This Fascinating Animal World

This
Fascinating
ANIMAL WORLD

by

ALAN DEVOE

ARTHUR BARKER LTD.
LONDON

First published Great Britain 1954

The author wishes to express his appreciation to the Fish and Wildlife Service, United States Department of the Interior, for the use of illustrations from *American Wildlife and Plants*.

Printed in Great Britain by
MORRISON AND GIBB LTD., LONDON AND EDINBURGH

Contents

The Nature of This Book

When I was a boy, fascinated then as now by our fellow creatures, the animals, I used to be full of questions about them. Though I lived reasonably near a good library, and pored over its books about animal life at every opportunity, I was disheartened to find that the answers to a great many of my most urgent questions seemed never to be discoverable.

There were plenty of books giving specific information about specific kinds of creatures: How many eggs does a golden-winged woodpecker lay, and how many eggs does a wren lay? There could be found a "bird book" which would contain this information. But the sort of questions that occur to a boy—or to any other inquirer, when an interest in our fellow creatures begins to be aroused—are questions far anterior to these particular and specific matters. They are basic questions. Long before we want to know about woodpeckers' eggs, particularly, or wrens' eggs, particularly, we want to know: Does a bird lay all its eggs at one sitting? Why are some eggs plain-colored and other eggs speckled and streaked? What makes a mother bird brood her eggs, and is she the only one to do so, or does the father bird sit on them too? If two kinds of birds are about the same size, why does one lay bigger eggs than the other? How does a baby bird get out of the egg? Most fundamental of all, perhaps: Do all birds lay eggs; and do any other creatures?

It was questions like these—about birds, mammals, snakes, fish, and all the rest of the animal company—to which I used eagerly to seek an answer; and it was questions like these which sent me hunting through all the rows of library books from Chester A. Reed's terse little *Land Birds East of the Rockies* to a staggering volume, written by a Victorian clergyman and illustrated with wood engravings, which was called with a fine comprehensive complacency, *The Animals of the World*. Sometimes, by vast delvings, I found the information I wanted. More often I did not.

In a sense, that is why I have written this book: it is because I wished so heartily, once upon a time, that such a book existed. But I have been further urged and encouraged to compose this volume by the discovery, in my adult years as a writer-naturalist, that inquirers into animal life are still asking, today, just exactly the same sort of questions that I used to ask, and that they are still finding it difficult to turn up the answers quickly in the ordinarily available books. The inquirers write me letters:

How many different species of animals are there? Can a fish see out of water? Are birds able to distinguish colors? How does a snake effect its locomotion, and how fast can it go? Do insects breathe through mouth and nose, as we do? What actually is the difference between a moth and a butterfly? How much do baby birds eat? Do other mammals have the same temperature we do? How do nocturnal animals see in the dark? In muddy water or at night, why don't fish bump into obstacles? What's the biggest mammal in the world, and does any bird ever fly backward?

Over the years, these questions have come from persons of every age and from most of the countries of the world. They are the primary questions, evidently, that most often occur to people wondering about animal life, whether in Kamchatka or Kansas City, and they are questions to which answers cannot always readily be found by consulting generally available books. Some of the questions (as, for instance: How do parent birds make sure that all their nestlings share equally in the food?) have come to me scores of times and even hundreds of times. The questions seem to be the universal "how?–why?–what?" wonderings about the lives around us—those creatures that companion us, and of whose company we are ourselves a part. The questions add up to something like a thousand. They have set the scope of this book.

I have taken the thousand questions (more or less), given them a degree of classification, and set out to answer them. Some can be answered in a line or two. Others need a fuller answering to provide groundwork and a filling out with related information. What I have wanted to do is to provide as completely as possible in one volume, informally readable and without the dense technicality of a textbook, the sort of general and foundational information about animals which I wish had been handily available to me twenty-five years ago, and which, as my mail tells me, is the information still most frequently sought and still not easily unearthed or compactly available today. How long do animals carry their young? Why don't sleeping birds fall off their perches? Are there any mammals that can fly? As I say, there are about a thousand of these queries. This book is to pose and answer them, and by that means to provide an introduction to a field amply covered by specialists and technicians, but insufficiently covered still, it seems, with regard to the primary and universal queries. (There stands at my elbow an enormous and learned work about ants. Its range of data is vastly impressive. It is a great work of entomology. But an inquirer might read through its hundreds of pages in vain, seeking to know—what is surely the first thing a nature-questioner wants to know—why do some ants have wings and others not? It has not occurred to the learned myrmecologist that in our curiosity about ant life, as in everything else, we begin at the beginning.)

What *is* an animal, exactly? A great many readers have asked me that. We may as well start there. To write even an introduction

A*

to animals—to answer even the thousand commonest questions—will take a good many pages. The reader is urged, of course, to plow straight through, from "What is an animal?" to the last question about the final animal considered. A book, naturally, is written as a book; and it is better read so. But on the other hand, of course, those who have an insistent preference for hopping and jumping around a bit may open these pages at any point and read where and when they please. For using the book as a reference work, to answer (as I hope it will) some particular question about animal life, the reader is referred to the index.

Are there any questions? There are indeed! Suppose we proceed to them.

ALAN DEVOE

This Fascinating Animal World

Animals in General

What is an animal?

Perhaps the easiest way to put it, in a rough, nontechnical fashion, is to say that animals are all of earth's living creatures that are not plants. An animal is a being able to make locomotor movements and perform actions that appear to be what we call voluntary. It shows a certain quickness and "aliveness" in its responses to stimulation. It ingests and digests foods consisting of other animals or plants, and it doesn't contain chlorophyll or perform photosynthesis. Not every animal need meet every one of the requirements; but in a general way this is the stuff of the definition.

Where the higher animals are concerned—a deer, say, or a raccoon or a squirrel—an animal's animality of course seems abundantly obvious, and a need for definition may appear a little absurd. But the kingdom of the animals runs right down to the roots of things. There are animals that consist of only a single cell. There are animals in which there is scarcely discoverable any distinct nervous system; and there are plant forms that look, at least to casual observation, a good deal livelier than these least developed animals. Down in the very lowest life levels, in the elementary ooze, so to speak, of the creation, animals and plants are so almost indistinguishably alike that it seems hardly possible that the one life line leads to oaks and redwoods and the other one to rabbits and foxes. Hence we have to take at least this brief cognizance of their technical division.

Few of us, unless we are going to become biological scientists, are likely to be much concerned with the life-ways of the tiny protozoa and their infinitesimal animal kindred; but it is important, in even an introduction to a book about animals, that at least we realize that a paramecium, for example, is an animal as much as a possum is.

A paramecium, one of the most easily identified (because slipper-shaped) microanimals to be found teeming in a spoonful of common brook water, is far tinier than a grain of sand. About 120 paramecia would have to be lined up to span an inch. It is as transparent as water. It has no legs or fins; no lung; no ear; no eye. We may safely guess that its awareness of the life experience, if it has any such awareness at all, is unimaginably dim and tiny. But all the same, it is an animal. It is a fellow being of ours. It takes in food and assimilates it. It excretes wastes. It undertakes travels. With waving cilia—delicate threadlike filaments that are the animalcule's version of legs or wings or fins—it propels itself through its water world. It feeds; it breathes; it voids its waste. Further, it responds to the flow of the current against its flesh. It retreats from too-warm water. It hurries away from salt. It does battle with other protozoa, exploding its tiny organs called trichocysts and hurling out from them a mass of grappling threads. A paramecium has no reproductive organs. It reproduces by what is called binary fission: the splitting of its nucleus and the division of itself into two new selves. But as a usual, though not essential, preface to that happening, paramecium lies with paramecium in an embrace. There forms between the two bodies a protoplasmic bridge. A part of the nucleus of the one animal flows forth and fuses with the nucleus of the other. There takes place a mutual blending of living flesh.

Such protozoa as a paramecium are very dim little animals, very tiny ones, their animalness only a sort of basic hint of what animal life is like. But they are members of the kingdom. There is the beginning, among them, of personality. There are moving, feeding, reproducing, and combat. There is spontaneous motion, quick reaction to changes of circumstance. With even the humblest of the animalcules, animal has parted from plant. There has come into life and being, in its small way, a brother of ours.

Conversationally and informally, we use the word "animal" for creatures that we mean to distinguish from, say, birds, or fish. We use it to mean warm-blooded beasts that suckle their young. The term we ought to use in that connection is "mammal." The mammals are but one part of animaldom. Rightly speaking, an animal is any one of our fellow beings that appears, to the spontaneous judgment of a primitive philosopher, to possess an *anima*. *Anima* is soul, breath of life, the indwelling self at the core of being. Our sense of our own *anima* is what Coleridge called a primary intuition. It does not come naturally to most of us to think of a rosebush as a "self," an animated being of this sort. We don't go into a garden as into a gathering of companions. (Some of us, uncommonly responsive to all sentiency, may indeed do just that, of course. There is nothing in the least absurd about it. The thing is the very heart of primitive poetry. But it is not a kind of sensitive sympathy developed in us all.) We do spontaneously take it, however, that a robin, a coyote, or even the cricket on the hearth, is at least in some degree, after its fashion, akin to us. It looks out on the world, as we do; it moves and seeks; it experiences. Its life is not exactly our life, of course; we are to beware of anthropomorphism, which means reading the human into the not-human. But even a cricket, we take it, in its crickety little way, is a being, a life, a self. *Anima* glimmers here; and our own responds, in brotherhood.

Such is the great company of the animals. A little boy who had been asking me questions once summed up the nature of animals perhaps better than a biologist would do it. "An animal," he said, "is something you feel like talking to."

How many different kinds of animals are there?

It always comes as a stunning surprise to inquirers taking their first full look at the facts about animals to find by what a huge and various throng of these fellow beings we are companioned. Biologically speaking, we human creatures are just one species of mammal among some four or five thousand other species. The whole of this vast mammaldom which so dwarfs us is itself no more than a tenth of the entirety of the vertebrates (the backboned animals). There are more than 2,000 species of snakes. There are something like 15,000 species of birds. Turn even to what would surely seem one of the littlest categories of our fellow creatures—turtles—and it turns out that there are more than 300 varieties.

If the numbers and diversity of the vertebrate animals are startling, a greater astonishment comes with the realization that these thousands of kinds of backboned beings make up only one part—and incomparably the lesser—of the two subkingdoms of the animal kingdom as a whole. It is the invertebrate animals with which our earth really teems. The tiny protozoa ("first animals"), such as the paramecium we were talking about, include at least 15,000 species. There are nearly 4,000 species of roundworms, even more species of flatworms, and in a complete catalog of mollusk species there would be almost 100,000 entries. No naturalist has any idea how many species of insects there are. We know that at least three-quarters of a million have been discovered and labeled; but new ones turn up virtually daily, and the extent of the remaining unknown is of course unguessable.

How many species of animals are there? The more we look into the matter, the more it becomes evident that Noah's ark, containing representatives of all these living beings, two by two, must have been remarkably spacious. Just the crustaceans—the lobsters and crabs and so on—amount to at least 20,000. There are over 3,000 species of sponges. (Are *sponges* animals? Most of us perhaps suppose, and Biblical writers almost certainly supposed, that sponges are vegetations. But they aren't; they are animals. A sponge takes food into a gastral cavity; it passes out wastes through an opening called its osculum. It begets young sponges by means of fertilized eggs. The sponge in our kitchen or bathroom is the bleached, dried-out skeletal remains of the animal.) There are about 30,000 species of arachnids: the spiders and their relatives. There are hundreds, even thousands, of kinds of just myriapods: the centipede-like animals.

At the lowest estimate, the number of different species of animals now living all around us is at least three million.

How are animals classified?

The division of the huge animal population into classifications is the science of taxonomy. It abounds in difficulties and disputes which still continue. To put it roughly, however, a naturalist thinks of animals like this:

First, they are split into massive divisions called phyla. A phylum is a broad, comprehensive assemblage of more-or-less-alikes. For instance, crabs, insects, and spiders all go into the phylum of arthropods. (They all have jointed limbs.) All segmented worms are put into the phylum of annelids. (*Anellus* is Latin for a little ring.) And so on.

The phylum is then broken down into classes, the classes into orders, the orders into families, the families into genera, and at last the genera into species and subspecies. Almost all of us have a stage, in our early years of the extraordinary adventure of self-awareness, when we find it exciting to "locate" ourselves by writing something like this: Jack Jones, Elm Street, Centerville, Random County, State of Illinois, United States, North America, Eastern Hemisphere, World, Universe. The classification of animals "locates" each creature in much this way.

This book is not a text of technical science, but a book about animals in their everyday livingness. Still, to discuss animals at all, it is a help to know at least the framework in which they have their identities. Take a common woodchuck:

This woodchuck is a species (*Marmota monax*), inside a genus (the marmots), which is contained in a family (the squirrels), which belongs to the order of rodents. The rodents are part of a great class, the mammals; and the mammals, of course, having backbones, fall into the vertebrates. The vertebrates, finally, belong in the broad phylum or subkingdom of chordate animals: all the ones having (more or less) spinal chords.

Species and subspecies are the "pin-point" identifications. They designate groups of animals having such close commonness of characteristics that they are not further subdivisible. Thus, the order of rodents contains a big family of squirrels. That family itself can obviously be divided into a number of "subsorts" of squirrels. The subfamily Sciurinae can be taken apart into genera: the marmots, which are woodchucks, and the otospermophiles, which are rock squirrels, and so on. But when we get down to *Marmota monax*, our woodchuck himself, we have come to the end of possible narrowing. A *Marmota monax* is a *Marmota monax;* and one of these chucks doesn't differ from another one except in the minor details which distinguish subspecies and varieties within what is clearly one specific and indivisible category of animalness. We look at our woodchuck and say, This is a *kind* of animal. It differs from every other kind. Let his name be Woodchuck, *Marmota monax*, the name for a particular and unconfusable species of creature under the sun. A relative of squirrels, yes; in a bigger sense, a relative of moose and antelope, yes; in a still more expansive sense, the co-tenant of an animal category with *us*. But, in his particular *Marmota monax* woodchuckness, unique. Demarked from every other animal but his fellow *Marmota monaxes*, whistling in the clover field, and his only tinily variant brethren, *Marmota monax rufescens* and *Marmota monax ochracea* and *Marmota monax preblorum* . . . *Marmota monaxes* all. This is a species of animal; a kind; an identity not to be divided. "A species," as one easy old rule of thumb puts it, "consists of a group of closely similar individual animals that don't mate with individuals of other species."

Taxonomy is a horribly intricate and technical science, and we may seem here to be reducing it to something of a child-simplicity. Why not? As has already been remarked in these pages, and will probably be remarked a good many times more before we are done, the lore of animals, like all other knowledges, has to begin at the beginning. How does the tribe of animals split up? Well, it splits up more or less so and so. There are plenty of textbooks of taxonomy. But first questions first. Are all squirrels rodents? Yes, we see that they are; for they are a family within an order. But are all mollusks oysters? No; for mollusks are the great grouping called a phylum, and oysters are only one class in it. (Snails are another; squids and octopuses are a third.) If we want to look up butterflies in a big reference work, why should we look for them in the same general section—most improbably—that treats of seashore crabs? Answer: their common membership in the phylum of arthropods, the "jointed-legs." Why aren't earthworms and eels and snakes all pretty much the same sort of animals? Answer: Earthworms have no backbones, so they belong in the invertebrates. Eels and snakes both have backbones, which makes them cousinly to that distant degree; but an eel has gills, which puts it in the fish class instead of the class of snakes.

A little rough-and-ready taxonomy is enough to give us the "feel" of how animals are grouped. We see that their groupings are based on blood relationships. Merely superficial resemblances don't count. Each phylum holds all the animals that, according to the best scientific guess, had a common ancestor. The split into classes, orders, families, and all down the line, is according to the same principles of genealogical descent; and a taxonomist establishes grandsonship, cousinship, and nephewship by the study and comparison of anatomies.

There is no occasion for us here to go delving into the vast technicalities of the numerous phyla that contain the hordes of very primitive creatures—the echinoderms (starfish, sea cucumbers, and the like), the coelenterates (jellyfish, corals, etc.), or the molluscoids, ctenophores, and porifers. It will probably be enough for us just to know, among the invertebrates, the divisions into such great phyla as we have already talked about: arthropods, mollusks, annelids. The vertebrates (omitting some lampreys and sharks that needn't bother us) break into the familiar classes: fish, amphibians, reptiles, birds, and mammals.

Before we get along to something else, we may like to have a look at how one class of animals—the most familiar class of animals, the mammals—divides into its component creatures. Mammals are probably the most interesting and appealing animals, to most of us. They stir our early curiosity, and prompt some of our first questions. What sorts of mammals are there? They go like this:

First, there are the prototherians: such primitive and peculiar beasts as the duck-billed platypus. Then there are the metatherians: opossums, kangaroos. And then there are the eutherians, which are the placental mammals and which include just about all the beasts that most of us commonly encounter. They fall into these groupings:

Insectivores: These, obviously, are mammals that eat insects. Moles do, and shrews; likewise hedgehogs.

Edentates: These ought to be the mammals that don't have any teeth. We encounter here, however, what a naturalist gets used to encountering in learning about animals: the occasional complete misleadingness of a name. Most of the birds called warblers don't warble. June bugs aren't bugs, but beetles, and they appear not in June, but in May. Most insects with the suffix "fly" to their names are not in fact flies, and a water thrush isn't a thrush at all, but a warbler. Many of the edentate mammals do have teeth. However, they are in most other respects a primitive order. They cover armadillos, sloths, and anteaters.

Chiropters: These should be "hand-wings," and are. The chiropters are the bats.

Rodents: These mammals are all the gnawers: mice, beavers, porcupines, rabbits, and their kindred.

Carnivores: The meat eaters, ranging all the way from cats and dogs to walruses.

Cetaceans: A ceta is a whale; this order holds the aquatic mammals: whales, dolphins, porpoises.

Sirenians: This order will scarcely concern most of us, for it consists solely of the big herbivorous aquatic mammals called sea cows. There is a charm in their name, though. Why sirenians? Because a siren is a mermaid, and some romantic sailor's hasty view of a full-breasted sea cow nursing her youngster probably started the legend of the existence of mermaids.

Ungulates: An unguis is a hoof; and this great order contains all the wide range of hoofed animals—from horses, elephants, deer, and hippopotamuses to the barnyard pig.

Primates: This order, named to indicate the "first, principal, or chief" beasts, is the one where you and I belong. We share it with the anthropoid apes, lemurs, and marmosets.

How long have there been animals?

In our traditional religious account of the beginning of things, the Creator willed the world into existence, gave it seas and air and light and darkness, planted it with vegetations as a garden, thronged the green garden with all the animals, and finally breathed spirit into one portion of animated dust to make Man, all in a matter of seven days.

It wasn't long ago that learned experts were still making careful calculations to set the year in which that momentous week occurred. Bishop James Ussher, in the seventeenth century, established probably the most generally accepted date for the creation. He placed it in the year 4004 B.C.

Nowadays, of course, in the light of rock reading, fossil studies, and a hundred other means of shrewd estimate (such as, for instance, computations based on the disintegration rate of uranium), earth-scientists reckon our world to be enormously older than that. Its life is not calculated in centuries or in thousand-year terms, but in thousands of millions of years. How long have there been animals prowling around on it, swimming in its waters, nibbling at the greenery of this long, slow garden? Well, if by "animals" we mean all the sorts of creatures down to the humblest, we have to make a flying guess at something like ten or twelve hundred million years. There seem already to have been animals as complex as some segmented worms back in the almost immeasurably ancient mists of the Proterozoic. But even if by "animals" we mean animals of a much higher sort than that—even if we mean animals at least recognizably akin to the ones we meet now in the nearest woods or pasture lot, the sort of animals that the questions in this book are about—the answer is still a tremendous time-figure. When did the reptiles begin to come creeping ashore? It looks very much as though that must have happened some two hundred million years ago, give or take some millions. When did there start to be mammals and birds? A hundred and fifty to a hundred and ninety million years ago, probably. Many mammals seem to have been becoming specialized in very much their present mammalness thirty or forty million years ago. And our human selves? . . . the creatures whose stock split off from our fellow animals, so that we became, while still of their fellowship, also possessors of that distinguishing kind of spirit—rationality, self-consciousness, capacity for abstraction—that the religious record talks about? We are to think of that split beginning something like six or seven million years ago. We are to think of man, even in the fullness of his manness, even in the complete humanity of body and mind symbolized by the Genesis figure of Adam, as having been brought forth on the earth at least a million years ago.

The animal scene into which we go exploring nowadays may have the look of a set-scene: the rabbit on the lawn, the hawk overhead in the high sky, the minnows in the brook. Here lies the creation, with this look of yesterday-today-and-forever about it. But this hawk is not a creature that just burst into its present hawkness, *ex nihile*, all glittering eyes and broad wings and curving talons. Minnowness and rabbithood don't date from the first day. The animals didn't just abruptly *be*, in a dramatic instant of completed creation. They have *become*. What we see now, when we look at the animals, is final animals shaped by almost immeasurably long, slow workings of the process of evolution.

Evolution? There is a question about that that always comes up when we get to thinking about animals at all, and we must take a look at it:

Does evolution mean we are descended from apes?

There are probably no theories except Sigmund Freud's that have influenced our present thinking and affected our view of the world as tremendously as the concept of evolution. This being so, it is astonishing what inadequate notions, and what wrong ones, most of us are likely to be given about the thing. When I was a naturalist of ten or twelve or so, the air was thick with agitated flapdoodle about "God or Gorilla"; but few of the heated disputants ever seemed just to sit down quietly and write a statement of a hundred words or so to explain clearly what the doctrine of evolution really *is*. Simplified and unalarmed statements about evolution still don't seem to turn up very often. Turn to "Evolution" in an encyclopedia or a textbook, and we encounter forty pages of fine print, dense with learned technicality. Most of us don't want to become scientists. We just want to know what evolution is about. What does it say about our brother hawk and brother woodchuck and our bipedal self? It says, in essence, simply this:

When our earth had come into being and cooled off, and life began upon it, the initial creatures were not our present hawks, rabbits, minnows, and the rest, but simpler animals on the order, say, of the paramecium we were considering at the start of these pages. From a few kinds of such primitive beings (possibly from just one kind), there have developed all our animals in their variety. Life is changeable, modifiable, plastic. In adaptation to circumstances, animals have variously altered their shapes, sizes, habits—over aeons and aeons, that is, of slow, slow, graduality—becoming (some of them) bears, and becoming (some of them) mice, and becoming (some of them) this or that other species of the millions of animals now teeming. Way, way back in the far distances of time, the lighter colored animals inhabited some dark-colored environment, say, were the more easily seen by their enemies and killed off. So, in that particular branch of animal stock, the darker colored individuals tended to survive and beget. A trend of darkcoloredness was initiated. And then there were agility trends, too, and trends toward a particular way of effective food-securing, and a thousand other trends, tendencies, and developments, all inter-working, interacting, and at the end of some millenniums behold a catocala moth. Or behold, along another line, a giraffe; or along another, a minnow; or along others our rabbit and our curve-taloned hawk. Mostly, development has been from simple to more complex. Here and there among the animals a complexity has dwindled toward simplicity. Now and again a development has gone just so far, and then this particular tentative trend in animality hasn't, so to speak, "worked," and the beasts have withdrawn from the animal scene. (Dinosaurs, for instance.) Is there a perfectness about our animals? There is; for what is fit survives and begets and improves; what isn't fit disappears.

Now this is a primer-way, to be sure, of talking about evolution; but a primer, it strikes me, is what we want, to see very simply the elementary Idea of the thing and understand what it basically has to say about animaldom and ourselves in it.

Did Charles Darwin originate the idea of evolution? No. There had been occasional thinkers of antiquity who had entertained sur-mises about it. Darwin proposed a particular set of scientific ex-planations for the origin of species and the evolutionary develop-ment of man. He turned surmise into science, so that a naturalist today cannot seriously doubt the truth of evolution in the main, though there is still plenty of room for continuing disagreements about this or that aspect of it.

Is the doctrine of evolution hostile to religion? Why, not re-motely. It *is* hostile, of course, to the sort of small-minded literal-ism which would persist in taking the superb earth-poetry of Genesis for a scientific monograph. (As if one were to insist that a sonnet about the sunrise must be held to mean that the sun does in fact circle around the earth, and that any science which states the facts otherwise is hostile to the kind of tremendous truth that sonnets speak.) Genesis talks about "days." Evolution discovers that they were very long ones. Evolution finds that the garden (to continue religious metaphor) into which man was introduced at a late day has been a long time growing. It didn't start—bang!—in a fullness. It was shaped into being, if we like to think of it that way, from a start in seeds. Well? What central religious ideas have been damaged? Of the foundational matter of religion—the Power at the back of beyond, the universe's ground-of-being—science never has anything to say at all, one way or another. It is only a very simple-minded sort of scientist, or a very simple-minded sort of religious devotee, who can suppose that it has. Actually, evolution strikes a good many reverent-hearted naturalists as grandly enlarging the glory of things, not hurting it or reducing it.

Now how about that ape-grandfather of ours? Does evolution say we are descended from a gorilla? Emphatically, it says nothing like that. What it says is that both anthropoid apes and ourselves branched off—back in the ancient mists when the garden was far from being inhabited yet, either by gorillas or by naturalists—from a common ancestral animal form. Ultimately, over the aeons, there got to be gorillas; ultimately, over the aeons, there got to be ourselves. Is there then a relationship? Surely there is. *All* animaldom is related. (And so is the plant in the window and Betelgeuse in the night sky, if it comes to that.) Is there anything about it to depress or humiliate us? Is there anything about it to degrade our humanity, or to "prove that we're just monkeys"? Nothing.

What's the biggest animal that ever lived?

It's living right now: a blue whale. The vanished dinosaurs were enormous, some of them measuring nearly ninety feet in length and weighing probably upwards of forty or fifty tons; but blue whales (or sulphur-bottomed whales, as they are also called) dwarf them. Whales measuring well over a hundred feet in length have been taken, and their weight can go over a hundred tons.

Are there animals everywhere?

Just about, yes. This earth of ours swarms and teems with living beings. Not merely has "the breath of life been blown upon this star"; animaldom has come to throng it everywhere. It is one of the great advantages of being interested in animals that the objects of our interest are always at hand, no matter where we are. Go high, go deep, go to a hot region, go into the bitter cold, and there are animals, living out their fellowly lives, exploring after their fashions their various worlds of experience. Animals are endlessly adaptive, and wonderfully hardy. Frogs can be kept at a temperature of $-15°$F. and survive. Centipedes can endure $-25°$F. (By the way, to eliminate a lot of repetition of the letter "F." for Fahrenheit, suppose we agree here that whenever a temperature is mentioned in this book it will be in familiar Fahrenheit scale unless the more formal scientific Centigrade is expressly specified.) Snails have "come alive" in good shape after being frozen at $-50°$. On the other hand, amoebas and other animalcules can flourish in water heated well past $120°$, and fish sometimes go swimming through hot springs that aren't so very far below the simmering point.

Deserts cannot discourage animals. There are desert frogs, for instance, that store up water in their bladders. The ocean deeps hold populaces of animals. There are intricate and delicate animals down in the black abysses where the pressure is 2 or 3 tons to the square inch.

We live in an atmosphere of somewhere around 21 per cent oxygen. But many animals—even many mammals, our warm-blooded immediate brothers—can live contentedly when the oxygen content gets way down to 14 per cent or so. They can stay alive at 7 per cent. The oxygen has to go down to the almost-vanishing point of about 3 per cent before their consciousness winks out in death.

This is a stunningly animal-ful earth of ours, fecund with everything from paramecia to polar bears. We human beings, going through the life adventure, have a great, great host of companions.

Are there about the same number of male and female animals?

In the vertebrate animals, at any rate, the sexual proportions do stay strikingly stabilized in equality. This, of course, is an over-all picture. There are some odd deviations within it. What animal shows the broadest disproportion of the sexes? It's a dog—our common greyhound. For every 100 female greyhounds born, the males number 110.

Do all animals reproduce sexually?

Except for tiny animalcules and primitive hermaphrodites, all animals engage in specifically sexual relationships. Male lies with female; amatory and reproductive impulses are aroused; sperm makes contact with ovum to fertilize it. The kingdom of animals, we have seen, runs a great gamut. The gamut of love is nearly coextensive.

It is extraordinary how often the question of animal sexuality comes up, in one form or another. Is it true that insect life sometimes arises spontaneously from decaying matter? It isn't; butterflies copulate as animally as bears; but the question is asked as often by adults as by small boys. Do snakes have a hidden leg, which they sometimes extrude in emergencies? No. The "leg" we may occasionally see is a male snake's sexual organ. There are reptilian love rites comparable to those of any other animal. Is it really true that female opossums receive a pollenlike dust into their noses, and then, tucking their heads into their pouches, blow the magical stuff into those dark repositories where in time it forms baby opossums? It is pure fairy tale; but it was a popular piece of whispered "animal lore" thirty years ago, and the question goes on being asked. The small seed of truth, sprouting the fantasy, is probably the fact that a male opossum does have an anatomical peculiarity. Its penis is forked.

Some particular questions about animals' sexual behaviors can be brought up more appropriately in other parts of this book. But in this section where we are talking about the broad foundational questions that come up most often about animals in general, we may at least take a sort of over-all look at the manner of matings and pairings. Sexuality is how life goes forward. Sex is the source of animal variety. It is because the stuffs of two bodies combine to make a third that individuals come forth in their differences of individuality, instead of all animaldom having a monotone uniformity. It is evident enough, from the sex questions about animals that come up, how stuffed a lot of us have been on muck and moonshine. The drive of sex, of love, is as natural a thing, as clean and interesting and often lovely a thing, as any other animal event. It will answer a host of common questions at one swoop if we have a broadly surveying look here at how love expresses itself among a diversity of animals.

Snails are such primitive creatures that they are hermaphrodites. Each snail, that is, has both male and female sexual organs. But even among snails there can be seen the beginnings of lovemaking. When two snails come together in their version of love, they excite each other's sexual instincts by thrusting into each other's bodies sharp-pointed shafts made of the same carbonate of lime that forms their shells. The soberest zoologists, not given to lighthearted and romantic language, call these instruments of the snails' amatory expression their "love darts."

When they are aroused to love, even the dullest and most sluggish kinds of cold-blooded creatures can be kindled extraordinarily by its fire. Male toads experience a peculiar swelling of their thumbs in preparation for the act of union. As the male climbs upon the back of the female, he clasps her tightly just behind her forearms. He presses his enlarged thumbs hard into her sides, holding her in an almost unbreakable embrace. The pairing toads may stay thus coupled for many hours, sometimes even for days. Normally toads are hungry creatures, and also timid ones. When they are under the spell of mating, they give up eating entirely. They will not abandon their embrace even if they are picked up and handled. There is no relaxing of the toads' ardor until at last the female voids her eggs and the male pours over them his fertilizing cells.

As intense as toads' love-encounter, and stranger, is that of newts. The male of the common red newt, or spotted salamander, grasps the female with his hind legs just behind her front legs. Gripping her tightly, he arches and bends his body in an S-curve until he can lay his head against hers. Rhythmically he rubs his head back and forth, back and forth, against his partner's. Presently he brings his tail into play. He begins tapping it steadily against her body. On and on the love-play continues, in an absorbed devotion lasting for hours. Every now and then there is a crescendo, the male shaking and mauling the female, the two newts threshing and twisting their bodies in a wild agitation. Then the steady caressings begin again, the rubbing of heads, the rhythmic tail-tapping. At last the newts break their embrace. The male withdraws a little way and deposits a tiny white vase-shaped object called his spermatophore. As he leaves, the female comes to where the spermatophore has been deposited, creeps over it, and takes it into her cloaca. The mating of the newts has been completed.

Vivid rites of love occur among fish. Suppose we take a look at the love-play of betta fish, the so-called "fighting fish" of Siam, which many of us often keep in aquariums:

When the male betta feels the urge to mate, he builds a love-nest by taking gulps of air into his mouth and releasing them—each coated by a sticky casing—until the bubbles have formed a cluster. When he has finished his dome of bubbles, he ensconces himself under it and waits to lure a mate. His colors have become blazingly vivid. His gill covers are projected in alluring excitement. His fins stiffen. When a female ready for spawning comes by, the male swims around and around her, displaying his charms, and then he sidles closer and gives her a side-stroke with his tail. He slips away to the nest, adds a few bubbles to it, makes a provocative little rush at the female and then glides to the nest again. If she has been captivated, the lady betta follows him to the nest now and signifies her acceptance by nudging him in the side with her nose. This touches off the completion of love-making. The bodies of the two bettas come together. The male wraps himself in an arching half circle around the female's body. She turns on her back. Presently, she releases fifteen or twenty eggs. Clinging tightly together in a vibrant embrace, the two bettas slowly sink together through the water. Then they break apart and the male betta gathers the drifting eggs in his mouth. He carries them to the bubble-nest and stows them safely in it. Swimming back to the waiting female, he again seizes her in an embrace and the two bettas go through the same intense rite of love all over again. They keep repeating it with unflagging fervor until the female's body holds no more eggs.

From the most primitive animals to the highest, the fire of love burns all through the creation. Many kinds of birds, in the time of mating, become so carried away that their outpouring of love is spectacular. A common cowbird, addressing himself to his chosen lady, first points his beak skyward and compresses his feathers, seeming to hug himself in unendurable ecstasy. In a few moments the ecstasy reaches a release as his feathers fly erect and stick out in all directions, his wings and tail fan out as taut as they will go, he utters a shrill whistling hiss, and on quivering wings pitches forward almost in prostration. When waxwings are in love, the little birds caress each other tenderly, rub their beaks together after each separation of even a few minutes, and when building up to their final intimacy often spend long periods side by side on a twig, passing a ripe berry or small fruit back and forth from mouth to mouth.

The "drumming" of the ruffed grouse is familiar to many of us who are even moderately acquainted with animals. Less well known is the grouse's love-prelude when the male and female have actually come together. The male fluffs out his glittering ruff, struts to the hen, and begins a performance of arousal. He bobs and ducks, pecking at the ground. He comes closer, closer, until the two birds are face to face, expectant. The cock sways his head from side to side. Now faster, faster, until his motion has become a quivering blur of intensity. With each shake and sway, he makes a quick little sound like panting. Finally, when it almost seems he must fly to pieces under the urgency of what he would utter, he moves in directly in front of his chosen one, stiffens his legs, emits a final prolonged cry, and suddenly turns his fanned-out tail laterally so that the full splendor of it bursts flashingly upon the female. The climax is almost always quick to follow. The European grouse called a capercaillie works itself into such a love-frenzy that in the peak of the performance it gnashes its beak and foams, closes its eyes tightly, and undergoes such a swelling of its soft palate that the bird is temporarily deafened. When capercaillies are in the throes of love-excitement in a treetop, they often cause the whole tree to tremble.

When egrets reach Louisiana from their South American wintering place, their flock presently breaks up into pairs. Each pair chooses a nesting site and withdraws to it together. But the couples don't immediately start home-building and raising a family. First there is a honeymoon. It has such qualities of passionate happiness and devotion that when it was first witnessed by Dr. Julian Huxley, the English scientist, he could scarcely believe it to be a regular practice in these birds' lives. But it is; and "honeymoon" is the only possible word.

For days the two egrets are always together. By the hour they perch motionless, the female on a twig just below her mate's, her head pressed against his flanks. Every so often, as quiet delight

surges into ecstasy, both birds raise their wings, stretch up their
long necks, and then with an outburst of love-cries intertwine their
necks together. The egrets' necks are so long and supple that
each of them actually makes a complete turn around the other.
The birds are locked together in a true lover's-knot. Then each of
them takes the fine plumes of the other (the famous "aigrettes")
in its beak, and nibbles them lovingly, giving each plume a long
sliding "kiss" from its base to its tip. As the egrets' love-play sub-
sides they untwine their necks and relapse once more into their
sharing of a quiet happiness: side by side, always touching one another. The honeymoon of the egrets often lasts as long as four
or five days.

The love ways of the highest and most familiar animals, the
mammals, are by far the most difficult to learn about in the field.
Mammals like to keep their mating ways secret. We know at
least a little, though, about the ways of a few of them.

Deer and antelope in mating time are stimulated by the excitant
of a powerful musk exuded by special glands. As they respond to
its influence, they fondle each other's necks and heads with gentle
gestures. The doe uses coquetry: pretending to run away in
alarm, stopping and looking back at the buck, timidly returning
to just beyond his reach. As excitement mounts, the buck stirs it
to further pitch by "running down" the doe. The two animals
gallop at full tilt in rushing straightaways, their excitement mount-
ing with each run until the last one when the doe suddenly stands
still with heaving flanks and allows herself to be taken. This sexual
run is so much a part of antelope nature that a lonely buck, unable
to find a doe, will make the passionate run all by himself, spreading
the white hair of his rump and going through all the motions of
antelope endearment. Theodore Roosevelt on one of his western
hunting trips once watched a solitary pronghorn staging this
phantom love-making.

The musk of the deer family has its counterparts in numerous

B

other perfumes and essences that accompany and stimulate mammals' love-making. Bull elephants express their love expertly with their trunks, which can be as delicately gentle in fondling a female as they can be mighty in lifting a teak log; but the effect of this elephantine trunk-play is heightened by the bull's use of a potent amatory perfume discharged from a gland in his head. A bull elephant in his time of love looks almost as though he were weeping, as the perfume trickles down his seamy cheek between eye and ear. Beavers' love-making takes place in a heady haze of the beaver musk called castoreum. Castoreum has such strangely exciting properties that it is used by trappers as a lure for all sorts of animals. Perfumers have incorporated it in their products. Martens, weasels, foxes, and many other animals use similarly strong scents. Even the fearful sulphide used by skunks as a weapon serves also as a love-lure. Outdoorsmen have often remarked that skunk scent, when it is very faint and diluted, is not unpleasant. To skunks in love, apparently, it is maddeningly irresistible. A female skunk, ducking away from the male's first clumsy approaches, walks teasingly in front of him with arched back. He stamps and patters with his forefeet, grunting excitedly. She pauses, lifts her plumy tail, and lets forth the tiniest jet of scent. As it drifts on the heavy spring air, the male rushes to seize her.

Among primitive animals the initiative in love rests almost entirely with the male. It is only among the mammals that the female's role becomes the important one, and she develops the arts of teasing and enticement. A female gnu in love-time has a winning trick of dropping to her knees and bumping her male with her heavy head until he can no longer resist. Female giraffes tease the males into chasing them, and then run with a strange swaying gait that proves irresistible. The male giraffe signifies that he has succumbed by cornering the female, stretching out his long neck, and nuzzling her flanks. At this sign of conquest, a female giraffe quivers and trembles with pleasure from one end to the other of her great gawky body. Llamas incite their males by rubbing their necks softly, persuasively. It may continue for a long time. Then suddenly the male llama twists his neck violently around hers, and in a savage gesture of possession forces her to her knees.

Female enticement, and intensity of love-making, reach their greatest height in the big cats. Tigers in love are almost terrible to see. Slowly the female walks back and forth before the male. If this lounging provocation does not arouse him, she glides closer and pads sinuously in front of him, almost touching his nose each time she goes by. She begins to flick her tail. Now as she passes before him she draws her tail softly, slowly, across his muzzle. She does it again, again, until the growlings start in his great throat. She prances lightly away. Now a little wait, while the male stares at her, growling throatily, kneading with his claws. She circles him, rippling her tail down his body, across his muzzle again. She throws herself on her back, four paws in the air, and lies waiting, purring. A well-known animal painter who was fortunate enough to see two tigers at their love-making has said that its climax has so furious an intensity that nothing can be seen but a vibrant blur of tawny colors.

The fire of love burns all through the creation, now bright in passion, now a steady flame of quiet happiness. It is more than just sex. A pair of old apes, long past days of passion, will sit by the hour with their arms around each other, petting, comforting, in the quiet joy of togetherness. A gander, while his mate broods her eggs, will lie patiently with his long neck stretched protectively across her back. Love is a fire of many degrees, at which all animals may warm themselves, after their fashions. It is the central fire of life itself, and it's what makes the world go round.

"To go to the animals," Johannes Jensen said, "is to go home." It is to find, that is to say, the basic stuffs of ourselves. It is to look at plain reality. From even the brief survey we have been making here of some representative animals' sex ways, it ought to become evident to us that sexuality is no more to be sniggered at than sleep. It isn't funny; it isn't nasty; it oughtn't to be, to any of us who have the health of creatureliness, embarrassing. It has a great many oddities in it, yes; but we can stop looking for the sort of erotic fantasticalities that the whisperings and titterings we heard in our childhood may have led us to expect to find among the animals. Is it true that porcupines mate at long distance? It is nonsense. Porcupines couple like all other mammals, from mice to mankind. Will birds' eggs hatch if there hasn't first been a mating? Why, no; how could they? Is sex a "beastly" thing? Only if we use "beastly" to mean what it rightly means—"pertaining to the beasts"—and only if we never, never forget that the kingdom of the beasts extends right down to the primal stir in the single cell in the morning of the world.

Do male animals ever give birth to young or lay eggs?

There is a straightforward answer to this, and a quibbling one. Straightforwardly, no. In a few rare cases, however, disease has caused sex reversal. Hens have grown spurs and taken to cock-a-doodling; roosters have laid an egg. By the way: Are the very small and misshapen eggs that we find in our poultry houses really what farmers usually call them, "rooster eggs"? No; they are just hen eggs that have developed improperly.

Do all animals have to have air?

Yes; at least they all have to have oxygen, which they get from the air either directly or indirectly. What about those everlasting toads and frogs that are continually turning up fat and chipper in cornerstones and similar places, where they are supposed to have been sealed for ages? Is it possible? No. In a really airtight chamber, no animal can live. Imprisoned in, say, a block of porous limestone, a toad can live for as much as a year or perhaps a year and a half. It cannot live for ages, or even for anywhere near a decade; but if it can get a tiny minimum of oxygen it may survive until starvation occurs. Which brings us naturally enough to the very frequent question:

Do all animals need food?

They do, to live. This isn't a willfully ambiguous answer. Some animals—May flies, for instance—have an adult life span of only a few hours in any case. It is of no consequence whether they eat or not. Brief-living creatures sometimes have no mouth parts at all. There are several moths that don't. But all animals that live for any extended length of time require nourishment for their aliveness.

What gives rise to the widespread notion that there are animals which never eat is probably the fact that some animals can survive such long intervals between meals that they may live out what looks to be a whole lifetime without feeding. Snakes don't even lose weight when they are able to get a meal only once every ten or twelve days. They can fast for weeks and months. Salmon feed only in salt water, which means that they do not eat at all during the entire spawning voyage upriver. (What happens to their stomachs? They shrink. At the end of spawning season a salmon's stomach has shrunk to such tininess that a regular meal couldn't be forced into it.) As we shall be seeing when we get to the section of our book that deals particularly with birds, these hot-blooded and vibrantly alive creatures are ordinarily enormous eaters. But even among birds there can be an exception. Take penguins. From mating until egg laying there is no feeding. This means a bird-fast of anywhere from eighteen to twenty-eight days.

Some years ago a museum snail gave an arresting display of fasting power. The snail, of course, was "dead" when it was put on display in its case. Glued neatly to a card, the "specimen" stayed put for what anyone might excusably imagine to be a whole snailish lifetime. Then one day it yanked loose its big snail-foot from the card and went creeping off to look for something to eat. It had been sitting motionless on its card, with nothing to eat, for three years.

Do all animals drink?

No. All animals do need water; but a great many manage to get it without ever drinking, and still more need drink only very seldom. For instance: Giraffes can go weeks without drinking. They manage to extract enough water from the foliage on which they browse. Most sheep very seldom drink. There are some tree-dwelling porcupines that virtually never descend to the ground to go looking for water. They quench their thirst on leaf juices and dew. Do lizards drink? Most do, yes; but there are some kinds that have a rough hygroscopic skin so absorbent and retentive of moisture that they can live indefinitely in the most parched deserts. Are there any mammals that don't drink? Yes. Fur seals absorb water directly through their pores. The commonest of all the questions along this line, of course, is about camels. How long can they go without a drink?

Camels store fluid in their fatty humps, and in some other body tissues, and most of us get a notion in childhood that they can draw on these internal reservoirs almost indefinitely. They can't. An average camel can survive between a week and two weeks without drinking. In extraordinary cases, less than perfectly authenticated, a camel seems to have survived a drought of about a month.

Are most animals harmful or beneficial?

This is a question, of course, for a lifetime of philosophy; but it is continually coming up in one form or another, and some elementary consideration of it is essential to our basic understanding of the texture of animal life.

Very often, the question takes this particular form: What *use* is a woodchuck? (or a bumblebee or a rattlesnake or an ichneumon fly or whatever the animal may be). Putting it that way, we indicate clearly the viewpoint underlying—perhaps unconsciously—our thinking. We are saying: What use is the creature to *us?* We are assuming that the entirety of the creation has been, so to speak, devised with us in mind. There is our human self, and there is "the rest" of nature; and "the rest," we are taking it, is to serve, help, guide, support, and generally further our supreme and central self. The sun shines to give us light; the darkness comes to give us rest; birds sing to make a music for us, and flowers bloom to provide us with the enchantment of a garden.

It is when we find an animal that appears flagrantly to be violating this scheme of things—a woodchuck despoiling our garden faster than it can grow, and not rewarding us even with a song or a shimmer of beauty—a bee stinging us though we have laid our hand on it by however innocent an inadvertence—that we are moved to the familiar pouting outcry: What *good* is such a creature?

Old Adam, the tale has it, made a primary and fundamental error of soul. He thought he was master of everything. He thought he was central and supreme. Instead of directing his awed homage to the Creator, and his reverent respect to the whole expansed creation wherein he found himself creaturely, he took the notion that he was a very god himself, and that all things must be ordered according to what *he*—peeking through his tiny peephole upon the staggering operation of The All—judged to be wisdom. All of us (so the tale continues) have had an inveterate tendency to the same nonsense ever since.

We have indeed; and naturalists and animalizers no less than everybody else. We may grin easily when we find one of the old theodicists pointing out, as a sign of divine beneficence, the fact that so many large cities are providentially equipped with rivers flowing handily close to them; but we all have a psychic disposition to the same sort of absurdity. What reason can there be, we keep asking, for this or that animal that does not directly serve *us?*

(By the way, this is as good a place as any for an interjection. The word "animalizer," just used above, isn't in the dictionary. Apparently it is not, or hasn't been until now, a word. But I propose that in this book we *make* it a word; for it is beautifully useful. It comes from an old farmer neighbor of mine, over across the hill from the hundred-and-some remote acres of woods and fields that surround my house and that constitute, so to speak, the living laboratory in which daily around the year I do my animal-examining. I encountered this old neighbor one day some years ago, when I was following a deer track or trying to locate where the crows were roosting or some such thing, and he halted me to ask some question or other about the outdoors. "I thought perhaps you'd know," he said, "you being such an animalizer." "Animalizer." Could anything better describe those of us who go poking into chipmunk burrows and snooping into birds' nests and probing around under old stumps, wanting to find out all we possibly can about our fellow animals and their world?

"Zoologist" is a chilly, formal word. It stands for scientific technicality; it has hints of cold Greek about it; it conjures the vision of white coats and glittering instruments and long hours devoted to dissecting the trigeminal ganglia of *Rana clamitans,* the green frog. "Biologist" is as bad, and much too spacious. "Naturalist" means a man seeking to know about all nature; and life is hardly long enough for getting to know even a little something about just flowers, or just minerals, or just stars. But "animalizer" . . . well, this not only limits us suitably to just animals, but it has a fine *lively* sound to it, a homely sound, an animals-in-the-field sound. Do woodchucks often climb trees? A zoologist might or might not know. He'd know, of course, the woodchuck's scientific name; and he might very likely know how many millimeters long its second southeast whisker is; and he could probably draw a chart showing precisely the animal's relation to the subspecies of marmot found in the environs of Basle. But do woodchucks very often climb trees, and why, and what do they do when they get to the top? That's the sort of thing that an animalizer would very much want to know. He'd want to go out into the actual meadow, and watch excitedly the actual tree, and get to know these living details about the living woodchuck. He wants to know some zoology, naturally; but what essentially he wants to know about is *animals* . . . animals as they actually live and breathe and feel and think, animals as our creaturely brothers, animals known in intimacy and their animalness, so to speak, entered into.

What we are wanting to do in this book, it strikes me, is *animalizing*, in an introductory sort of way. We can go on, if we like, after the animalizing, to become scientists, specialists, or this or that kind of technician. But the sort of thing we're about, here, is some plain and primary *animalizing:* getting the lay of animal land, trying to find the answers to the questions that come to mind not when we are deep into the minutiae of special learning, but when initially we step into this actual meadow, this actual piece of woods, and see an animal track or hear an animal sound and we start thinking, Well, now, by George, what's this all about? "Animalizer." It may not be in the dictionary; but it is going to be in this book.)

Now back to our question of what use a particular animal is.

The "use" of an animal, as an instructed naturalist or animalizer properly thinks of it, is its use to the totality of things.

The creation is an entity, a whole. This whole is sustained in its health by an intricate interdependency of all its parts. "We are all members of one another," the religious phrase used to put it. That truth remains, whether in religion or natural history. It is the thriving of The Whole that is served by particular creatures and events; and all things, everywhere, are linked together in a web of being. However "useless" a creature looks, in the little view that would comprehend only patent use to *us*, it has its use in the complex economy of The Whole wherein we are ourselves ingrediential. We know that it has its use. If it hadn't, the great over-all crush of the totality of life, bearing down, as it were, on this one little creature "out of function" in the functioning entirety, would eliminate it.

Some animals are of clear and immediate service to us.

An earthworm? There are 50,000 worms, more or less, in an acre of soil. In a year they carry to the surface about 18 tons of earth castings. In twenty years they carry from the subsoil to the surface a layer of soil about 3 inches thick. They honeycomb the earth. They aerate the soil. They "plow" it and turn it and make it good for agriculture.

But other animals are of no evident service to us. They are actively hostile to our prosperity. Their "use"? Here we go into the labyrinth of the study of indirect uses, uses to The Whole.

Is a fox "any good"? We can find out that it is. But to do so we have to find out how many mice a fox eats, how many deer mice, how many grasshoppers, rabbits, and porcupines; and then we have to find out what *they* eat, and also what other creatures beside foxes depend *on* them for food; and we have to open up some hundreds or thousands of fox stomachs and find how many bushels of grass are in them. (*Grass?* Does a fox ever eat *grass?* Yes it does, frequently. It eats grass directly; and it also eats grass indirectly, by eating herbivores that have eaten it; and the study of the different grasses in fox stomachs, and the study of vegetable distribution thereby involved, can comfortably keep a team of investigators with a brace of slide rules busy for a lifetime). In Eric Gill's words about the creation, "It all goes together." It goes together with a most beautiful exactness.

The study of animals' individual "niches" in the architecture of creation's flowing stability, its repose in progress, is called ecology. We can't very well go into it very far in this book. It needs shelves full of books all by itself. But we can get the sense of it, in an easy and memorable way, from a whimsical situation suggested by Huxley as an extension of an example of Charles Darwin's. Animal goes with animal, all in a linkage, and Huxley expressed it like this:

Suppose you know that in a certain village there live a good many old maids. What can you confidently guess as to the flora of that region? You can guess that it will be an excellent place for crops of red clover. How do you perform this singular guesswork? This way:

The only bees that can reach the nectar in red clover blossoms are bumblebees. Red clover can't grow at all except where there are bumblebees in abundance. What thins down and keeps meager the bumblebee population? Field mice do. Where there are lots of field mice, destroying bumblebees' nests, the bumblebees dwindle; which means that red clover does also. But where the field mice themselves are kept down, the bumblebees thrive, and the red clover flourishes. And what keeps down field mice? Nothing does that more effectively than a plenty of mousing cats. And where, notoriously, can you count on cats abounding? Why, in the households of lonely and affection-starved spinsters, to be sure. Presto! Count the old maids and you have as good as weighed the crop of red clover, without ever going near the place.

The addendum of the "old maids," of course, was Huxley's fun. The rest of the factor-linking was Darwin's, and it makes sober sense enough. It describes exactly, in its preposterous way, the fashion in which the close-textured web of animals' interrelations is composed; and it makes plain what an enormous and frequently impossible question we are really asking when we ask what is the "use" of any animal. No living thing in this world stands alone. It has its connection, literally, with every other thing, everywhere. When a mouse sneezes in Patagonia, there is a connection with how many eggs a catbird lays in Wisconsin. We cannot, naturally, always follow all the workings of all the strands in all the web. We have to go groping and peering, and at best we can make out only a little. But at least we can make out enough to know how very little it is.

Are most animals harmful or beneficial? A wise animalizer ought at least to be wise enough to know that that is not the right way to ask the question. Do we want this world to be this world? Do we accept it? We do? Then we have answered—pre-answered—our question about all the animals in it. For it is *all* the animals—connected each with each, linked unseverably all in all—that effect the serene entirety. There are foxes on this acre because there are woodchucks on it, and there are woodchucks because there are these particular vegetations, and there are these vegetations because certain birds migrate here and feed and leave droppings, and these birds are here because the Mississippi River, which they follow when traveling, is where it is, and the Mississippi River . . . the whole thing goes round and round in a continuum, and we are reminded of the old definition of God as the Power whose circumference is everywhere and center nowhere. What use is a woodchuck? Come now. What use is the Mississippi?

How long do animals live?

There are almost as many answers to this as there are kinds of animals; but at least we can say a few things about the subject, by and large, and look at a few common cases. By and large, then, life span and size go together. Big beasts endure longer than little ones. Among the mammals, vegetarians and animals that eat mixed kinds of food live longer than meat eaters do. Animals that mature early also die early. Those that come late to maturity are also slow to "wear out." Sluggish cold-blooded animals can live longer than hot-blooded mammals. What's the longest living of all the animals? A giant tortoise, probably. Tortoises not infrequently weigh five or six hundred pounds, and it seems a safe guess that one this size is two or three hundred years old.

Do elephants live for centuries? No. It is a very rare elephant that reaches one hundred. Most elephants have begun to become decrepit at fifty or sixty.

How about carp and pike? Surely *they* live for centuries? Doesn't "everybody say" that they do? Well, yes, a great many people do seem to say it; but the fish don't say it. This is not a coy and prankish way of speaking. Fish, no less than trees, "tell" their age with considerable exactness to an examiner. Concentric rings on fishes' ear bones (and rings, too, on their scales) show their periods of growth. How long do carp really live? Not more than sixty or perhaps seventy-five years. The ages of other fish? Trout, bass, perch? Rarely fifteen years. A common crawfish? About the same. Minnows, sticklebacks, and such small finny ones? Half that, or even less.

Many insects (like the May flies we were talking about a little while ago) are ephemeral. Their adult life is reckoned in hours. Other insects are more durable. How long can a queen bee live? Fifteen or twenty years, at least. A termite? Thirty or better.

Birds? Vultures (which live, by the way, entirely on meat; animaldom at large does not support a vegetarian argument) often live well over half a century. Do parrots reach great ages? For birds, yes, they do. A parrot lifetime as long as a human lifetime is not uncommon. Parrots share with owls, ostriches, and eagles the longevity record among birds. Do any of these birds ever get to be centenarians? Almost certainly. How about our common small birds, the songbirds? Their lives run, putting it broadly, anywhere from about five or six to about eighteen years.

If there is one thing we want to avoid in this book of informal animalizing, it is that chill and dreary adjunct of textbooks, the *table*. Animals are alive things, warm things, fellow-being-things; and nothing can make them seem less so than charts, graphs, and lists. Still, risking it in this instance as we risked it in talking about

how animals are classified, here are a few representative probable
life spans, in years, of some other assorted animals:

Our brotherly ape	50
Bat	3–5
Bear	20–30
Camel	45
Cat	15–20
Crocodile	40–50, plus
Crow, raven	25–30
Deer	18–25
Dog	15 (the record's about 25)
Fox	8–10
Goat	15–20
Horse	20–35
Lion	20–25
Mouse	3–5
Newt and lizard	25
Ostrich	60
Pig	20
Rabbit	8–10
Rhinoceros	50
Snake (a big one)	25
Squirrel	8–10
Toad	30
Wolf	10–15

These animal ages aren't exact. They are based on the ages to
which captive and domesticated animals have lived, the ages at

which they attain sexual maturity, and the ages at which they stop breeding, and similar useful factors for calculation. But there is always to be understood the silent qualification, "more or less."

Also, though most of us may not stop to think of it very often, the terms "life" and "death" don't stand for a clear-cut difference. When is an animal alive and when is it dead? That's easy enough to say, when the animal is a deer or a fox or you or I; but it gets less and less easy among simpler animals, and among very simple animals it gets pretty nearly impossible. We ought to have a look at at least one instance, to understand the difficulty. Take the small animal called a bear animalcule.

This microscopic fellow lives in water. While the water remains, the bear animalcule is obviously and thrivingly alive in it, pursuing its animalcule destiny with lively activity. But now suppose the water dries up. The bear animalcule dries up too. It shrivels and shrinks and presently becomes desiccated into a mere fleck of powder, a particle of organic dust. Is it dead? Quite clearly.

Now suppose that we keep the bear animalcule like this for a week, a month, a year. Suppose we keep it for years. And then, when the years have gone by, suppose we pop the dust grain into water.

Some hours pass, and then, very very slowly, the bear animalcule begins to move. The speck of dust swells and fills out into a body. Movement becomes more and more vigorous. Behold now: the bear animalcule, pulsingly alive, goes creeping off upon its rounds. It had been only dead, dry dust, and now it has resumed its living exactly where it left off living years before.

Life? Death? There is nothing better than animalizing for getting rid of any tendency to a too-cocksure dividing of truth into tight compartments.

What do animals die of?

The very humble animals, such as the one of which we have just been speaking, can scarcely be said to undergo "death" at all, in the sense in which we ordinarily understand the word. It is not altogether a fantasy to think of a protozoan as immortal. Our paramecium, the representative animalcule into whose life-way we were looking in the beginning of these pages, does not *beget* new paramecia. It *becomes* them. The individual paramecium divides and becomes two new individual paramecia. Each of these divides and becomes two more. Each of *these* divides . . . and so on to infinity, by geometrical progression. (Or nearly so. In strict fact, this sort of fission does not go on endlessly without any addendum of "new" stock. After a number of generations, paramecia do come together in pairs, as we saw, and a part of the one's nucleus fuses with a part of the other's, in an act of conjugation. But individuality has such inexact boundaries, at this animal stage, that death can only with difficulty be thought of as the passing of a self.)

All the higher animals, however, come to the end of their life adventure in a death such as we recognize. Squirrels, coons, possums, mice, robins . . . all the animals are under the same terms we are. They all meet death. How?

The great majority of animals die by violence. They are killed by other animals or by natural mishaps and disasters. Life feeds on other life. As a classical phrase of naturalists puts it, in another connection, *Omne vivum ex vivo*. Death, for most animals, means being caught and eaten by another animal. At one moment, a rabbit is nibbling the moonlit grass; the next moment, its spine has been snapped by a fox. At one moment, a song sparrow is trilling on a twig; the next moment, it has launched into rushing flight, with a lean gray shadow pursuing; and presently it is beaten to earth and clawed and clubbed to death by a shrike. To go outdoors at all into animaldom is to find death happening. Death by storm, death by starvation, death by freezing, death by fire or drowning, death inflicted by an enemy. There is also death by disease.

Do animals get ailments like ours? They do indeed. Microorganisms and bigger parasites invade them in legions, so that they weaken and sicken. Bacteria, viruses, mold growths abound in animaldom and feed on it. Appendicitis? The coccidia that get into the caecum of, say, a common thrush, give the mottle-breasted little bird an inflammation that is almost exactly like our appendicitis. Malaria? Even a phoebe may have that; even a toad; even a snake. (Do mosquitoes bite even birds and animals, transmitting disease from bloodstream to bloodstream? Oh, yes. We are only one of numerous animals visited by mosquitoes.) Animals get tumors and cancers. They get infections and impactions of their teeth. They get skin and circulatory disorders. An epidemic paratyphoid often sweeps the great migrating flocks of birds. A naturalist studying what kills animals has to have almost as fat and numerous reference books as a doctor.

Are we to feel, then, a lessening of our spontaneous sentiment that the garden of the creation is a good, glad garden? We step outdoors, and breathe deep the air of the June morning, and hear the tumult of ten thousand exuberating bird songs, and we say to ourselves: What a health and happiness there is about all this! It is natural and native to us to feel that moss smell and earth smell and woods smell are tonic scents to breathe, that animaldom has a joy and lilt to it, and that when we go animalizing we are doing a somehow restorative and wholesome thing. Is all that a sentimental delusion? Are animals, in sober truth, as harried and fretted a lot as we ourselves unfortunately often are? No.

No; and no again. We aren't deluding ourselves, in those moments of simple Adamite spontaneity about the excellence of earth. We're reading animaldom right. Animal life does have, in the profoundest sense, a soundness and happiness at the heart of it. ("Their world is instinct and joy and adventure!" the grand old naturalist of Slabsides cried. "It is our childhood come back to us.") A little knowledge about animals, like a little knowledge about anything else, may be a dangerous thing. It may let us know about the deaths and diseases which in our original naïveté we had scarcely thought about. It may make things look grim. But then if we persist on to a further and deeper knowledge about animals we are bound to come around full circle. It is a matter of realizing this: that delight and fear, happiness and unhappiness, do not lie just in events that occur, but in the quality of the mind that experiences them. It is a matter of getting inside animals and knowing the quality of their psyches.

A rabbit, living in its rabbity little world of the moment, is full of the joy of function: this taste of grass, this feel of the earth underfoot, this sensorimotor excitement of being. The pounce of a fox is startling, yes; but it is not an *understood* thing. A rabbit does not know what death is; it cannot look forward to it. It cannot conjure the past; it cannot think about all the connotations of the present; exactly speaking, it cannot worry. Our thrush, dying, does not—*cannot*—know that it is dying. Is it a tragic thing to be dying? Not if the dying one does not know it has a self to lose. What is jeopardized, in its mind? Nothing. Pain depends on what mind receives its message and reflects upon it. We cut our finger and "suffer." Our hound dog tears through the brambles, hot on a trail, and rips its hide to shreds; and an unprejudiced man needs only to look at that joyously lolling tongue, those shining eyes, to know that, though "pain" may have touched the flesh, our hound (so to put it) has not heard of it. Animals are engaged in being animals: putting forth their powers, exercising their superb senses, responding to the drive and thrust of animal aliveness. The dark agonies of apprehension, the worries of self-concern, have no entrance into that world of creation's morning.

We shall be talking again and again, in this and that connection, of various aspects of animals' inner lives.

The animals' mind is one of the biggest and most difficult and most fascinating of all questions about animals. It is the question on a broad consideration of which this first section of our book may suitably conclude. The answer to it has to be long, and it may make dense going in spots; but it is superlatively important if we are to have any real and right understanding of the animal life around us. It bears upon the question of animal suffering; it involves our interpretation of every act we see an animal perform; it is nothing less than the centrally intimate question of what being an animal is like. So then:

Are animals' minds like ours?

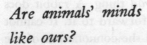

This is such an enormous question, requiring such a deal of background data, such scrupulosities of definition, and such an entering of exceptions, qualifications, and nice nigglings of one sort and another, that about all we can do is try to establish here a sort of general answer, and then let that be amplified, qualified, and illustrated by particular answers to particular other questions later on.

Books, of course (books?—*libraries* of books) have been written about the animal mind. Comparative psychologists have studied it in the laboratory and subjected it to scientific tests. Field naturalists have studied it outdoors, in living action. Theologians and philosophers have considered it in theory. Beliefs have come and gone. Arguments have flared up and died down. (There was the great controversy about "nature faking" in the early years of the twentieth century, with a popular naturalist, Dr. William J. Long, asserting he had seen an oriole do thus and so and a woodcock do thus and so, and with the President of the United States, Theodore Roosevelt, roaring "nature faker!" and insisting that the limitations of oriole mind and woodcock mind could not possibly have permitted the birds to act in any such way and that Dr. William J. Long was a sensationmongering fraud. It was a painful and disedifying business, a lot fuller of heat than of light.) Are animals' minds like ours? Well, cautiously, suppose we tackle it like this:

It is obviously impossible for us, by however earnest and instructed an effort of the imagination, to project ourselves inside an animal and see with its eyes, hear with its ears, feel with its feelings, and entertain altogether its content of consciousness. Old Uncle Zeke, who has hunted raccoons so many years that he virtually feels he *is* a coon, can't quite do that; and neither can Professor X, with five scientific degrees after his name, who has tested raccoons in scientifically designed mazes, subjected raccoons to bell ringings, saliva tests, and blindfold tests, and written a shelfful of impenetrable monographs on *Behavior Studies of Procyon lotor and Related Forms.* A man is a man and a coon is a coon; and when we look into the deeps of the dark eyes of our ring-tailed brother, *Procyon lotor,* it's a good idea to retain a large humility in making our reckonings of what may be going on behind them. We learn all we can, fact-wise; and then—and this goes for the best of us—we guess. Scientists will guess like scientists. Poets will guess like poets. None of us can guess with the certainty of insight which could be ours only if, like our subject, we were a *Procyon lotor* ourself.

However. We can bear a good many things in mind which keep our guesses about the animal mind from being merely wild ones. We can get down to probabilities. We can avoid the absurd. We can be completely sure of a number of things, and *pretty* sure about a whole lot more. The whole study of animals has no adventure more fascinating than the attempt to get, as accurately and vividly as we can, inside these furred and feathered brothers of ours. Does a rabbit think and reason? Does a fox? Does a fish? Can an earthworm learn anything?

Well, now. Introspection is not a scientific method. But it's a practical human method; and we can most usefully start with it here. You and I, at this moment, have no doubt, do we, that we are creatures with reasoning minds? We are agents aware of our agency, consciously employing means toward envisaged ends. We can reason in abstractions; our thought is lit by the light of universal logical concepts. By an act of imagination, we can fore-inhabit the future. By an act of recollection, we can call the past into presence. We can conceptualize in universals: roundness, triangularity, symmetry, and, more rarefied still, fairness, duty, or whatever. Our minds, in the fullest human sense, are what we call rational.

All right. We are now a reasoning animal. But now go back some years. Go back, say, to when we were about ten. Was our world of consciousness, then, as wide and full and deep as it is now? Clearly, it wasn't. General concepts were fuzzy around the edges. When we looked into the future, it wasn't a vast stare into vistas of infinity. It stretched only to the next vacation, perhaps not quite that far. The past? No long, ordered vista there, either. Memories were wavery, jiggly things, the time sense incomplete. But did we have intelligence? Why yes, of course we did. We were capable of learning, and learning fast. Our minds were agile enough, but in—so to put it—a small way.

Now let's go back further together; back to well before we were seven, which is the classic age for the beginning of reason. When we were three or four, our eyesight was at least as keen as it is now. It was probably a great deal keener. But when we were three or four, did we really "see" the far hills that our elders contemplated? We know we didn't. What we really "saw" (for seeing takes mind as well as eye) was just the immediate world right around us: this beetle, here beside our foot, this toy we were holding in our hand, this one human being, right beside us, who was our mother or father or playmate. Sensorily, we were keenly alive, animally alive. Did we do any thinking? Yes, very actively, in a tinily circumscribed world, in a world with no far insights. Future and past? "Today," "tomorrow," "yesterday" . . . a little child jumbles them all around. We had not entered into that reality. Death? Quite unimaginable. A little child doesn't even understand what is meant by anything coming to an "end." You and I were learners, in those days; we had alertness; we made a stab at "figuring things out." But our whole world of consciousness was a little bit of a world. It hadn't become enriched and thickened out with implications. We lived and moved and had our being in a Now, and the lively realities of the Now were things like feeling hungry, feeling sleepy, feeling obscurely "cross," feeling startled, or feeling secure.

Back before that we were infants; and before that we were newborn babies who had wide-open perfect eyes but didn't "see" at all because vision was not backed by enough mind to report and interpret the images; and back before that we stirred and sometimes squealed as a foetus inside another body; and way back at the beginning we were a wiggly little blend of ovum and spermatozoon.

Does it become clear what we're doing, in this backward look along our lives and along the states of our consciousness? Each one of us, in his life's history, recapitulates the whole evolutionary history of our kind. There's a stage where we show our gill slits. We show tails. We live through a state of being as elementary as a tadpole's; we live through dawn-consciousness; we progress through growing and growing awarenesses; we learn to put two and two together, and after a while a million and a billion. We start by making little whimpers of obscure discomfort or satisfaction; we arrive at the last, perhaps, brooding on the meaning of the universe. In a word, the development of mind, like the development of body, is a long, infinitely gradual thing. Are animals' minds like ours? Now we can say it: Yes, they are; but any given animal's mind is like ours at that given evolutionary stage of development.

Is a tadpole filled with dread when it sees a kingfisher diving down upon it? No more, we can be certain, than a newborn baby is dismayed if the doctor speaks in its presence of a war rumor in Malaya. Were we alarmed by the darkness in the womb? Does our coon think, when he hears the hounds, that the hour of death may be drawing near? Consider: Did *we* have an idea of death when we were two or three? Did it cross our mind, for that matter, when we teetered joyously along the top of a picket fence even when we were ten or twelve, that perhaps we might slip and that this might cause thus-and-such injury and that this would mean going to the hospital and that this would mean pain and expense? The far, far thoughts of adulthood are not the thoughts of childhood; and they are not the thoughts of animals, either. It is an old and natural figure of speech to call animals the "children of nature"; and the figure will do us excellently, in the matter of understanding animals' minds, if we hold fast also to one or two other considerations.

Animals, all animals, can learn. Their *understanding* of the life experience—their comprehension of what they are doing and why, their insight into the fullness of reality—may not expand beyond this or that child-stage; but this has nothing to do with the acquisition of cunnings and ingenuities that can total up impressively into what I think we may usefully call practical intelligence.

There is a saying that a cat doesn't sit on a hot stove twice. Exactly so. An animal tries, say, first one way and then another of catching fish. By trial and error, it discards the ways that are unrewarding, or that bring pain, and so on. It hits on a way that works. By practice, it perfects that way. The result is finally a fishing technique that cannot possibly be called anything but intelligent; but the animal using it is displaying *practical* intelligence, as distinguished from the insighted intelligence that would have gone straight to the heart of things in the first place by direct why-and-wherefore understanding.

Intelligence is one thing. Insighted reason is another, and very special, thing. Do worms have any intelligence? Yes, some. Under patient training, they can learn to find their way through simple mazes. Has a cockroach any capacity for learning? Oh, yes. Cockroaches have even been taught, completely against the whole instinct of their nature, to prefer light to dark. One biologist has put it this emphatically: "Even protoplasm has brains." That's slangy and inexact, no doubt, but it is substantially the truth. Every living animal can learn. It can make experiments; it can profit by them; it can get to be, in its maturity, the harborer of a large lore of practical intelligence in living. Is a veteran fox adept in woods cunning? Yes, indeed. But—and this puts a difference just about as simply and crucially as it can be put—does the canniest old fox know that he *is* a fox? The realizations of self and of otherness, the concept of identity, the concept of number . . . all these come only with insighted reasoning, and it is only we human creatures whose minds advance into that gigantic new area of understanding.

There can be a great deal of "wisdom," of course, that has nothing to do with reasoning. There is flesh wisdom, body wisdom, nerve wisdom. Animals are largely guided through their lives by that prerational intelligence. It is "wisdom" to bat our eyes when a fist is brandished at our faces. But we don't have to "decide" to do it. We don't have to "think it out." It is a wisdom of reflex. We were talking about toad-mating a while back. It is a "wise" thing, certainly, that a male toad's thumbs swell up before copulation so that he is enabled the better to grip the female. But it is flesh wisdom. It is caused, quite involuntarily, by a change in hormone secretion.

Animals' lives are full of acts that look thought-out, or seem to show penetrating astuteness, but that are in fact as unconscious and unplanned as a toad's physiological preparation for coupling. How does a baby turtle, newly hatched from the egg on a sand dune, know which way to head to find water? It has an inborn drive to go down hill . . . the kind of inborn and hereditary drive that is called a tropism. There are dozens and scores of tropisms (and similar kinds of natural inborn inclinations) in animals' lives. Why do moths come to a flame? That is a positive phototropism, serving in a state of wild nature to pull them toward the glimmer of flowers in the dusk. What holds queen bees to the dark interior of the hive? A negative phototropism. It is the pull of hydrotropism that brings housefly grubs to moisture. Why does a snake insert itself thus and so in a crevice, and not otherwise? Because it is impelled willy-nilly to establish a certain peculiarly satisfying kind of contact with its environment. It is under the compulsion of a stereotropism. Subject a cockroach to a weak tactual stimulus; which way will it turn? It will turn toward the stimulus. Why? Because it thinks that is wise? Because it has learned? No. Again it is a spontaneous compulsive thing. (The name, thunderously enough, is positive thigmotaxis.)

All animals' unconscious and reflexive behaviors are popularly summed up in one handy word: instinct. Strictly, instinct is defined as an established and transmitted pattern in animals' central nervous systems; but it is an invaluable word, in a more spacious sense, for all the things that animals do prementally, subrationally, of whatever sort. "Instinctive" covers admirably the way animals "get the feel" of a situation, where a human philosopher would insist on trying to understand it. It covers the inner urgencies that set otters to playing, and birds to singing, and skunks to dancing in the moonlight. Instinct, in this wide sense of the un-thought-out, the spontaneous, the impulsively done, the hereditarily native, undoubtedly covers an enormous amount of all animal activity.

But are we to think of animals, then, as just mechanisms, as just automata? No; not at all. A mind, as we saw in our backward introspection, can be a very humble little mind and still have begun, in its limited little way, to put two and two together. The two-and-two of an earthworm is a dim and minuscule arithmetic; but the arithmetic has begun. The robin on our lawn is thinking no large thoughts about ornithological theory; but after its bird fashion it is entertaining at least fragmentarily and in glimmers a little of something that must be called thought. (Had we *no* awareness when we were in our perambulators? Why, if psychoanalysts are not mistaken, there was a faint, faint stir of consciousness in us even before we got ourselves born.) Look now into the eyes of *Procyon lotor*, our coon. What looks out at us is a fellow *anima*, a coon consciousness, a coon wit. Enough mind to do trigonometry? Of course not. But enough mind to learn the more appropriate skills of luring a coon dog to water to drown him, and of putting mussels on a sun-hot rock to make them open their shells. Here, in a worm, mind flickers feeble and small. Here, in an ape, it has grown to a brightness and quickness. But it is all Mind; all part of the one seamless continuum.

The hereditary skill of instinct gives animals, so to speak, a basic instruction. It is immeasurably added to, and may be modified, by learning: by what is picked up in the trial-and-error school of living experience. There grows the thing called practical intelligence. There is added at last, in all the higher animals, the occasional gleam of putting two and two together; the flash of insight, at least of a sensorimotor sort; the perception, to some degree, of relationships of things. Do animals have minds like ours? Being duly wary of anthropomorphism, and remembering that the animals are not ourselves as we are now, but in the more spontaneous and less intricately analytical days of our various stages of childhood, there can be only one answer given. It is Yes.

In the attempt to get inside an animal and understand what life is like to it, from the inside looking out, we have to remember one more thing particularly. We have to keep in mind animals' vivid sensory aliveness. Our own senses are dull. When we use the words "consciousness" or "awareness," we ordinarily mean intellectual awareness and thinking-consciousness. We forget about sensory awareness. We can think much bigger thoughts than a moth; but a moth is keenly alive to subtle scents two miles away. We think our way through life. To a great extent an animal smells its way, feels its way, hears its way, finds its way by touch and taste. In answer to specific questions later on in these pages, we shall be encountering a good many rather stunning facts about what a fish can feel, or a viper detect in the air, or a bat "see" on a black night.

Is an animal's experience of life like ours? Yes, with the intellectual content diminished; yes, with emotions more direct and simpler, because free of the elaborations that come with fuller understanding; and yes, finally, with this to be borne in mind: that an animal is constantly receiving and interpreting an inflow of sensory advices which "tell" it things as our intellectualizings tell us what we require to know. Do we want to know what time it is? We look at our watch, or make a computation. Bees *feel* the passing of time. How far away, on a dark night, is the obstacle we are approaching? We light a light, or try to "think out" the answer. A trout knows it by pressures felt along its median line.

All animals, in their ways, are knowing. John Burroughs, who struggled for half a lifetime to express some of the nearly-inexpressibles of how animals think and feel, once spoke a phrase of deceptive simplicity. "The animals know," he said, "but they know without knowing that they know."

This just about completes our considerations of the broad thematic questions that are most often asked about animal life in general. Suppose we go ahead, now, to animals in particular. We start with mammals.

Mammals

Mammal means "breasted." A *mamma* is a milk-furnishing teat. The mammals are all those fellow beings of ours which, diverse as they may be in other respects, suckle their young. They are all warm-blooded. They all have hair, and they never have feathers. The great majority have discernible tails, and with negligible exceptions they have claws, fingernails, or hoofs. Mammals are the warm, appealing, "animally" animals. They are obviously the closest of all our brother creatures. It takes a certain effort of mind, and a certain breadth of vision, to be aware of our fellowship with fish or lizards; but we can all feel an immediate intimacy with rabbits and foxes. We ourselves, whatever else we may be, are mammals. However near to angels our psychic nature may put us, everything else about our nature puts us very close indeed to all the warm-blooded beasts of the creation.

Mammals are what in ordinary popular language and conversation we call simply "animals," intending to distinguish them from birds, reptiles, or whatever. Since "mammal" is not a familiar and congenial term to some of us, why don't we—for the duration of this one section of our book, that is—agree to use the plain familiar word? Having established that we know better, we can comfortably use the language of simplicity and every day. All right, then. Now about *animals*. . . .

Do all animals have hair or fur?

Yes, they do. There are no exceptions to this. Animals' hair may be thick and cohesive, so that we call it "wool," as in the case of sheep; or it may be composed of stiff outer hairs and soft, dense underhair, so that the outer hair has to be removed in preparation of the commercial "fur," as in the case of sealskin, which is in fact the seal's underhair only; or it may be so fine that we scarcely realize it exists at all. (Does even a hippopotamus have hair? Yes; hair covers almost its entire body, but it is so short and scanty we may not notice it. Surely *we* don't have hair except in particular areas? Yes, we do. We are a very hairy animal. There is fine hair virtually all over us except on the palms of our hands and the soles of our feet.) Dense fur keeps animals' body heat from escaping. It affords protection from injury. Often it is erectile, under the control of muscles, so that animals can "bristle" or signal with what among deer we call their "flags." Do any creatures but animals have hair? No.

Do animals ever develop from eggs?

Sometimes, yes. Rightly speaking, of course, we *all* develop from eggs. What happens is simply that an animal's egg hatches before it gets outside the mother's body. But even this is not always the case. The primitive Australian animals called platypuses and spiny anteaters lay eggs. Platypuses—famous among naturalists as probably the oddest animals now prowling our earth—have ducklike bills and webbed feet. They nest in stream-bank burrows, lay eggs much as a kingfisher might, and hatch forth naked baby animals which are then suckled. They also have another oddity, which leads into a very common question:

Are there such things as poisonous animals?

There are extremely few of them; but, yes, they do exist. For example: on the inner side of a male platypus's hind leg there is a sort of spur. It is hollow and connects with a poison gland. It makes the platypus, in its way, as truly venomous as a stinging insect or poisonous snake.

Though poisonous animals are very few, there is one other one we ought to know about. This one isn't an obscure zoological curiosity like the platypus. It is the common little mouselike American animal called a short-tailed shrew. This tiny animal is very unlikely to bite any of us—a shrew being a nervous, skittery little fellow with such a tense and delicately adjusted nervous system that when a shrew is caught in our hand it frequently dies instantly, then and there, from the shock of the experience—but it does have a toxic bite.

When we get to know animals, we get to find out that a great, great many popular notions about them aren't true. (Do bats snarl themselves in women's hair? No. Does a skunk's bite always give you hydrophobia? No. Do falling cats always land on their feet? No. Are elephants terrified by mice? Not in the least. These "things which ain't so" about animals are legion; and we shall keep finding out about them again and again in this book.) But every now and then, entertainingly enough, another sort of thing happens. We find out that some nonsensical old backwoods superstition, some long-debunked bit of animal folklore, turns out to be true.

Can a toad give you warts? And, if it can, will an application of stump water take them away? When we know nothing at all about animals, we are likely to believe both those propositions. Didn't an old gardener tell us something of the sort in our childhood? Isn't it the fact that "they say" you get warts from handling toads? If later we take up the study of animals in anything like a serious way, we soon learn that the toads-and-warts notion is a baseless old superstition. Toads do give off an acrid and slightly irritating exudate which discourages predatory animals from eating them; but the substance is powerless to cause a wart. Further, a caught toad often voids its urine; but again, while this may startle or repel the capturer, it cannot cause warts to appear. At this stage, we are wonderfully superior. *We know about animals;* and we are eagerly ready to go about disabusing the myth-laden and instructing the ignorant. It is a grand and bracing stage in every naturalist's life. It may last clear through his teens. (Should he be a permanently teen-minded man, of course, it may last him with a bright cocksureness through a lifetime.) But if, following persistently the Huxleyan injunction to "sit down before fact like a little child," we go pressing on into more and more years of thoughtful and inquiring animalizing, we have the surprising adventure of coming around back to where we started.

Can a toad give you warts? Yes. Can stump water get rid of them? Yes. Or, to put it with the nicest exactness, we can be given warts by whatever we *think* can give us warts; and we can be cured of warts (or at least of one of the commonest kinds of them) by whatever we devotedly believe will cure them. We have gone far enough, at last, to have passed through the reaches of sophistication and come out on the other side, arriving back at the simplicity of the immemorially ancient truth that matter is extraordinarily worked upon by mind.

By what goes on in our minds, we can make blood flow or coagulate. We can feel pain as a trivial nuisance or feel it as a dire agony. We can get well or we can dim and darken our spirit toward death. Do we expect, with a sure confidence, a crop of warts from that toad we picked up in the woods the other day? We can get them. Do we expect, with a sure confidence, that this dab of stump water (applied, perhaps, in the full of the moon) can make the warts disappear? It can do it. So can milkweed juice, or a spider web, or throwing a dead cat over our left shoulder. Mind and body interact in continuum. We find out, the longer we go investigating "this green-kirtled earth," that things in this garden aren't quite as simple as they look. (Or perhaps, and not to be willfully perverse about it, they're simpler.)

This isn't a book of philosophy, but of animals. What were

we talking about? Oh, yes: shrew bites. Trappers and woodsmen and such-like ignorant fellows had been saying for ages that these shrews were venomous. Mammalogists and such-like learned persons had been smiling their chilly little superior smiles and deploring the superstition that there could be an animal with a venomous bite. They were still tut-tutting about the thing when I was a boy. It was only a few years ago that an investigator in an idle hour at last got around to injecting a bit of shrew-spit into a rabbit, and discovered, in confirmation of Trapper Joe's wildest whims, that the rabbit quickly keeled over, twitched briefly, and died.

Said Henri Fabre: "Human knowledge will be erased from the archives of the world before we possess the last word about even a gnat." A good animalizer might do worse than paste the observation in his hat.

Are animals ever iridescent, as some birds and insects are?

Like venomousness, iridescence among animals is exceedingly rare; but again the answer is Yes, it does occur. There are two or three kinds of African moles and water moles that gleam and glitter with the iridescence of hummingbirds.

Do any animals migrate, the way birds do?

Yes, quite a number. The most celebrated animal migrants are probably Scandinavian lemmings. These are little mouselike animals 4 or 5 inches long. Hordes of them at intervals go traveling from central Norway and Sweden westward to the Atlantic, and sometimes—what gives them their special celebrity—they continue into the sea. Spitzbergen reindeer regularly migrate inland in summertime and back to the seacoast in the fall. There are seals that make an annual migratory circuit of pretty nearly 6,000 miles.

The most truly "birdlike" migrating animals are bats. Do all bats migrate? No. The greater number, in northern climates, travel only as far as the nearest cave or big hollow-tree shelter, where they congregate in numbers, hang themselves up, and hibernate. But several common bats—red bats, hoary bats, silver-hairs—undertake in the autumn a true migration. Some travel down from the northern United States and Canada to far southern seacoast points, even to Florida. Bats from the North have arrived in early autumn in New Mexico. Now and then, astonishingly, they turn up in Bermuda.

Bats are the subject of an uncommon lot of animal questions. Among them are:

Are bats "as blind as bats"? By no means. They have complex eyes, fly with no indication of being dazzled in the brightest sunshine, and, as far as a naturalist can tell, have very fair daytime vision.

How do bats find their way around and avoid obstacles in the dark? By radar. The extraordinary quality of animals' sensory abilities, which we have to keep remembering if we are rightly to imagine their world of experience, is vividly illustrated by the commonest little bat that goes swooping and skittering around our heads in the dusk. We hear the bat emitting now and then, as it flies, a sharp little squeaking. We suppose that that intermittent squeak is the bat's only utterance. But it isn't. It is just the occasional part of its utterance that *we* are able to hear. Actually, a bat in flight through the darkness is continually "talking," but its voice is supersonic. It is outside the range of sounds we can hear. The bat's supersonic cries are bounced off the objects in the landscape, reflected back to the bat, and tell it unerringly how to guide its swift flight so that it never bangs into anything. A blindfolded bat, set loose in a dark room all cross-strung with piano wires, can flit around at top speed and never touch a wire. But stop up the bat's *ears*, and it blunders hopelessly, for it can't hear the guiding echo of its supersonic voice.

Are there such things as vampire bats? Lots of them, throughout Central and South America. Vampire bats make delicate little nicks with their sharp incisors in the skins of all sorts of animals— man is only one among them—and feed on the blood. Do they "suck your blood"? No. They lap up the droplets the way a kitten laps up milk. Do they hover over the victim, hypnotizing him? Do they fan him to sleep with their wings? Do they cause ex- cruciating pain? None of these things. Are they menacingly huge? No animalizer goes animalizing for very long before he finds out that the actual animals of this actual sun-warm and sea-wet planet are rarely indeed as alarming as the animals of mythical invention. The biggest vampire bat has a body about 4 inches long.

Will bat dung cure scorpion bites? It might soothe them a little, but no more than mud. Do bats teem with vermin? No more than any others of our brotherly animals, and less than large numbers of ourselves. Do bats lay eggs? Never. They are as com- pletely animals as rabbits or squirrels. How are their young born? The mother bat hangs head downward, suspended by her hind feet and her thumb claws, and by curving her tail and body forms a sort of receiving apron for the baby.

Most of our common bats breed in the fall and bear their babies in the spring. That doesn't mean, though, despite what we may often hear said, that bats' gestation period is a fabulously long seven or eight months. Almost immediately after mating, hibernation sets in. The bat sperm lies immotile and undeveloping in the hibernating female's reproductive organs until hibernation ends in the spring. The actual gestatory period for bats is about three months.

Bats are very "old" animals. They have been fluttering around in our night sky for probably more than sixty million years. They are a part of the magic of the country dusk—the hour of whip-poorwills, and the rising moon, and hawk moths hovering around the glimmering garden—and we don't want to go on thinking a lot of alarming nonsensicalities about them.

By the way: How big do the biggest bats in the world get to be? They occur in the Old World tropics, and are popularly called flying foxes. Their wingspread reaches about 5 feet.

Are there any animals beside bats that can fly?

No, there aren't. Many animals are *called* "flying" this or "flying" that; but actually they are animals equipped simply for soaring or gliding. Can't flying squirrels fly? No. These beguiling, soft-furred little animals have folds of skin which, when their legs are extended, become furry "wings" of a sort; but the squirrel doesn't flap or beat them. It just uses them for soaring through the air from a high point, like a treetop, to a lower point such as the bole of another tree. The performances of "flying dragons" and "flying lemurs" are similar. How about flying fish? Again, there is no true flying. The fish pushes itself out of the water, spreads its broad fins rigid, and skims through the air as far as gliding power will carry it. Then it drops back into the sea.

Every now and then we're likely to see references to a flying *snake*. Is there such a thing? Well, put it this way: No snake can fly, strictly and technically speaking; but it is true that there are snakes that can manage an aerial gliding. Some tree snakes can launch themselves in a leap from a treetop and soar to another tree 10 feet or more away. Preparatory to its "flight," the snake flattens and pulls in its underside until it becomes a widened concavity, offering remarkable air resistance. Some of these soaring tree snakes are also great leapers in other ways. When striking, they can hurl themselves clear off the ground. One Asiatic tree snake, a gold-and-black one, sometimes catches small birds in flight by leaping up into the air after them.

Speaking of leaps and jumps:

What do animals use their tails for?

For just about every purpose imaginable. A squirrel's bushy tail, for instance, is a steering rudder when the squirrel is making its big arboreal jumps and a balancing parasol when the squirrel is picking its way along fine twigs. When a squirrel misses its footing and falls (they sometimes do), the plumy tail acts as a parachute so effectively that squirrels often plunge 50 or 60 feet to earth without suffering any injury. A bushy tail is a warm wrap-around in cold weather—a winter fox, for instance, sleeps with his tail curled around over the tip of his nose—and a tail is also of incalculable help in making a predatory enemy misjudge a pounce. A predator, rushing after its victim, is likely to jump at the waving tail. It gets a mouthful of tail fur and the tail-owner gets away.

Is it true that mice use their tails to get food out of inaccessible places, such as out of bottles? Unschooled animalizers have always believed that, but some others have dismissed it as folk myth. It is no myth. It is true. If a mouse finds an unstoppered jug of, say, molasses, it will sit itself atop the neck, lower its tail into the jug in a mouse version of the gesture of a man lowering a bucket into a well, and haul up the sweet stuff tail-ful by tail-ful. Most of my own animalizing is done in the woods and fields of my land, along the brook and over in the heron swamp and in places like that; but it is a beauty of animalizing that it can go on anywhere, and I have done some of it in the old earth-floored farm cellar under the house. A year or two ago a deer mouse—a white-foot, that is—devoted an evening, while I watched him, to half emptying a small honey crock, stored on a shelf there, by this adroit tail technique.

Back in the ancient distances of time, we animals managed to get ashore at all in the first place, so to speak, by virtue of our propulsive tails. Our human fragment of tail today, our coccyx, is an inheritance from the immeasurably long-ago time when we were fish. For fish, and most aquatic creatures, tails are simply organs of locomotion. On land, tails have developed into an enormous number of other uses and animal adaptations.

To what use does a kangaroo put its great heavy tail? It leans back and props itself on it, as a man does on a shooting stick. Many lizards use their tails that way too. The original monster lizards, almost certainly, swung their tails as weapons, in a carry-over from the tail-swinging technique of fish. And today? Is it true that a crocodile uses its tail as a weapon? Yes. It can knock a man over with one wallop. Do any warm-blooded animals do the same sort of thing? Yes again. Take an ant bear. It thwacks with its tail as powerfully as a bear with its forepaw.

Tails serve animals as fly-swatters, as signals, as instruments of communication, as extra hands and tools of many uses. A woolly monkey curls the tip of his tail into a circle, plants this loop on the ground, stiffens the rest of the tail into a supporting column, and has a portable chair. A honey bear, raiding a nest of bees, hangs head downward and then, when it wants to make its getaway, climbs its own tail. Pangolins, which are scaly anteaters living in West Africa, block their burrow entrances with their armored tails.

There are almost as many tail uses as there are animals. There are also, however, some popular notions about animals' tails that aren't true.

Is it a fact that if you pick up a skunk by the tail the skunk can't discharge its malodorous spray? As a good many outdoors-explorers have learned the hard way, it isn't. It is true that sometimes a skunk, captured by the tail-grabbing technique, fails to loose its stench. This may be either because the particular skunk is exceptionally affable (*all* skunks, by the way, are placid, friendly animals, and don't ordinarily discharge their sulphide unless extremely frightened or harassed), or it may be because stench-loosing ability varies from skunk to skunk. The fact to be remembered is that a great many skunks can and do function just as effectively when hoisted by their tails as under any other circumstances. How about squirrels using their tails as sails? The story goes that when numbers of migrating squirrels come to a river, each squirrel takes off from shore on a bit of bark or a big leaf, hoists its tail as a sail, and the whole squirrel horde goes whisking adrift in a great flotilla. True? No.

This brings up the matter of beavers' tails, and so of beavers in general. Few of our furred brothers are the subject of more frequent animal questions, the list of them being headed by:

Do beavers use their tails as trowels?

In the animal books of our childhoods, and particularly of our fathers' and grandfathers' childhoods, there used sometimes to be wonderful engravings showing beavers piling heaps of mud on their broad flat tails, toting the mud to their lodge, and then slapping and smoothing the mud into place like plasterers. They were enthralling pictures. They weren't, however, reliable. Do beavers use their tails as mortarboards and trowels? They never do. What *do* they use them for? Three things: They use them for swimming-rudders. They use them for props, to sit back on when they are gnawing at a tree. They use them to sound alarm signals. They slap them against the water with a resounding "whomp," and every beaver within earshot dives to safety.

When beavers are carrying sticks for their dams, do they transport them in bundles tied together with a reed or a strip of bark? No. It is a rather delightful notion, somehow, but mythical.

When beavers start their dam, do they first fell a tree across the waterway? No. Their usual beginning is to cut willow or alder branches, carry them to the bottom of the stream, and fix them in place with their butt ends upstream. The beavers then add mud, gravel, and stones; then another layer of brush and saplings; then more mud and stones; and so on until the dam is as high as required.

Do beavers always fell a tree so that it will fall in a particular direction? Do they avail themselves of wind stress? Do they "suck the air" from logs to sink them? Do they use their tails to drive stakes? These questions are asked so often that any experienced beaver-watcher is filled with a kind of baffled wonder at their origin and persistence. The answer to all the questions is No.

There are plenty of true things about beavers to give a naturalist a lifetime of speculating about their minds and personalities. Is it really true that beavers sometimes construct canals on which to float their cuttings to their pond? It is. Sometimes such a canal may be as much as 750 feet long, and sometimes it may have two or even three water levels. Is it possible that beavers can fell a tree 10 feet in circumference? They can. One lone beaver, in one night, can cut down an aspen half a foot thick, reduce the tree to neat 6-foot lengths, and haul all the sections to the pond. Do beavers talk to each other by "sign heaps"? Yes, in the way the dogs of a countryside "talk" to each other by their voidings of urine. Beavers carry in two pairs of glands a musky substance called castoreum—we were speaking of it back in our consideration of animals' mating ways—and their communicative "sign heaps" are little cakes or patties of mud which they place in shallows or along the shore and anoint with castoreum.

There are two things about beavers that sound especially fanciful but aren't. Has some old woodsman said, improbably enough, that beavers' teeth are orange? Or has he insisted perhaps that a beaver has a special double claw for combing its fur? The claw is quite real, and the beaver does so use it. A beaver's incisors *are* orange-fronted.

When we see beavers at work, we get to wondering—as we do continually, of course, in all our animalizings—about just what is going on inside the minds of these furry engineers. What about instinct? What about intelligence? We have to keep coming back and back to this, to know the animals. There is an extremely common question, not about beavers but about something more everyday and universal, that it might be a good idea to bring up here next in this connection.

Do animals have instinctive enmities for other animals?

No. Bring up a puppy and kitten together, and they are as congenial and devoted as any dog to another dog or cat to another cat. Dogs' cat-chasing is a learned thing. The better we get to know animals, the more we find that their personalities (using that word always, of course, with a recognition of its animal limitations) are shaped by experience and learning, not wholly preformed in an automatism.

Do ducklings take instinctively to water? Are young otters instinctive swimmers? Do chicks instinctively peck at grains of corn? Do cats instinctively kill mice? Do birds have an instinct not to eat nasty-tasting caterpillars? Do young mammals have an instinct to suck at their mothers' breasts? The answer to all these questions is No; and the same answer is the right one for hundreds of other questions of the same sort.

Animals have a certain number of innate drives and propensities; in the more primitive animals, a creature may live out its lifetime with very little altering or modification of the pattern to which it is instinctively persuaded; but all animals whatsoever—all of our fellow creatures in which there burns a spark of consciousness, dim or bright—go through the life experience, as we do, as through a school of learning. The native instruction of instinct may provide, so to speak, an equipment of First Things; but there is many
C*

another thing to come afterward, in the forming of a functioning personality, and these things come by acquisition, by learning. In the higher animals, the hereditary equipment of instinct is less and less, the extent of learning greater and greater. A dog chases cats because other dogs have led him into it, or because he has in some similar way picked up the idea that it is the thing to do. He is not born with an anti-cat "instinct."

Baby elephants often suck hopefully on their mothers' trunks and tails. They have no "instinct" for the breast; only hunger, and a smell of milk, to guide them. Young chicks, however thirsty, don't instinctively recognize water. They peck at it in the random way in which they peck at everything else; and only by experiment do they find out that it is drinkable and thirst-quenching. At first, they peck with equal enthusiasm at pebbles or at corn grains; they have to learn to know their food. Kittens have no instinctive inclination to kill mice. Sometimes they may play with them, as with any other small object. Often they are afraid of them. Often they are affectionate toward them. It is the mother cat that arouses a kitten to mousing and initiates it into the lores of the kill.

Go down to however primitive a level in animal life, and "instinct" is still not the whole behavior story. An angleworm in a Y-shaped experiment-box, in which one path of the Y leads to a pleasant experience and the other path leads to an unpleasant one, can learn after a few trials which path to take, and in its obscure angleworm fashion can remember it. Herbivores can learn to eat meat, carnivores to live on grass. Life is a fluid thing, constantly being reshaped. To live is to learn.

Silkworms, we are pretty sure to have been told in school, live on mulberry leaves. So they do. They are habituated to mulberry leaves; the smell of mulberry leaf is with them from birth; they are mulberry-leaf-conditioned. We say, speaking loosely, that they have an "instinct" to eat mulberry leaves. But *must* they? Is it an iron and foreordained thing? It isn't. Under training, a silkworm can learn to eat some other sort of leaves altogether.

The whole matter of instinct and learning, of instinct and adaptation, must keep coming up again and again in our considering of animals and of what their inner lives are like. This seems a good place for two illustrations: one of instinct operating in its strictest and most rigid "instincticity," and one of a creature's basic drives being modified—indeed reversed—by the force of encountered experience.

Henri Fabre experimented with processional caterpillars. These are a kind of caterpillars that habitually march in a close-ranked file, spinning a thread as they go. Fabre artificially deflected the course of a caterpillar column and caused them to start marching around the circumference of a large vase. The procession formed a string around it, a completely closed circle of caterpillars, no leader, all followers, an endless file along an endless track. It was at midday on a thirtieth of January that Fabre got the caterpillars thus started on the circle. When nightfall came, the caterpillars were still marching around and around; when the next day dawned, their interminable procession still followed undeviatingly its endless route; on the third day they had not halted or swerved. Frost chilled the air, numbing the caterpillars, and they grew weak from starvation, but never could they break their everlasting circle or escape from the inner compulsion toward following-the-leader which for millenniums in the wild state had been innate in their being. More days passed, and still the caterpillars marched onward along their endless way. When at last the spell did finally break, it was only by an accident, and it was in the eighty-fourth hour of the caterpillars' continuous marching. Driven by the undeniable compulsion of instinct—unable to break away from its tremendous behests even to avoid freezing and starvation—the caterpillars had marched more than a quarter of a mile.

That is instinct in operation with nothing to modify it. The mind of a caterpillar is a very dim little mind, not easily educable. But now suppose we consider a second illustration, to let us see how even at these humble levels of animal life a creature *can* "change its mind" . . . can learn something, in fact, vividly enough to inhibit a tropism. J. S. Szymanski, in 1912, taught a cockroach to that end.

Szymanski placed the cockroach in a box, half of which was made of glass and thus flooded with light, and half of which was cozily dark. The cockroach, in the powerful grip of negative phototropism, naturally sought to hide in the darkened end. Every time it did so, however, it received an electric shock. Again and again it obeyed its tropism; again and again it was shocked. After a number of trials, the cockroach would run to the edge of the dark end and would then hesitate there, brushing its antennae furiously, which is the cockroach indication of high excitement, before going in to be shocked again. Gradually, these hesitations became longer and longer. Finally, on a day of triumph, the cockroach stayed firmly in the lighted end of the box and did not even go to the threshold of the dark area for nearly a full hour. The tug of tropism had been overcome. The cockroach had transcended the mere mechanism of essential cockroachness. It had learned something.

The power of tropism being what it is, and the learning power of cockroaches being what it is, the cockroach could never be made to hold fast to its new behavior for much longer than an hour. But, to that little degree at least, it could demonstrate that it was an animal. It was not a plant. It could assimilate simple facts of experience, and (as it were) keep them briefly in mind.

No; dogs don't chase cats because of any simple "instinct" to do so. They have learned it. . . . And hawks have learned the nice calculation of the swoop on prey, cats have learned to pounce on mice instead of loving them, beavers have learned, in maturity, how to deal with logging problems as they could not do when they were beaver kits. Instinct, if you like, is the primer. But the developed lore of the higher animals' lives comes in the living and the learning.

Can water animals stay submerged indefinitely?

No. No animal (by which, as we'd better repeat, we mean in this section a mammal) is equipped with gills; and no animal, however devoted to water life and adapted to it, can stay underwater very long. All animals have to come up to breathe. This is true even of whales, and brings up two common questions:

When a whale "blows," does it spout water? A great many thousands of observers would swear that it does; but it doesn't. Whales are true mammals, wholly air-breathers, and can no more tolerate water in their respiratory apparatus than any other mammal can. It would drown them. When a whale dives (and by the way, how deep can that be? Almost incredibly, it can be more than 3,000 feet), it fills its great lungs with air on which to subsist until the next time it surfaces. Then, when it comes up, it blows out the air in a great blast through its two nostrils, its "blowholes." In the whale's warm-blooded body the air has become heated and moist. As it's exhaled into the cooler outer air, what we see is jets of steamy vapor. Why do whales seem to "blow" more often and more spectacularly in cold climates than in mild ones? That's why.

Whales, we say, are true mammals. That means they must suckle their babies. Why in the world, then, don't the babies drown, as they feed at the underwater teats? The answer is this: When a mother whale feeds her youngster, she heaves herself over on her side, so that her breasts are just below the water line. As the baby whale attaches itself, its "blowholes" are above water.

Valvular nostrils and slow respiration can enable water-frequenting animals to stay underwater so much longer than we can that it is not surprising there should be a notion that these animals are "part fish." One or two questions ago, we were talking about beavers' dam building. As they work away at their log-fitting and mud-patting, how long can beavers stay submerged? At least ten minutes. The great marine animals can do much better than that. How long can a whale stay down? Well over an hour.

It is impossible to speak of whales at all without bringing up that question that is one of the most persistent in the world. In short, what about Jonah? Could that whale really have swallowed him? When as animalizers we have had a few years of learning animal lore, and consequently feel a complacent superiority, we are ready to dismiss the Jonah story as beneath contempt. A great blue whale may weigh almost 300,000 pounds, true; but it has a tinily narrow throat, lives entirely on minute sea creatures, and could scarcely engulf anything much larger than a duck. Swallow a man? Absurd. But then, later on, we may get to know about sperm whales, the very different whales that some mariners call cachalots. Their gullets are amply big enough to swallow whole the huskiest man in the world. Could a cachalot have gulped down Jonah? Easily. There remains, of course, the problem of whether a swallowed man could long avoid being digested. That must strike any naturalist as unlikely. But we have come a long way if we come from the fierce intransigence of "absurd!" to the gentle cautious- ness of just "unlikely." We have traveled along the wisest of all the trails that a naturalist can follow.

When they are walking and running, do all animals move their feet in the same order?

No. Animals use two different ways of maneuvering their four feet. A horse, for instance, is a "diagonal" runner; a deer's foot- work is "rotatory." Rotatory sequence goes like this: left fore- foot; left hind foot; right hind foot; right forefoot. Diagonal se- quence goes: left forefoot; right forefoot; left hind foot; right hind foot. An animal, of course, may choose to move any one of its four legs first; but the movement of its legs then follows one of those two patterns. The deer and antelope are all rotatory runners. So are dogs and foxes. Diagonal movers, in addition to horses and cows, include bears. How about insects, by the way? They have *six* legs to manage. Most insects have such a wobbly, bumbling gait that it scarcely looks as though they moved their legs in any particular order at all. But they do. Two legs on one side and one on the other always operate simultaneously. An insect, so to speak, moves along on a tripod.

Why do animals' eyes shine in the dark?

If we like to be stickling, we can say, with strict truth, that they don't. In complete darkness animals' eyes don't shine; they don't give off a light of their own. Technically, the question ought to go like this: Why do animals' eyes reflect light directed into them? Go into the woods at night and flash a torch, and eye-shine everywhere glitters at us: little pricks and glitters of topaz to let us know that there is a spider hiding in this shrubbery, glints of green witch-fire to betray the presence of a stealthy fox behind that fallen log, a quick blaze of glowing red that means our light has discovered a rabbit. If we shine our light into human eyes, we rarely catch a glint; but the animals' eyes blaze at us from the darkness. Why?

Animals are very largely nocturnal. The dark hours are when they do most of their hunting and prowling. Behind the retinas of these night explorers' eyes, instead of a dark layer of pigment, they have what amount to mirrors. The faint light in which they have to do their seeing—moonlight, starlight—is reflected by these mirrors and thereby multiplied. (This puts it a little crudely and oversimply, perhaps, but we're not wanting a treatise on optics.) Nocturnal animals' eyes shine for the same reason that roadside reflector buttons shine. They are the same kind of reflectors.

Can cats see in total darkness? No; but they can utilize a minimum amount of light much better than we can. With such sensitive vision in very dim light, then, why aren't they blinded in brilliant

sunshine? Because they have slit pupils. They can narrow the
slits, at noontime, until less daylight enters than through a pinhole.

While we are on this matter of animals' vision, there occur
several other questions needing answer.

Is it true that a rabbit can see what is going on behind its back?
Empty-handed hunters have often sworn this must be the case;
and as a matter of fact, it is. Rabbits' eyes have such a protruding
convexity that they can contemplate virtually a full circle.

Why are bulls particularly excited by the color red? Here, with
no stickling or quibbling at all, we can give a forthright answer:
They aren't. Bulls are color-blind. Repeated experiments by a
number of investigators of animal life have made it certain that
bulls inhabit a visual world of only black and white and intermedi-
ate grays.

How about other animals? Are they *all* color-blind? We can't
say with absolute certainty, of course, for there are a good many
thousands of kinds of fellow animals of ours, watching with their
various eyes the world around them, and not all of them have
been tested; but among all the animals that have been studied in
this respect color blindness has been found general with only one
exception. That exception is the monkeys and apes.

Why do some animals' eyes at night gleam redder than others'?
The "fire" of nocturnal animals' eyes depends on the number
and distribution of their blood vessels.

When I was a boy there used to be lively arguments about "the
power of the human eye" in quelling hostile animals. Does our eye
in fact have that power? The eye, No. But a steadily quiet eye, of
course, is likely to mean a steadily quiet man; and animals do
respond to that. In their world of subtly experienced sensings and
feelings, animals are delicately responsive to moods. We can fairly
say—putting it deliberately vaguely and leaving it at that—that
they "feel" it when fear and excitement are in the air, and they
"feel" it, too, when there is serenity. All this, of course, is a very
unscientific way of talking; but it is a truth that all experienced

animalizers get to know; and we may permit ourselves the reflection that a great many of the most significant truths in the world are likewise best put unscientifically. A good animalizer needs to be, among other things, a good animal; and that means sometimes "knowing" things the way the animals know them, not by hows and by whys but by just *is*. Can animals "feel it" when they are stared at by a hidden watcher? A good many Trapper Joes and Chippewa Petes are certain that animals can; because, as they say, *they* can. Is that true? All we can do is go on with our animalizing, and get more and more the "feel" of animals, and the feel of the woods and wild places, and the feel of our long-blunted animal senses roused to fresh vividness again, and then, each of us for himself, make up our own minds, out of the stuff of living experience.

One final eye question: Do animals ever have periscopic eyes, the way so many fish and crabs do? Well, no, not exactly—but in a way some do. Take a hippopotamus. A hippo's eyes are so protuberant, and so near the very top of its head, that it can lie almost completely submerged in the muddy river shallows it loves and still keep a lookout.

Do father animals help the mothers tend their youngsters?

By and large, no. The family unit is such an established entity in our human lives that we are likely to take it for granted, until we have gone exploring into animal life for a while, that the same pattern of two-parent care which characterized our own childhoods must exist in all young animals' lives. It usually doesn't.

As soon as baby animals are born, if not before that, their father usually removes himself completely and reverts, either temporarily or permanently, to a separate existence. It is very natural, when we think of animals' home life, to have mental pictures of a buck and a doe standing guard together over their fawn (there used, in fact, to be a very famous painting of just this, by a painter who was not a naturalist), or of mother and father squirrel taking turns warming and feeding the babies in the nest high in the old oak tree; but when we go out animalizing into the real woods and fields and treetops we find that these things don't happen. A doe and her fawn are alone. A male squirrel stays with the female only long enough for mating and then is gone. Male and female bears are sometimes so devoted in mating time that they have what without vulgarizing we can call a "honeymoon" (after all, we spoke of the honeymoons of herons, back when we were talking about animals' sexuality in general), but when that season is over they go their separate ways. There are a great many children's tales about Mama Bear and Papa Bear and the Little Bears all together, and it is hard to rid ourselves of the pictures these stories conjure up; but we have to.

Aren't there *any* father animals that stay with their families? As a matter of fact, quite a few do. What we have been speaking about is the general all-over pattern of the thing, as it looks when we consider animals broadly. But patterns, rules, and generalities, as we find as we get to know animals better and better, are constantly having to be modified by exceptions and qualified by on-the-other-hands. Animals differ tremendously from species to species. More than that, individual differs from individual within the same species. That's one of the great drawbacks to textbooks. A textbook may say, "Male animals rarely assist in raising the young," and then whiz off to something else. If we memorize that sentence about male animals, we have, in a way, learned something. But in a very real sense we haven't learned anything at all. A generality, when it pertains to animal life, is almost a piece of noninformation. The entity "animals" is only slightly more a consistent entity than the entity "mankind." An animal is a being, a life, an individuality. It is not just a congeries of predictable chemicals, and not just a statistic; and if we say, without any explainings and exceptions, that "animals do thus and so" we have not said anything much more really informative than when we say that "mankind does thus and so." Are animals gentle or fierce? Answer it this way: Are *we?* Do animals prefer solitude or sociability? That is no more susceptible of categorical answering than the corollary question: Do people?

All of which is by way of caution, and also by way of explaining one of the reasons why some of our answers in this book have to be long. Do father animals stay with their families? On the whole, no. But. . . .

A father cougar (mountain lion), though he may stay away from the den when the cubs are newborn, generally comes back while they are still little and heads the family. Lynxes stay together in a family band for months, usually until the next mating season. Other big cats have the same sort of closely knit family life. What about wolves? Father wolves help feed the youngsters, and they keep watch on high lookout places; but as a rule they don't come into the den. Foxes? It is pretty sure that foxes mate for life. It is at any rate certain that father fox stays around home, helps feed the family, and is devoted to the youngsters. Otters? Here is the same thing. But rabbits? Father rabbits have gone their way long before the babies are born. Porcupines? They are as casual. Beavers? Father beavers are likely to stay away from the family during the summer, but rejoin them in the autumn.

It becomes clear that the way to get to know about family life of animals is to go into the outdoors and know them at firsthand, not try to learn a set of book rules. If we must have any rule at all to bear in mind as a help, we can most serviceably put it like this: Among animals that are polygamous (and this means statistically "most" animals), the father pays little or no attention to the babies; but among monogamous animals (which in a given naturalist's field of interest may also turn out to be "most" of them), the father usually shows devoted fatherhood.

There was a magazine story not long ago that depended crucially on the appearance together of a skunk family: mother skunk, father skunk, and a parade of skunklets. The magazine's letters column was soon filled with indignant objections, pointing out that father skunks never stay with the family. These objections must have entertained any long-experienced animalizer. "Never" is an imprudent word to use, if not about the physiological facts of animaldom, at least about the behavioral and psychological. Do father skunks stay with the family? Not usually; not often; hardly ever. But occasionally? Yes.

Where animal lore is concerned, a soft answer is always better than a short one; and any naturalist must constantly be reminded of it when he sets out to answer animal questions. We were bringing up the matter, in considering another question, of whether woodchucks climb trees. Do they? A woodchuck may live a lifetime without doing so. Ten woodchucks may, or perhaps a hundred. But the hundred and first . . . *that* one goes tree-climbing, and may scamper among the branches 50 feet above ground. (And drink maple sap? And come down the tree headfirst? Yes, even those things. I watched woodchucks for ten years in the living laboratory of my country acres and never saw it; and then I did.) Do fly-catching birds, such as phoebes, ever pull up worms robin-fashion? We'd never find that in any ornithological textbook; but it does sometimes happen. Do wrens always build in cavities, such as birdhouses? Indeed they do; except, as the Irish naturalist remarked, when they don't. A wren, very rarely, may pile up a great bulky twig-nest, almost like a crow's, in an open place. Do rabbits swim? Exceptionally they do. And frogs exceptionally catch birds, beavers den up in a hole without building any lodge, herons nest solitarily instead of in colonies, and May-nesting robins start building during a late autumn snowstorm. "If you would see new things under the sun," a great naturalist of my boyhood used to say, "the path to take today is the path you took yesterday." It is true. We don't know everything, yet, about a dooryard cottontail; nor shall we, ever.

Before we leave this roundabout consideration of the question of father animals, there is one other query in the category that comes up very often. Are there any animals among which the father plays the *more* important role in tending the youngsters? There are. As soon as a baby marmoset is born, the mother hands it to its father. It is the father that does all the baby-rocking, soothing, and petting . . everything except the suckling, to which the mother marmoset attends only as often as essential. As we shall see when we get to Birds, there is a similar entertaining reversal there too.

How long do animals carry their young?

With this question, we are back again on the solid ground of straightforward factuality and can be terse. It looks, in fact, as though this is unavoidably a place for one of those tabular "lists." It's the only way to answer a lot of common animal-gestation questions quickly. Here, then, are the average lengths of time for which some of the most often asked-about of our brother animals carry their babies:

Beaver	About 3 months (94–128 days)
Big cats (Mountain lions, etc.)	3 months to 100 days
Black and brown bears	About 7 months
Bobcat	50 days
Cat	53–63 days

Chipmunk	1 month (31 days)
Cow	9 months (280 days)
Deer	About 7 months, average. Species vary widely
Dog	63 days
Fox	51 days
Goat	5 months
Guinea pig	Just over 2 months (66 days)
Grizzly bear	Just over 6 months
Horse	11 months
Lion	105–110 days
Mink	6 weeks
Mole	About 30 days
Moose	A little over 8 months
Mouse	21 days
Muskrat	About 30 days
Opossum	10 days to 2 weeks
Otter	9 weeks (61 days)
Porcupine	About 4 months
Rabbit	About 30 days
Raccoon	9 weeks
Rat	21 days or a little longer
Sheep	5 months
Skunk	8 weeks (51 days)
Squirrel	40–45 days
Whale	9 months to 1 year
Wolf	2 months (63–66 days)
Woodchuck	About 4 weeks

Questions about the sexual aspects of animals' lives, as we were saying earlier, are extraordinarily frequent; and also they show forth extraordinarily some persistent myths and misinformations. Is it true that elephants carry their babies for many years? No. Their period of gestation generally runs about twenty months.

How about the other biggest animals? Rather less than that. The gestation period in giraffes, for example, is about fifteen or sixteen. In hippopotamuses it's only about eight months. Are baby porcupines and similar quilly animals always born headfirst, so that the mother isn't injured by the quills, or are they born quill-less? Neither one. All placental mammals are covered at birth by membrane; and the slippery membrane around little porcupines renders them nonscratchy, whether presentation is headfirst or tailfirst.

Do baby animals' sizes vary with the size of their parents?

Not by any means always. Young animals are born into the life adventure at various stages of advancement, and their size depends a great deal on that factor. A baby whale, obviously, has to be a pretty proficient whalelet immediately upon birth. A baby whale therefore is not only the biggest animal baby in the world, but also the biggest in relation to the size of its mother. How big is a whale infant? A young sulphur-bottom may weigh around 15,000 pounds. And its *relative* size? It may be almost half as long as its mother. On the other hand, take bears. Most bear babies are born during the latter part of their mothers' drowsy winter den-up. A naturalist poking into a bear den may take quite a while to realize that there are babies there at all. An adult black or brown bear may weigh from 200 to 500 pounds. Her newborn baby weighs only about 8 ounces. The tiny little mite is undeveloped and helpless. A newborn bear cub is smaller than a newborn baby porcupine.

Some of the very littlest animal babies are born to the pouched animals, the ones called marsupials. These, as we found out when we were speaking of animals' classification, are primitive animals. They belong to a prehistoric era when, in fact, they were the commonest of all mammals; and they exist now only in a relatively few species. A kangaroo, one of the best-known of them, may get to be as large as a big dog. (Is it true that kangaroos can be taught to box with human ring-opponents? Yes indeed, they often are; and they make formidable fighters.) How large is this big beast's baby? Just about an inch long. The tiny infant, using the claws of its forefeet, hitches along through its mother's fur until it manages to scrabble into her pouch. It rides there for three or four months, till it's capable of venturing into the world on its own. (By the way: How does such a tiny baby, so undeveloped that it is still almost like a foetus, have the strength to suck milk? It doesn't. The milk of a mother kangaroo is automatically pumped.)

Most of us are perhaps likelier to encounter opossums than kangaroos. A possum baby is even more spectacularly little. There often are as many as fifteen or eighteen in a litter, and each baby is littler than a bee. The whole brood can nestle in a tablespoon.

We may as well interject here a couple of other questions about opossums.

Is it true that after baby opossums have emerged from the pouch, they often go riding on their mother's back, clinging fast to her curved-over tail? Yes, that's true. There are few more beguiling things to see in the woods than one of these opossum caravans.

And: Do any animals besides opossums "play possum"? Yes, quite a few do. Animals succeed in life not merely by savagery or speed or the like. They also succeed by trickery. There is a lot of trickery of one kind and another throughout nature. Patterns of deception and camouflage recur again and again, and we ought to have a look at this.

Perhaps the commonest trickery is that basic form of camouflage in which an animal so resembles its general background that it disappears against it. An underwing moth, resting on the striated and mottled gray bark of a tree, vanishes from observation. A checkered-and-banded snake, lying immoblie and silent among the withered leaves of the forest floor, can defy discovery. It's a commonplace among animalizers that a spotted fawn, dappled as the underbrush is dappled with sunlight, needs only to remain still to remain nearly invisible.

Even this most elementary form of trickery isn't quite as simple a matter of resemblance as it may at first seem. Mere harmonizing of color with a similar background isn't enough for invisibility. An animal colored all over like its background would be given away by the shadow it cast, and by that play of light and shade upon its body which would reveal contour and make it stand out from its background. It's necessary, for the success of the trick, that contour be minimized and a semblance of flatness achieved. The natural effect of lighting is to make a creature's underside appear darker than its upper. For successful falsification this has to be neutralized. Nature has achieved that nullification of the giveaway by the equipment of every animal with a back that is darker than its belly. Is this always true? Not quite, no. The exceptions furnish proofs of the rule. Suckers which swim upside down have blackened bellies and whitened backs. Snails which regularly thrust their shell-mouths upward have the tip of the shell-spire darkest. How about sloths, the animals that live head-downward? They're similarly reversed in their areas of light and dark.

In the simplest camouflage trickery, an animal wears always the same garb. In the next further elaboration of the trick, dress alters with the alteration of environment. A deer, dappled in fawnhood, loses its spots with maturity and never again makes radical change in appearance. But every spring the backs of our northern weasels turn brown, to the color of the earth, and every fall turn white, to the color of the snow. Seasonally, in the same way, arctic foxes and varying hares metamorphose with rhythmic duplicity. Among ptarmigans, which are particularly defenseless birds, the changes increase to three: a dark summer feathering to match the tundra rocks, a delicate gray autumn feathering to match the silvery lichens and the rest of the graying scene, a white feathering to go with winter snow. Finally, among lots of frogs, fish, lizards, and other preyed-on beings with thin, naked skins, the changing of color to match background becomes almost continual. Why are fish often so hard to see? Suppose we consider a common perch. Gliding from open shallows into a dark pool, our perch's color deepens and darkens as though the shadows had stained it. Or again: What color is a prawn? A prawn is now the color of weeds, now of sand, and now, at night, of the deep blue sea.

In the simpler forms of invisibility tricks, an animal's contribution to the illusion is to keep perfectly still. A startled hare "freezes"; a fawn is as quiet as a rock. But mere immobility merges into a more thorough furtherance of illusion. This is achieved by a special and particular posture. Have we ever seen a bittern just walk away from the brook and disappear? How does it do it? A striped bittern doesn't merely halt; it halts with its head and long neck pointing upward, so that the stripings parallel the reeds in which it takes cover. A striped snipe? It halts, to the same effect, with its head downward and its tail pointing up. Among some of the nightjars and similar birds which match the mossy bark of trees, the "freeze" is always bolt upright so that the bird is the more indistinguishable among the stubs and stumps of branches.

Disguise by form and color ranges all the way from what camouflage experts call "self-contained" camouflage—camouflage that breaks up the animal's outline with a dazzle pattern—to the most literal and scrupulous mimicry, and from simulation in which behavior plays a minor role to simulation that is almost wholly by deed. A tiger's stripes break up its body surface confusingly; a zebra's dazzle-striping doesn't literally imitate anything, but, when the zebra is feeding on the moonlit veldt, it gives it a kind of phantom checkeredness in the general harlequinade of the moonlight. As disguise becomes more literally imitative, it becomes more astonishing. As it is supplemented by behavior that is also imitative, it sometimes becomes almost incredible.

Our common walking-stick insects exactly resemble twigs, in both coloring and shape; and they walk with a stiff and exceeding slowness, in perfection of the illusion. Some of them change color faithfully with the greening and withering of the plants they inhabit. The insects called walking leaves are so exactly leaflike (and, more, lay eggs so exactly like plant seeds) that there is an enduring belief that they *are* leaves, miraculously animated. Sea slugs imitate the anemones on which they feed. Anemones imitate the coral they inhabit. The spider crabs that live in the same undersea domain carry imitativeness to a fantastic length. The crab takes cuttings of seaweeds, chews and frays the ends, and affixes them among the hairs on its carapace and legs. The cuttings take root, and presently completely conceal their harvester in the likeness of a bunch of vegetation.

There are not only trickeries to escape notice. There are trickeries to invite an attention that will be a misunderstanding. The simplest of these are those cases in which a defenseless creature has the color or form of some dangerous creature or object. What are those small insects that appear to be bees and wasps, but that turn out, when we look at them closely, not to be? Those are hover flies. Harmless? Entirely. If our hover flies aren't decimated by birds, it's chiefly because they look like wasps. The acridity and uneatableness of the butterfly called a monarch gives protection not only to monarchs but also to the nonacrid butterfly called a viceroy, which counterfeits the monarch's appearance. Harmless snakes take security from resembling venomous coral snakes and water snakes. A plant bug makes the pretense of being a prickly burr. Caterpillars are marked with body designs that make them seem to have terrible eyes and intimidating faces.

Perhaps most remarkable among the trickeries are those that are wholly of behavior. Stranger than deceit by appearance, they are deceit by act. They may be seen by any animalizer who has ever caught opossums, or startled meadow larks or killdeers from their nests, or surprised a common hog-nosed snake by the wayside. When danger overwhelms, is inescapable, an oppossum relaxes into an immobility and inertness that counterfeit death. When danger approaches, a meadow lark slips from her nest, emerges from cover some distance away, and with trailing wing and piteous cries pretends to be badly injured. Faking crippledness, engaging the molester's attention, she lures him ever farther and farther from the nest. A frightened hog-nosed snake, harmless as an earthworm, first fakes dreadfulness—swelling and flattening its head, rearing, striking, hissing furiously—and then, if this stagey terrorizing fails, abruptly opens its mouth, gives a gasp as of despair, collapses, and rolls over on its back in a semblance of having died.

So here we are, back around to our possum again. Do animals "play possum" on purpose?

The question of the extent and quality of consciousness among animals, as we keep finding out, is never easy to answer. We want to go carefully. By and large, as we've seen, it seems presumable that animals aren't very reflective upon what they do, or why they do it. They take dress and habitat from evolution, and much of their behavior from (so to speak) the unpondered promptings of their senses and their juices. A viceroy butterfly doesn't knowingly imitate a monarch. A ptarmigan does not "choose" to change plumage, or know it changes. A meadow lark may not grasp the why of its malingering. Opossums "play possum" through an involuntary trick of the nervous system.

All very simple. But one moment, now. There's a little something else to say. . . .

If a fox, uncharacteristically, should feign death, that might give us pause. It would be difficult to avoid ascribing to such a fox at least a glimmering consciousness of the intention of such a trick.

Nearly half a century ago there was published an allegedly true story of a fox that, in desperate circumstances, had foiled an enemy by playing dead. The story was shouted down in an uproar of derision. Its teller was laughed out of countenance for ascription to a fox of the capability of such a cunning. Then a few years ago the tale of a new adventure was told. This time a man had surprised a fox in his henhouse, and the fox, unable to escape, had simulated death. It lay inert and limp while the man carried its body outside the henhouse and deposited it on the grass. Its freedom gained, the trickster fox sprang to life again and dashed away into the woods. The story came, this time, with its truth a little too massively attested to be ridiculed away. Its attester was the President of the Association for the Advancement of Science.

Do many kinds of animals sometimes play possum? Yes. Can we say what is going on in their minds when they do? On that matter, we want to go as cautiously and soft-footedly as a fox when the snow lies deep.

Do animals educate their young?

The word education has the same Latin base as the word educement. It means a leading out, a drawing forth. It means arousing and stimulating the young personality's latencies, and doesn't mean merely, as we're likely to think, stuffing wholly new things *into* it. We have been seeing in our consideration of animals, again and again, that all animals do a certain amount of learning. They start with little knowledge, dim knowledge, imperfect knowledge. They start with not much more than instinct and awareness. These develop into intelligent behavior under the influence of living experience. What animals receive from their parents is a quickening of that development.

This seems, perhaps, like a lot of words; but we have to be scrupulously on guard, as usual, against thinking of animals in too fully human terms; and it always takes quite a parcel of careful words to formulate just the viewpoint we want. Now: Does a mother bird teach her babies to fly? In a sense, yes; and in a sense, no. When they're ready to fly, she does coax and urge them. She does a lot of teasing and luring; and always, of course, she holds out to them the example of herself. We may take it, safely, that she has at least an obscure feeling that they ought to be getting out of the nest, and that she is moved to a variety of gestures to suggest that and bring it about. But: if the babies were brought up with no mother at all, would they learn to fly anyway? Yes, they would. Man-reared birds are likely to be rather bumbly little fellows. They have to learn their bird lore the hard way. But flight is at least latent in all winged things; and an "uneducated" robin can in time take to flight as do the winged insects, which of course receive no parental instruction at all.

Are we to read conscious intention into the teaching that parent birds do? Remembering the brotherhood of all things, minds as well as bodies, we're bound to posit some. How does a golden eagle persuade her eaglets to leave their cliff-nest for the first time and launch into the air over the gulfs of nothingness? She hovers before them; she nudges and urges them; she stands off farther and farther from them with food morsels; finally she even drops bits of food in mid-air, a few feet from the nest, until the eaglets' hunger and the sight of these tantalizing morsels combine to persuade them to launch forth. Does the mother eagle have, at least in her eagle way, some "idea" of what she is doing in all this? Unless we are going to suppress our sound spontaneities of judgment and our straightforward common sense, we have to say that surely she has.

When we ascend from birds to animals, we find teaching becoming more and more evident. Always bearing in mind the limitations of animal consciousness, which we have talked about such a lot, we also find the "on-purposeness" of the teaching more and more plainly evident. Do young otters take instinctively to water? No. The mother otter endlessly coaxes and wheedles them; and, as often as not, she ends up by *tricking* them into swimming. She takes them out for a swim on her back, and then ducks out from under them. Mother sea lions do the same sort of things to get their babies to swim. Bear cubs have to learn to be quiet. A she-bear "tells" her cubs that, in an instructive growling; and then if they disobey the instruction she cuffs and spanks them vigorously until they *do* learn the lesson of obedience. Watch any of the higher animals with their youngsters, and we see encouragements being held out, punishments inflicted, play-ways guided, all to the end that the young ones' native propensities are sharpened and trained and their growing personalities shaped into effectiveness.

Are we to call that education? We can't very well call it anything else. The thing we have to keep in mind is just that all this activity, like most else in animals' lives, has a kind of "feltness" about it, rather than a "thought-outness"—a kind of quality of immediacy and impulse—a texture, so to speak, of active livingness, rather than of the planned and meditated. The animals' world is not the world of reflection. It is the world of urge and action. Is it true that mother animals shape their children's personalities? Indeed yes. How fully do they "think out" and "realize" what they are doing? We can illuminatingly employ some of that introspection we were practicing when we talked about animals' minds in general. Back when we were around three and four, we used to educate our dolls and Teddy bears and lead soldiers. We disciplined and loved, cradled and drilled. How much was going on in our minds, back then? Nothing? A complete understanding? Why, neither of these, to be sure. Unawareness does not issue abruptly into the full blaze of knowing. There is a great glimmering borderland, a twilight, a graduated dusk of emergent understanding. It is where the animals live.

Do all animals have voices?

As far as naturalists have been able to examine into the matter, it looks as though the answer is probably Yes. There are a good many animals that haven't yet been *heard* to utter sounds, and of course a good many animals haven't been under close-enough study for us to say for sure; but it seems nearly a certainty that every one of our animal brothers, as it prowls through the life experience, is able, so to speak, to comment on it.

Isn't it true that giraffes are mute? No, it isn't. They used to be supposed to be, as lately as my boyhood; and their muteness is still mentioned in many books; but they have voices. They utter a murmurous lowing and mooing, like a very soft version of the voice of cattle.

Can mice sing? Every now and then there is a newspaper story telling how some astonished housewife has heard, or thinks she has heard, a mouse song. The stories are likely to be written facetiously. There's no reason for facetiousness. No animalizer can go attentively exploring the night woods and fields for many years without finding out that mice do have singing ability. What they make is a high, wiry, warbling little trill, somewhat canarylike. Why don't we hear it oftener? Probably, though not certainly, because mouse music, like the bat cries we were recently speaking about, is mostly supersonic. Only occasionally does part of the song fall within our auditory range.

Do rabbits have a voice? Yes; unforgettably. In mortal danger, or when seized by a predator, a rabbit utters screams; and they can be an appalling sound to hear. We ought to settle here, while we're about it, one of the most popular and disputed questions about the animals of the American outdoors. Does a cougar scream? Perhaps because these mountain lions are capable of keeping wonderfully quiet, there is a persistent belief among lots of old-timers and outdoorsmen that they never scream at all. It isn't so. The big cats can emit, when they're in the mood for it, a tremendous and unearthly yowl.

Many animals are able to make sounds which they use only very rarely, so that even if we spend a lifetime investigating outdoors we may still hear every now and then an animal-utterance we can't identify. What's bullfrog talk like? Mostly, of course, it's the deep bass "jug-o'-rum" croaking. But then sometimes, when a bullfrog has been grabbed or terrified, it's a shrieking. What noise does a coon make? Well, ordinarily, a kind of "churring" and gutturalizing, as if in mild puzzlement or complaint. But then suddenly, some midnight, we hear what sounds like the tremolo "hoo-loo-looing" of screech owls, only sounding from the ground. What's that? That's a coon too.

Considering animals' voices leads us naturally enough into a very frequent question:

Do animals talk?

The best way to answer this, perhaps, is in a sort of two-part consideration. First, then:

Speech, meaningful speech, is the product of a human world of ideas, values, linked awarenesses, and intellectual insights, over the threshold of which no animal crosses. The simplest noun has behind it an idea-content, an immensity of abstraction, which are not part of the psychic world in which an animal moves. The crows, keenest of birds, don't have one kind of caw to designate a pine tree and another caw to designate an oak. They are not aware of oaks and pines; they are not aware that trees are trees; they are not indeed aware of themselves and of otherness. It is the function of an animal to *be:* to experience life, and respond to it, and be influenced by it, and dance (as it were) to its felt tune. But it be-

D

longs exclusively to humanity to pass beyond being and achieve the kind of perception-of-being that can issue in comment-upon-being.

On the subject of the highest apes, our most immediate animal brothers, there isn't a greater authority than R. M. Yerkes. He has said: "It may not be asserted that any one of the anthropoid types speaks." Furness spent a whole half year in intensive efforts to teach an exceptionally acute female orangutan to master the words "papa" (as a designation for himself) and "cup" (for the vessel from which she drank). The ape did learn to make, occasionally and indistinctly, the two sounds. There is no good evidence that she ever acquired any understanding of their signification, or learned to use them purposefully as communication.

Many animals are imitative. Where the structure of their vocal organs permits it, they may be expert in mimicry. A bluejay can "speak" an imitation of a hawk; a parrot can make noises like the noises man makes. But of "speech"—the conveyance of idea in symbol—there is no trace, from the squeak of the smallest field mouse to the growl and mutter of the biggest of the apes.

Very well, then. But now to the second part of our answer:

There are modes of communication below the level of speech. There is the language of gesture. There is the language of scent. There is a language which is a thing of sensings, feelings, unconscious sendings of impulse, and unconscious receptions of impulse. For the purposes of animal practicality, there is no need of words. It isn't necessary, to animal welfare, that there be reflection. It is necessary only that there be action. And at *this* level—at this degree of consciousness where the world is all emotion and action and the practical intelligence of sensorimotor insight—animals are excellently equipped with language of their own.

A bird is seized by a snake, and screams. The scream is not a "word"; but it is the sound of danger, and the birds of a whole countryside will come excitedly flocking to it. Or a snake is enraged. It can't utter imprecations; but, all unconsciously, it looses

a musky sour-sweet smell and, all unconsciously, the creature that
has enraged it takes warning of its anger. A doe is feeding with
her fawn when danger comes on them. The doe bounds away. As
she bounds, her tail is flung up like a white signal flag. She has
"said" to her fawn, "Quick! This way! Follow me!" And the fawn
has "heard" and—at the animal level—"understood." There has
been no deer speech consciously and intentionally uttered; there
has been no deer speech consciously comprehended and obeyed.
The world in which an animal moves is a world of sensing, feeling,
acting; a world less of thought than of impulse and of the un-
rationalized wisdom of the muscles and nerves; a world of awareness and response, and not analysis. It has its own kind of language,
subtle and diverse.

Do dogs talk things over together? The psyche of a dog speaks
with the psyche of a stranger-dog, when they meet, not by means
of anything like human words, but quite otherwise: by the significance of a smell, by the significance of muscle tenseness, by the raising of hair or the thump of a tail, by a dozen kinds of animal
indications that are meaningful to dog-consciousness. When a
worker bee has found nectar, it returns to the hive and "tells" the
other bees; but it "tells" them by a ritualistic dancing. It has no
intention, probably, to speak a message; and the fellow bees have
no intention to receive and interpret. The bee dances spontaneously; and the fellow bees are stirred, and moved to follow, by a
contagious excitement that lies far, far below the quality of
comprehension. But it is a kind of language, nonetheless; a language effective in the realm of being of a bee.

Any of us who have played tennis know how, with the growth of
skill, it becomes possible to anticipate with greater and greater
accuracy where an opponent is about to place a shot. That's an
unconscious skill. It isn't a thing of the thinking mind. It is a sensorimotor understanding. Similarly, anyone who has ever been closely
intimate with another human being knows by what small and
subtle manifestations moods may be expressed and understood,

intentions hinted and guessed, unspoken things divined as though by telepathy. Such things as these are close to the quality of much of the "language" of animals. Dog meets dog and they are in communication without a syllable. A vixen commands her brood of little foxes, and needs "speak" only with a muscle, only with a look. An animal trainer becomes a little rattled, and instantly the tiny tremor of his hand, the infinitesimal edge of anxiety in his voice, has told his beasts that the instant is right to strike and overpower him.

Can animals talk? Why, certainly. We have been taking the question pretty solemnly; and all the while there's a very neat and wonderfully unscientific summing up of it in something an Indian guide once said to a writer-sportsman, John Durant, who relayed the story to me. The Indian was telling about two deer that he had watched carrying out a curious woods-maneuver together—the details don't matter here—and he spoke of how the deer "talked" together. "Or, well," he added thoughtfully, "maybe animals don't exactly *talk*, but they sure know what they say."

Our considerations of a good many animal questions have a way of turning out to be long. It's partly because animals have full and subtle personalities, and we have to go into that pretty thoroughly and precisely; and partly it's because, in this book of ours, it seems like a good idea often to group numbers of common questions together in clumps and let ourselves go meandering through a whole wide range of question territory in the course of answering one main, thematic lead question. That makes for a kind of connectedness that wouldn't otherwise be possible; and it gives us a chance to get something of the feel of "over-allness" about animaldom.

There are a lot of particular animal questions, though, that come up extremely often and that don't always lend themselves to incorporation in these ranging, over-all considerations. They're better asked and answered, I think, just as they come, staccato. Before we take up one or two remaining animal matters of the leisurely and long-way-round sort, suppose we address ourselves now for a while to these. These are the top-ranking questions, judged by frequency, about Animals Miscellaneous:

Do elephants drink through their trunks?

No. They suck up water with their trunks and then squirt it into their mouths to drink it. Don't baby elephants use their trunks to suck milk? No again. They grasp their mothers' nipples directly in their mouths.

Is it true that an elephant never forgets?

Well, not really, of course; no. Like mice, rabbits, wolverines, or you or me, elephants forget a good many things. Recall, among all the creatures born into the life experience on this earth, is a good deal less than total; and we needn't be anything very profound in the way of philosophers to agree that perhaps it's just as well. At any rate: What *is* true is that elephants have a good deal longer memories than most animals do, and likewise they do retain exceptionally the recollection of injuries. If an elephant has been done harm by a man, and then doesn't see him again for years, may the big beast blaze up in a renewal of hatred if they do meet again? Yes; that has happened often enough to be beyond any doubting.

Do dying elephants make their way to an elephant graveyard?

This is the last of the common elephant questions, and it must be one of the most popular animal questions in the world. The answer to it, almost certainly, is No. Most animalizers who have had long experience in elephant country don't hesitate to omit the cautious "almost certainly." Still, perhaps we'd better keep it filed away in the back of our minds. No one seems ever to have located an elephant graveyard. The records present one long, persuasive blank. Still . . . well . . . we might notice, without comment, the matter of Levick and the seals.

Surgeon Commander G. Murray Levick was with Captain Scott on his last antarctic expedition. At one time, when he was at Hell's Gate, near the Drygalski ice barrier, some hundreds of yards from the sea ice, he came upon something very strange. To the commander and his companion it appeared to be, unmistakably, a seal cemetery. The frozen and mummified bodies of a great number of seals were lying on a patch of ground in a group, as though they had been carried and left there by human beings. The varying ages of the seals' bodies, as best the surgeon-commander could determine them, suggested that the group of the dead had been added to and added to for centuries. The throng of dead seals was out of sight of the ice-foot from which, as it looked certain, the animals had crawled from the sea to that particular lonely spot to die.

That was what Levick saw. What Dr. Robert Murphy of the American Museum of Natural History saw was something else in the lonely ice-covered land of South Georgia. Why were the dead bodies of penguins almost never found? He had wondered about that. One day at the crown of a long hill he came upon a clear little lake of snow water. Around its edge stood several strangely quiet penguins, drooping, seemingly exhausted. Dr. Murphy walked to the pool and peered into its clear depths. There, with their flippers outstretched, lay hundreds, perhaps thousands, of dead penguins.

It doesn't do for an animalizer to jump to conclusions. No. No, indeed not. It also doesn't do for us to get to supposing that we know everything about how the world works, or everything about what goes on in animals' minds and hearts and the deeper unnamable deeps of them. Do elephants have graveyards? Well—no, probably not.

Can a pig swim?

We're in surer territory again. Yes, pigs can swim. There's a prevalent notion that if a hog takes to water its flailing sharp-hoofed forefeet must cut its throat. A prodigiously fat and jowly pig, I suppose, might suffer this disaster; but, generally speaking, yes, pigs can swim as well as most other animals. By the way: How about pigs' being immune to snake bite? They're not. Inject venom deep into a pig and it will die. Practically speaking, however, a fat pig almost never does die of snake bite; but for a reason other than actual immunity. The pig's thick blubbery outer layer so slows the absorption of venom received into it and so modifies its danger that by the time the inner hog, so to speak, is reached, no harm is done.

Can skunks breed with dogs?

It's out of the question, this, no matter how many "stink dogs" may continue to be exhibited in backwoods sideshows. Dogs do breed with their wild brothers, the wolves, but that's all. There are a lot of astonishing questions about animals' interbreeding that are constantly coming up; and, though by this time in our animal investigations we may feel pretty sure what the answer to them is, perhaps we ought to bring one or two of them up specifically. Do cats and rabbits sometimes mate, producing a long-legged cat-rabbit? Never. Cat-rabbits are as persistent as picturesque, but however far into the wild places our animalizings may take us we can count on never seeing one. How about that recurring tale of a buck deer getting in among the sheep and impregnating one of them? No. If the fence around the pasture doesn't prevent it, the zoological fence of family division does.

Not to become too offhand in our dismissals of the possibilities of animals' interbreeding, however, we'd better also raise now one or two other questions. Is there really such an animal as a "tiglon," begotten by a lion and a tiger? Yes; that interbreeding is possible and has happened. Back in the first part of this book, when we were talking about animals' classification, we mentioned the informal rule of thumb that defines a species as a "group of closely similar individual animals that don't mate with individuals of other species." It's a simple, useful rule; and now we have the salutary experience of also finding out that it doesn't always work.

How about that strange alleged animal, the "cattalo," that's supposed to be born sometimes to a cow and a buffalo or bison? That's a real animal too.

Are moles blind?

Substantially, yes, they are. A mole can tell brilliant daylight from darkness (after all, an eyeless earthworm can do as much; it "sees" to this extent with its photosensitive skin), but little more than that. How big are moles' eyes? No bigger than pinheads.

Must skunks aim backwards when they fire their scent?

We were talking a little while back about the unsafeness of picking up a skunk by the tail. It's even less safe to repose in the belief that a skunk must wheel to fire. Skunks commonly do swivel round in this way; but it can't be relied on. A skunk's anal scent-thrower is protrusible; our brother *Mephitis* can thrust it out and aim it in virtually any direction.

Nearly as popular as this commonest skunk question are these others:

Do skunks always give warning before they fire? Not invariably. A skunk usually performs a cautionary head-lowering and a pitter-patter stamping with its forefeet; but it may omit the ritual.

How much fluid does a skunk discharge at a time? Incredibly enough, hardly a twentieth of a teaspoonful; but it comes out under pressure in a very fine, carrying spray.

How far can a skunk send it? In the neighborhood of 10 or 15 feet. Received in our eyes, can it cause at least temporary blindness? It can, yes. And how far away, finally, can a blast of skunk musk be smelled? The odor of the two or three drops of sulphide can be detected easily at half a mile.

Skunk smell, close up, can be formidable. But the far, faint drift of it, tingeing the woods in the dusk, is a wonderfully exciting animal-thing, an earth-evocative thing. It's a grand smell for arousing what a naturalist crony of mine calls the "primitive sleeper" down inside us. He's likely to drowse and dim away, that sleeper of ours, as our childhood dims away. There's nothing better than skunk smell for waking him to fresh responsiveness to the old excitement of the earth. For that matter, there's nothing better than animalizing of any sort. Perhaps, when we come right down to it, that is after all the really fundamental reason for this book.

Do bears kill by means of a "bear hug"?

Very simply and shortly, no. This green garden of our earth has its rigors and dangers and sternnesses. It's part of the business of being rightly creaturely that we learn to know and meet them. But as we get to know animals as they really are, we find out that more and more of the *eerie* dreadfulnesses, the nightmare happenings, don't happen. Does a cat, perched on our chest while we sleep, "suck our breath"? Do bears and wolves commonly go out of their way to attack us? Are wildcats likely to drop on us out of a tree? Is it true that if a dog foams at the mouth it always has hydro-

D*

phobia? We can put away all these alarming notions about animals with a simple No. Bears don't give bear hugs. They kill with a fore-paw wallop, and with teeth and claws. Bears hardly ever attack without provocation. If a bear does attack, we're in serious trouble, of course. But will a grizzly chase us up a tree? No. And we can be sure that no bear is going to embrace us in that slow, crushing dance of death that used to be described with such a vivid awfulness in the fairy tales of our childhood.

While we're speaking of bears: do they hibernate? This query landed in bales on naturalists' desks a few years ago, as the result of a syndicated newspaper statement by a university zoologist that the hibernation of bears is mythical. Is it? The question comes down to a quibble.

What is hibernation? Exactly speaking, it is a deep unconscious-ness, and a slowing almost to arrest of all the body processes, that in the winter months many kinds of animals undergo. What animals? Well, woodchucks, for instance; chipmunks; bats . . . there are a lot of them. Padded with autumnal fat, the animal with-draws into its winter burrow or cranny, slips into a drowse, and then into a deep, deep oblivion. In summertime activity, a wood-chuck's temperature averages within a degree or so of our own. As hibernation deepens, the chuck's body heat diminishes . . . ten degrees, twenty degrees, thirty. When the completeness of winter dormancy has been reached, its body temperature may be down around 38° or 40°. In summertime activity an animal like a wood-chuck breathes thirty or forty breaths a minute. Under excite-ment, it may breathe perhaps a hundred times a minute. In hiberna-tion, breathing grows slower, slower, until finally the sleeper is drawing a breath maybe only ten or twelve times an hour. A hibernating animal's pituitary becomes inactive. Its blood circu-lates sluggishly, unevenly. A hibernating woodchuck, down under-neath the frost line below our snow-drifted meadow, has with-drawn from aliveness into a profound nonbeing that is nearly death.

That is what hibernation is like. Do bears hibernate? Not in that full sense, no. In cold weather, bears do den up and sleep. They have long, long periods of deep drowse and lethargy. (The tiny cubs, to which we were referring recently, are commonly born to the mother while she is in this denned-up, half-sleeping state.) But bear sleep isn't the spectacular diminishment, with all the extraordinary changes in body processes, that the fully hibernating animals undergo.

Do bears hibernate? Common-sensely, yes. In the strictest, nicest, technical sense? Well, all right, maybe not.

When chipmunks carry acorns in their cheeks, why don't the nuts' sharp points scratch them?

Because, in a characteristic display of the thing we have been calling animals' practical intelligence, a chipmunk neatly nips off acorn tips before stuffing the nuts into its cheek pouches.

Why isn't there a telltale pile of earth beside a chipmunk's hole?

Chipmunks, and similar small burrowers, must be among the most-watched animals of our earth. This is one of the commonest of all questions about animals. Its answer? When a chipmunk digs a burrow, what it does is this: It throws the excavated earth behind it, in regular digging style, disregarding the telltale mound of dirt it necessarily leaves. It completes its burrow . . . a slanting tunnel down to below the frost line, then lateral corridors, storage rooms, and so on . . . and then the chipmunk comes tunneling upward and makes an exit hole from below. Because this hole has been dug from underneath, there is no accumulation of excavated earth around it. It is a neat little circle, invisible in the grass. The chipmunk pops out from it, scampers back to the original entrance hole, and there stuffs the loose dirt back into that hole, tamping it with its paws and scattering the surplus. The hole that was dug from underneath is now hereafter the chipmunk's doorway, and is almost undiscoverable. Why don't the chipmunk's comings and goings there leave a visible trail? A chipmunk approaching or leaving its doorway moves in high, springing jumps, and thereby avoids beating a track. Further, a chipmunk almost never leaves or enters the burrow twice in succession by the same route.

Instinct? Intelligence? We might look back over some of the long and careful things we have been saying in our considerations of all that. And then, if we're half the animalizers we ought to be, we might also go out and sit down on a stump somewhere for a while and reflect that there is still plenty for us to ponder . . . even about the soul of a small chipmunk, going its chipmunk way and thinking its chipmunk thoughts, down in the humid root-smelling darkness under our lawn.

When animals such as snowshoe rabbits turn from summer brown to winter white, does their fur change color or is it new fur?

It's new. The summer coat is shed in the autumn, and the winter coat grows in white; in the spring molt the white fur is shed and the tawny summer coat grows to replace it. If a snowshoe rabbit loses a tuft of its fur in an autumn fight, the new fur that grows in the patch will be white. Contrariwise if a tuft is lost in early spring. A *fight*, did we say? Do such mild and timid animals as rabbits engage in fights? Quite often. Not only do males fight among themselves; a mother rabbit with babies will now and then turn and put up a fight even against a dog. Rabbits can lash out powerfully with their strong-clawed hind legs. The "rabbit punch" of a fighting rabbit can leave an enemy disemboweled.

Can porcupines throw their quills?

No. They can't, that is, shoot them forth or eject them. They can't fire them like arrows. Still, the whole neighborhood around a really angry or frightened porcupine is a fairly hazardous place to be. The reason is this: A porcupine, like most other animals when angry, lashes its tail. Every now and then, in the process, one of the quills may come loose and be sent whizzing at random through the air. Can a porcupine throw its quills? Any first-year animalizer who has read a shelfful or two of mammalogy can smile a superior smile and say Certainly Not. But may you be standing 10 feet from an agitated porcupine and nevertheless get a quill whizzing through your hat? You may; and it's to learn this sort of living animal lore, so to put it, that we need our years of going out to the animals themselves and adventuring into the day-to-dayness of their lives.

Some other popular porcupine questions:

Is it true that porcupines have a passion for salt? Yes. A porcupine will chew up a sweaty ax-handle for the trace of salt that's in it. Can porcupine quills kill even big animals? They often do. Even wolves, bears, and mountain lions have been found dead, riddled by the barbed quills that have worked their way inward. Do porcupines roll themselves into a ball? We often hear that they do, but they don't. The prickly animals that roll into a ball are the

Old World hedgehogs. What a porcupine does, under assault, is tuck in its nose as much as it can (porcupines' noses are uncommonly sensitive; a blow with a stick on a porcupine's nose often kills it), and then bring its feet close together, hugging the ground, and then erect all its quills until it bristles almost twice life size. How many quills does a porcupine carry? Putting it roughly, around 25,000.

How fast can a jack rabbit go?

When we see a jack rabbit make its spurting getaway and go sprinting across a field to elude a hawk or a coyote, it looks as though it must be whipping along almost as fast as a race horse. As a matter of fact, it is. A jack rabbit in a hurry can hit 45 miles per hour, and in brief dashes it can go even faster than that. Each of its bounds covers 10 or 15 feet; its major ones can span 25.

Questions about animals' speeds come up very frequently. This seems the right place in our animalizings to consider the commonest of them.

What's the fastest animal of all? A cheetah, probably. These leopards are often trained for hunting. There have been unusually good opportunities for timing them. How fast can a cheetah run? At least 70 miles per hour; cheetahs have been stop-watched at that. Can deer really "run like a deer"? A startled buck can plunge away through the underbrush at about 45 miles per hour. And gazelles? They do 50 easily. There are a few gazelles and antelopes that regularly exceed that. A pronghorn antelope often travels at 60. The spurts and sprints of animals make perhaps the most arresting statistics, but the endurance they show in maintaining steady speeds over long distances is in its quieter way as extraordinary. Carefully timed antelope have maintained an average speed of over 35 miles per hour for distances of almost 30 miles.

Can a lion run down a man? Effortlessly; for our top running speed isn't over 25 miles per hour or so, and a charging lion lopes

along at 50. Even a grizzly bear can lumber for short distances at
35. How about elephants? They thunder along at about our own
top speed.

Do hippopotamuses sweat blood?

No; but it isn't absurd for us to suppose they do, even if we have
been devotedly animalizing for years and paying attention to hippopotamuses particularly. When a hippo comes galumphing up
out of the water and its skin begins to dry out, the big beast does
start secreting red droplets that we may easily take for blood. Actually, however, the red secretion is an oily stuff that serves to
keep the hippo's thick hide from drying to the cracking point
while the animal is on land excursions under the searing sun.

While we're on this, we can't very well pass by the other most
common question about bloodletting. Is it true that a horned toad
can shoot blood out of its eyes? Astonishingly enough, it's perfectly true. As readers of an autobiographical chapter in another
book of mine may know, I had in boyhood an uncle who was an
artist-naturalist. His studio, with its cabinets of birds' nests, its
stuffed owl, its striped garter snake preserved in a glass jar, was
for me a place of enchantment. The long boyhood hours in it, and
the company of the extraordinarily happy-hearted and earth-daft
man who presided over it, were no doubt in great part responsible
for my having given my own life to animalizing, so that now my
years of presumable adult gravity are still being devoted, as in-
fatuatedly as boyhood ones, to an everlasting concern with such
matters as whether, if an earthworm gets broken in two, both halves
of the fellow can become new worms, and why it should be that
the wild geese, when they go honking and clattering through the
smoky-golden October sky, fly in a V-formation.

(If our earthworm is cut near its middle, or back of that, its
fore part grows a new tail but its hind part doesn't grow a new
head. If it's cut far forward, just a few anterior segments being

lost, the beheaded earthworm can regenerate those. And the geese.
. . . As far as we can tell, they fly that way for two principal reasons. Each goose can better keep an eye on the lead goose and each
goose avoids the tumultuous air-wake of the big bird ahead of it.
V-formation for geese isn't invariable, though. Sometimes, especially on blustery days in the latter part of their season of migration, we may see the honkers straggle out in single file.)

This book isn't a place for autobiography. It has seemed warrant-
able to stick in that small fragment of it because it was in that
magical studio, on a memorable day long ago, that I was privileged
to help unpack a horned toad that had been shipped alive from
Arizona. As the horned toad was lifted out of its box, the spiny
traveler immediately ejected from the corners of its eyes a spurting
spray of blood. To my entranced delight (we're not queasy in
boyhood; we learn our dismayed finickings later), my hands were
splattered with the evidence.

Since the blood-squirting story turns out to be true, is there
nothing about horned toads that we can learn to pooh-pooh as
myth, to show our learnedness? There's one thing, and quite impressive. A horned toad isn't a toad. It's a lizard.

Do raccoons always wash their food?

"Always," of course, is no sort of word for us to be using about
living animals. They're *alive* beings, which means that there's
nothing about them as rigid as mathematics or as unvarying as
mere chemistry. However, taking the "always" in a suitably easy-
going way, the answer to this is Yes. Coons feed a good deal on
such water creatures as mussels, which need to be washed free
of grit before they're eaten; and food washing has become such a
coon habit that most raccoons won't eat anything at all unless they
can first wash it. A raccoon's forepaws are nimble little hands. The
coon takes its morsel of food in them, dips it in the brook, and
often souses and swashes the thing for several minutes, turning it

over and over and peering at it periodically in an intense inspection.

When monkeys comb through each other's fur and pop tidbits into their mouths, are they catching fleas?

Not ordinarily, no. Monkeys have an enthusiastic appetite for salt. They are almost never infested with fleas. The tidbits a monkey seeks in its own or a fellow monkey's fur are usually tiny bits of salt exudate and skin.

Do rattlesnakes, gophers, and owls live together in the same burrow in a partnership?

Together, yes; partnership, no. The lives of animals aren't by any means all struggle and warfare. Partnership and cooperation are life patterns running all through animaldom. It was perhaps to give a vivid illustration of this important truth that this mammal-snake-bird story came into being. It happens to be a false one—rattlers and small ground owls do often show up in gopher burrows, but they are there for the purpose of catching the gophers or feeding on each other's youngsters—but the fact behind the legend has plenty of authentic and equally arresting illustrations. For instance: Is it really true that a crocodile holds its mouth open and lets a little bird pop in and out, picking its teeth? It would be hard to think of an animal tale that sounds more whoppery than that; but if our animalizing takes us into a sufficiently intimate acquaintance with crocodiles we find out that it's true. The little ploverlike courser and the big crocodilian have established a mutually useful association. Or again: The woodpeckery little African birds called honey guides regularly team up with honey-loving badgers. A honey guide feeds on bee grubs, but has hardly the equipment for tackling a hive. The badger loves honey but can hardly undertake, on its short legs, the enormous excursions necessary to locate it. When a honey-guide bird has found a hive, it flies to the badger and—if we don't mind putting it a little fancifully—"tells" the animal. With the bird fluttering and darting ahead, the two set off together; and presently are feeding together, on a meal which neither of them could very well have secured on its own. Animaldom, as we keep finding, is the subject of an enormous lot of myths. But also, and not infrequently, it presents vignettes —like this one of the trotting little badger and the eagerly urging little bird—that have the quaintness of a picture in a children's fairy tale.

Cooperation and mutual help among animals of the same species is very general. A wolf pack is all a unit. When an elephant has been hurt, fellow elephants in the herd will gather around and bear up and help the injured one. We needn't go to an elephant jungle to see the thing in action. Wherever our home woods, if there are crows there, that place will serve. Crows, as will be discussed later, often rally around a sick or crippled crow, helping the victim to shelter or even carrying it aloft.

We may say, if we like, that animal life is a struggle for survival. In a very wide sense, if we keep our thinking careful, that's true. But we come to realize, as we get to know animals better and better, that the "struggle" isn't all in terms of self-assertion. The struggle comprises all the modes that make for self-preservation; and one of the most important and widespread of all those modes, exactly speaking, is self-sacrificing. Among animals, as among ourselves, devotion of the individual to other individuals goes very deep. The one subserves the many. The impulse to cooperation, to mutual help, goes down and down to the roots of things, to the inmost tissue of livingness.

By the way, when animals of different species live interdependently together for their mutual benefit, there's a name for that. Probably we ought to know it. It's symbiosis.

Can a fox climb
a tree?

Yes; if it's the right kind of fox. The astonishing frequency of
this question, and the hot disputes over it, must come from a basic
confusion over the different ways of red foxes and gray ones.
Red foxes don't climb trees. (Or to be moderate, let's say that
they *hardly ever* climb trees. Even a fox terrier, after all, might go
lolloping up a tree in extraordinary circumstances.) Gray foxes, on
the other hand, climb low trees almost as readily as cats. Are "cross
foxes," by the way, cross breeds between reds and grays? No. Like
silver foxes, they are just a color phase of red foxes. The "cross"
name refers to a dark banding across the fox's shoulders. Intersect-
ing with the dark band along its back, it forms the shape of a
cross.

Another fox question: Do foxes scream? We don't need long
experience in the night woods to learn to identify the yapping
bark that foxes ordinarily make; but it may take us a lot longer
to find out what animal is uttering a loud, shrill squalling that
we're likeliest to hear drifting on the heavy air of early spring.
That's the mating yell of vixens.

And still another fox question: Do foxes sweat? The question
of animals' sweating comes up in connection with all sorts of
animals that never show any visible lathering. For some reason or
other, probably starting with some old hunter's tale, it's particularly
often said that foxes don't sweat. Well, do they? Yes, they do, dog-
wise. It's one of the reasons why a fox leaves such an easily per-

ceptible trail. A fox sweats chiefly through the soles of its paws. But don't dogs sweat via their muzzles? No. They're paw-perspirers, except for a small perineal sweat area, and otherwise they do their cooling off, as do a great many other animals, just by panting. An animal that does perspire on its nose is easy enough for us to find. It's our homely and familiar cow. Which brings up, naturally enough, this:

Do deer chew cud?

Surely. All the animals called ruminants are cud chewers. *Rumen* is Latin for a gullet-paunch. The ruminants, in addition to our cows, include all sorts of the earth's wild sheep, goats, and deer as well. And does a deer have four stomachs as a cow does? We need to straighten this out a little. A deer does have the same sort of interior arrangement; but instead of calling it, in either case, four stomachs, we might better call it a stomach apparatus with four parts. What happens in a ruminant animal is this: As it browses, the swallowed grass and leaves go into its paunch (its rumen, that is to say). From there the food proceeds into a second part, where it's processed into lumps or wads to form cuds. Our ruminant now brings up these grassy aggregates into its mouth, cud by cud, and at leisure chews each cud slowly into a softened, digestible mass. This goes to part three, and then gradually into part four, which leads into the animal's intestines.

We were finding out, a few pages ago, how fast deer go when they "run like a deer." How about "leaping like a gazelle"? Some of the African gazelles easily make sailing broad jumps of 35 feet. A little klipspringer, which is a small antelope, can make a vertical leap of 15 or 20. Most common deer we're likely to get to know in our close-to-home woods and fields have no trouble rising 6 or 8 feet off the earth, as they soar over a windfall.

On the high northwestern part of that patch of the planet where I do my animalizing, there is a hemlock-wooded area to which I go a good deal. I go there to do a variety of pleasant and impractical things, of the sort for which the trade of writer-naturalist offers splendid excuse: things like just sitting on a hemlock stump, smelling the earth smell, soaking up the sun, and quieting into the state of mind of a contented turtle; or perhaps, in a mood of livelier attention, watching a procession of ants marching from one lichened stone to another lichened stone and pondering upon what—as best our animal lore and a careful effort of our sympathetic imagination will let us guess—may be going on in those small antennaed heads on their thready little necks. On one of these excursions, always justifiable by any animalizer as research, I found out something a little comical about my deer. There's a three-strand fence through part of the hemlock woods, and I'd noticed the deer tracks on either side of it, and I had thought I'd measure the height of the fence, to capture, perhaps, a statistic. I had got as far as contemplating this activity, while sitting quiet on my hemlock stump, when two does appeared at the fence and, not noticing me, dealt with the obstacle while I watched. They didn't leap over it. Crouching and hunching themselves gingerly, they crept through it, between the bottom strand and the next one.

Are deer superb leapers? Yes indeed. Does any animal in all this green world always behave predictably? We need go animalizing only a little while, only around our home-acre woods and fields, to come to know the happy answer to that. It's one of the endless rewards of animalizing—along with the chance to get out under the sun, and feel the rain, and scuff through the autumn leaves, and generally revive the Interior Adam in us—that we are guaranteed against ever being bored. Our world on which each new sun comes up is in a very real sense a new one. And so is every deer we may meet on a familiar woods trail, and every white-footed mouse into whose runways we go exploring. The zoological facts, the textbook facts, take a lot of finding out. But then, on top of that, there are the living facts, to be found out in a lifetime from the living animals . . . and that learning never comes anywhere near an ending. An animalizer may be all sorts of things.

But one thing he can count on being. He can count each morning, when the sun comes up and he goes prowling off into animaldom, on the delight of being surprised.

Now, to wind up these miscellaneous questions about particular animals:

Are animals' senses keener than ours?

In specialized ways, enormously. When we were talking at length about the animal mind and quality of consciousness, we had a good deal to say about this; and here we must say a little more specifically. An animal's world is very largely a world of the impulsive, the spontaneously done, and, above all, of the felt. We may look at a scene and analyze it. A fox, so to speak, breathes it. We say to ourselves, What is Truth?, and we go racking our wits to discover it. A fox cocks its peaked ears and listens for it. An animal's knowing is largely what certain Indian interpreters used to call "deep-knowing," or what we may call "knowing in our bones." Again, it's a knowing in the nostrils, a knowing in the ears.

Dogs are the animals most easily tested, and inquiring animalizers have tested them exhaustively. What we know about dogs' sensory world tells us, by extension, about the sensory world of dogs' wild brothers. How sharply do animal ears hear? How vividly do animal nostrils catch the scents of the life adventure?

What a man can hear at 175 yards, by straining his unaccustomed ear, a dog can hear easily at a distance of a full mile. In comparison with our dogs, we go ear-muffed and deafened through the experience of life. Nor is it only with regard to the volume of sound that we are hard of hearing. Our ears are not merely weak receptors, animally speaking; they are undiscriminating among the sounds that do reach them.

In the early part of this century an investigator in the Berlin Physiological Laboratory (Dr. Kalischer) conducted a long and complex series of tests in the matter of tonal sense. He was able

to find that dogs have an astonishing gift for accurately discerning
the exact pitch of sounds. Not only can a dog distinguish between
two adjacent notes on the piano, the animal gift of auditory discrimination is so beautifully precise that the dog can distinguish
between two notes that are separated by *one-quarter* of the range
that separates the two piano notes.

As with the discrimination between sounds, so with the locali-
zation of them. The findings in this field were the work of another
German dog-experimenter, Engelmann. Professor Engelmann tried
ringing a little bell, first behind one of two paper screens, then behind the other. Gradually he brought the two screens closer and
closer together. Long, long after the keenest human "localizer"
had had to abandon the attempt to tell behind which screen the
bell was being rung, Engelmann's dogs were still accurately select-
ing the screen from behind which the sound came. (Would other
kinds of animals be as subtly discriminating as dogs? Engelmann was able to prove, as a matter of fact, that cats and even
chickens have an auditory gift of "localizing" that is superior to
ours.)

Important though hearing often is to animals, it's the sense of
smell that is probably a mammal's most constantly employed means
of knowing its universe and investigating it. Smell tells a fox that
the hunter is near, before it can see him. Smell brings a wolf its
meat. Smell says "weasel!" to a rabbit, in the darkest and most
quiet midnight; and smell says "female" to every male animal
from a mouse to a moose. Once upon a time, in the morning of
the world, it's likely, we ourselves must have had a pair of nostrils
that could tell us all that. Our brother animals still have.

Dr. F. J. J. Buytendijk of the University of Groningen conducted a great many tests of the olfactory sense in dogs. The animals which he and his collaborators tested proved able not only
to recognize the presence of nitrobenzol in a solution of $\frac{1}{200}$ of
1 per cent, but to have such marvelously selective noses that they
could still recognize the presence of this microscopic trace of

nitrobenzol when the solution was disguised with flower scents, tar, cinnamon, and as many as five other powerful odors.

You and I live in a good deal more elaborate world of thought than any animal does. We can think much farther thoughts than the best dog Buytendijk tested. But there's a world of smell-knowing, where an animal can go, that's closed to us. How keen can an animal's smell-knowing really be? This keen: The most alert and most animally alive of tested dogs have been found able to detect the odor of iodoform in a solution of just one part in four million.

Animals' senses are developed in specialized ways. We have already talked about bats' supersonic cries and radar perceptions, the humanly inaudible way mice sing, the slit-eyed vision of cats, and the like. We shall be coming to other sensory findings about birds, snakes, fish. To get to know our creaturely brothers is to come to realize, among other things, that "What is Truth?" is a matter investigated, on this green earth of ours, by a great range of very various cognitions, of which mind-means is only one.

Do animals doctor themselves?

It comes naturally to us to think of animals as fellow personalities. From the time when we begin to pay any attention to them at all, we see them feeding, mating, sleeping, playing, after more or less our own fashion; we notice in them evidences of love, hate, fear, joy, the whole gamut, more or less, of our own emotional range; and we take it, in an immediate inference, that in their consciousnesses there must be going on, at least in some degree and after a certain fashion, the sorts of thing that go on in our own. After we have made our way rather deeper into animalizing, we find out, as we have been finding out in all sorts of ways in this book, both how true these spontaneous judgments about animals are, and how very, very careful we have to be to bear in mind the limitations of animal mentality, the specialties of animal senses, and the innateness of animal instinct, if we are not to be led into misinterpreting our brothers with an overanthropomorphism. By the time we've got to this point in our book, we ought to be able to take up the matter of animals' doctorings without needing too many words of qualification and reservation.

If a fox or a muskrat has been caught in a trap, may it amputate its leg to set itself free? Yes. That happens often. Why not? It's a very animally natural sort of thing to do. It's practical intelligence, sensorimotor insight, at work. So next: When a bear has been wounded, is it true that the bear may stuff its wound with moss or leaves? Yes; that's true too. After all, it's reasonable enough, even to bear mind, to press something soothing against a hurt. In the same way, we may find injured animals that have dressed their wounds with resin, or swamp mud, or plant down. The dressings have been acquired in the very natural and elementary course of placing a wounded part in contact with something that assuages it. Long ago when we were small children, we didn't need any medical learning to go dabbling our cut foot in the brook or thrusting our bee-stung finger into the cool soothingness of the mud. But now we come to a lot of common animal questions that at first glance may look to be of the same sort as the ones we've just been raising, but that in fact, if we stop to think about it, we see are significantly different:

Do animals with broken legs mend them with splints? Do sick animals know what plants are good for their ailments and seek them out specifically as remedies? Is it true that when a bear's getting ready to den up, it eats a special vegetation that will serve as a laxative and clean out its system preparatory to the long sleep? When animals have been bitten by a poisonous snake, do they seek out snakeweed and eat it as an antidote? The answer to all these, and a dozen other similar questions about animals' self-doctorings, is No.

It's No for the same reason that our right answer has to be No to the question of whether an animal ever commits suicide. "Suicide" means, obviously enough, the destruction of the self; and the idea of destroying the self can occur only to a mind that has entertained the concept of the self in the first place. Self-consciousness may strike us, because we're so used to it, as a very easy and simple sort of notion; but actually it's a huge leap of awareness . . . a leap clear outside the whole psychic province of animality. Does an animal ever seek to destroy itself? We answer our question when we pose the analagous one: Does any little child do so? As we were saying when we were talking in an earlier question about the freedom of animals' lives from the dark shadows of worry, apprehension, and fear of death—the freedom that makes animaldom such a glad kingdom, all confidence, life acceptance, and an immediacy of Now—an animal cannot know, any more than a little child, that it has a self to lose. It cannot look ahead to self-ending; it can't contemplate a coming of non-ness.

Animals don't kill themselves, and they don't practice complicated self-doctoring. For a woodcock to thrust its fractured leg into mud, and for the mud to harden into what is in effect a cast, isn't at all an impossible thing. (There are some severe ornithologists who question whether it ever happens; but there are also dozens of outdoor animalizers, devoted to firsthand investigation of woodcock ways and equally devoted to earth-truth, who swear that they've known it to; and at least we can say, in an equable way, that it falls comfortably inside the area of animal reasonableness.) But the devising and application of splints is something very much else again . . . so much else again that we ourselves, historically speaking, have known about the principle only since yesterday. Snakeweed? If any fox knows that specific, it knows more than any of us.

Many animals—squirrels and some of their relatives, particularly —periodically put their bedding out in the sun and air it. All sorts of animals take sun baths, dust baths, and mud baths. A deer that's had to plunge through an icy stream "knows" it's unwise to lie down to sleep. It keeps starting up and running to warm itself until its hide has dried. A rheumaticky old buck "knows" the value of

sunshine and a warm mud-wallow. Almost any animal in all the
green woods "knows" the valuable therapy of licking a hurt. But
it is a long way—an impossibly long way—from sucking and
soothing a wound to understanding the nature of asepsis. It's a wide
leap—an impossibly wide leap—from the quality of consciousness
in a sick lynx, following an obscure instinctive impulse to eat grass,
to the quality of consciousness in an herbalist composing an herbal.

Do animals do some doctoring of themselves, and is there a
wisdom in it? Of a certainty. But the wisdom is animal wisdom:
the felt thing, the sensorimotor thing, the spontaneous act out of
animal urgency. The doctoring, exactly speaking, is animal-wise.

We ought not to leave this without bringing up briefly two
questions particularly. If baby wild birds are taken from their
nests and caged, will the mother bird seek out the cage and feed
her imprisoned youngsters poisonous berries through the bars,
preferring to see them dead rather than deprived of liberty? And
how about the way in which a fox is supposed to rid itself of
fleas? (We must all have heard this story. The fox takes in its
mouth a tuft of hair, or perhaps a stick or a bunch of leaves, and
slowly backs into a stream or lake. The fleas, as the fox submerges,
scurry higher and higher on its body to escape the water, and
presently, when all but the tip of the fox's muzzle has gone under,
the fleas quit the fox altogether and climb aboard the stick or the
bunch of leaves or the tuft of hair or whatever, which the fox
then releases to float away with its cargo of pests.)

How about these?

No matter what veteran animalizers we become, it doesn't do
for us ever to be brusquely contemptuous. These two old tales are
told and retold, all over the world, and greatly cherished. Suppose
we just answer the question about them with merely the suggestion
of an answer. Suppose we just let our suggestion take the form of
a few rhetorical questions and one homely experiment. For the
rhetorical questions, we might just raise these: Does a bird understand toxicology? Does it know the abstraction, Liberty, and has

it realized that death is a form of freedom from the tyranny of captivity? For the homely experiment, we might have a go at this one: We might try taking a docile and richly flea-ful dog, and very slowly dipping this pooch of ours into a tub of water, and watching to see whether the fleas ascend. (This is a little laborious, perhaps, for some of us. We may like to know the outcome in advance. What we find is that the fleas, clinging tightly to their nourishing host, and no more endangered by a few minutes' submersion than most small chitinous insects are, ignore the rising water entirely.)

However assiduously our deer takes the sunlight and our lynx nibbles minty grasses, all animals must die. We were investigating, a number of pages back, the ways in which death comes to the animals, and what quality the event must have in animal experience. Now we come to the very common question that logically serves as final question for this part of our book:

Why do we so rarely find dead animals?

There are a lot of reasons, of course. Most killed animals are eaten at once by others. Animals that die of disease or accident may be taken, depending on the part of the world, by various big scavengers: vultures, jackals, and so on. But an important part of the answer lies in the secretive, chiefly nocturnal activities of an extraordinary little creature called *Necrophorus*. It's a black and yellow-orange little beetle, smaller than a finger joint. Its role in the animals' world is plain enough from its name. It is the Bearer of the Dead.

A good many popular and colloquial names are used by naturalists to describe this scuttling little being that performs tremendous offices in the darkness of the night. Most shortly and aptly, it's called the sexton. In the living laboratory of my own woods and fields, I've spent a good many dusk and early dawn hours watching sextons at their work. It's a curious work; and we must have a look at how this last chapter in so many animal lives takes place:

Suppose, now, that a baby rabbit has gone blundering and crashing into the wire netting around our garden and has broken its neck. The small body twitches briefly and lies still. We notice it, perhaps, when we are out mulching the roses in the afternoon. We think: Tomorrow I must bury that poor beast. The tomorrow comes, and we go out, and there is no rabbit. Perhaps a fox or coon has found it and lugged it away? Perhaps, but not likely. The chances are that the rabbit is still near at hand, around our garden. But between sundown and sunup, it has been interred. In the black hours, the sextons have been at work.

In the darkness, there is a whirry little clatter of beetle wings, like a smaller version of the buzz of a June bug. There alights beside the rabbit's corpse a small black-and-yellow beetle with powerful black legs. It comes to earth a few inches from the dead body, and waggles its antennae inquiringly to catch more precisely the smell of death that has brought it to this place from perhaps a long way away. The odor of death, to a sexton beetle, carries great distances on the heavy night air. The sexton scurries closer to the body. It closes its heavy, beetlish wing covers over its flying-wings. It is ready to undertake its business.

For some minutes the sexton examines the corpse, touching it lightly here, there, with its feelers, pitter-patter, pitter-patter, as in a quick gesture of "running its fingers" over the body. What is it determining? We don't exactly know. To get inside the consciousness of any animal is hard. To project ourselves inside the insect-being of the sexton and know, so to speak, what is going through its mind, is all but impossible. Clearly, however, it is making tests of one sort and another; it is obtaining a picture, sensory or more than that, that is meaningful to it. Pitter-patter, pitter-patter, go the feelers. Then presently the sexton backs off a little. It knows what it must know. It approaches the corpse again, wedges its dome-backed body under one side of it, scrabbles away at the earth to roughen it and clear away a little patch, and then in an adroit gesture the sexton flips over on its back.

Farther, farther, lying on its back, the sexton insinuates itself under the dead body. Everyone who has practiced at all with weights, or who has watched "strong men" going through their prodigious feats, must know what tremendous weights can be supported by leg muscles when a man is lying on his back. We have two legs. The sexton beetle has six. As the sexton lies on its back, pushing upward with all its might with these six stout black legs, it is able to show a power almost unbelievable. The body of the rabbit begins to jiggle and rock. Farther, farther, the little sexton beetle works its way under the rabbit, sliding on its curved, polished back, holding the rabbit aloft by leg power. Finally the sexton is directly underneath the body. It is supporting the whole weight of it. It is at dead center. In a mighty pedaling motion, with all six legs, the sexton sends the rabbit's body lurching perhaps half an inch toward the edge of the garden bed. As the body drops to settle again, the sexton scoots out from under it, slips over (right side up) again, and now rests briefly, contemplating what it has wrought.

What the sexton is doing is moving the corpse toward a soft spot of soil which it has selected as a burial spot. It may need to move the body a foot. It may need to move it 10 feet. It is quite capable of doing so. For the strength and energy of the sexton are prodigious. It will work, hardly halting, all night long. And it is pretty certain to obtain, any moment now, a helper. Another little whirry clatter of beetle wings sounds in the darkness. A small form drops to earth beside the rabbit. A female sexton has arrived.

There is no courtship between the insects, unless their immediate joining together in the work of burial can be called one. They work together, in perfect team operation, as if the thing had been rehearsed.

When the male pushes, now, the female runs to the other side of the rabbit and pulls. When the male is under the body, supporting the cadaver on his legs and pedaling it forward, the female is at the rabbit's head, scrabbling frantically to clear away impeding twigs and pebbles. Are insects intelligent? Not fully humanly intelligent, no, of course not. But—well—*insectly* intelligent? It is difficult to doubt it. When a rootlet or grass blade gets in the way, one of the sextons hurries to chew it through and cut it. Beetle works with beetle in a team play like the nice joint expertness of acrobats. Inch by inch, inch by inch, the body of the dead rabbit is juggled forward. In an hour, two hours, five hours—the sextons are tireless—it is brought to the selected site for burial.

The sextons whisk underneath. They dig. Down, down, the rabbit sinks, in a slow, jiggly descent into its grave.

Now only an inch or two of it is still visible above the sandy ground; now even that has disappeared; now there is no rabbit at all, but only a heaving and rippling of the earth to let a watching animalizer know that the sextons are still at their dark work, down underneath the interred body.

When the corpse lies several inches deep, the sextons pluck away its fur and groom it and work it into a ball. They dig a side tunnel out into the earth from the burial chamber, and there the female lays eggs. The preparations for the next generation of sexton beetles are now completed.

Most insects do very little looking after their young. The majority, of course, don't tend the young insects at all. But sexton beetles do. While they wait for the hatching of the eggs, they feed on the rabbit's body. Then, when their yellow grubs hatch out, they take care of *their* feeding. What the parents do is to take mouthfuls of the decayed rabbit flesh and then vomit it up, partly predigested, for the babies. They keep up this feeding until the grubs have finished their moltings and have become ready to pupate and transform into adult sexton beetles. As soon as pupation has started, in a chamber under the soil, the young are in no further need of tending. The adult sextons come tunneling up from their fetid tomb, take to the air again, and go their ways.

That is the story behind the disappearance of many a small dead animal's body. A nasty story? Why, no; earth-terms must strike an animalizer as fair enough. Is it a bad thing that carcasses are removed and buried? Is it worse that a beetle should feed on long-dead bodies than that we should feed ourselves on recently dead ones? Meat is meat, flesh is flesh, and everything in the world lives on some other thing. If we don't like those terms, we are on the wrong planet. Vomiting may signify unhealthiness when it happens to *us;* but among a great many creatures it is as sound and sunny a part of natural living as the singing of songs. Hummingbirds, after their fashion, vomit food into their nestlings. Are they any the less lovely in their delicacy and grace? What's the "pigeon's-milk" of the poets? It's discharged cellular matter from the birds' crops. Are doves any the less dovelike and delightful, for all that?

There is nothing about the dying of animals, any more than about their living, to dismay any animalizer who looks at this green garden with candor and understanding.

And now let's get to birds. There have already been taken up quite a lot of bird questions, while we've in theory been talking about mammals, and no doubt there will be mammal matters popping up among the insects and a stray duck query or butterfly fact intruding amid the snakes when we get to those. Animaldom is all interrelated, and so are the questions about it. Still, animals do divide up, after a fashion, into groupings; and this book of ours ought reasonably to do so too. So what comes next is Birds; and here we go to the commonest questions that concern (mostly!) that particular section of the animal brotherhood.

Birds

The poetry of earth, of course, is to be found in every created thing. Our spirits, when they're tuned to the right pitch of primal astonishment and delight, discover enchantment in any sun-warmed rock, any whisking October oak leaf, any shimmering drop of rain on the nearest blade of dooryard grass. The creation is one continuous and inexhaustible glory; this garden is all magic. Still, we're likely, most of us, to grow a little dulled, from a sort of fatigue of familiarity. We forget to be feeling the sunlight on us. We don't hear any more all the astonishing little earth-musics, such as, say, crickets'. We tend to lose what in a beautifully exact phrase we call our animal spirits. It must be a very rare one of us, though, who isn't stirred to response by birds.

Birds pluck at our attention with their tumultuous songs and vivid colors. Our eyes are entranced by their flight against the sky. Whatever else we may neglect to notice, we are pretty sure to be struck and stirred by the tumbling, spring-bursting "conker-err-ee!" of red-winged blackbirds in an April marsh, the honking clatter of wild geese in their autumnal passing, the bell-clear singing and the sweetly dappled look of a thrush in our summer-evening garden.

Our poetry is full of birds. Our painting is full of birds. Our language abounds in figures taken from these winged animals.

E

Birds? Why, we can scarcely look out of any window and not
see the flash of feathered wings. We can't go for the most pre-
occupied little country saunter and not hear the songs and calls
of these brothers of ours. Birds, it seems likely, are the animals
that most often set us to our first animalizings. Robins nest outside
our window; we are immediately captivated; and also immediately
we are full of questions. Is it just the mother robin that builds the
nest, or does the male help too? How long does it take birds' eggs
to hatch? If an egg is taken from the nest, will the mother notice?
Can she count? When the birds roost at night, and fall asleep,
why don't they tumble off their perches?

We start with thronging bird questions like these in our childhood, and a good many of us may still be asking them years later;
for in providing information about birds, as about other sorts of
our fellow animals, textbooks are likely to have a maddening way
of being immensely eloquent upon the nature of dichromatism
and the subspecific classification of an obscure gallinule but altogether silent about such childishly straightforward and simplehearted questions as, for instance, Can birds ever fly backward?
and Do all birds lay eggs?

In this book of elementary and informal animalizings of ours,
we're not being ashamed to start from beginnings. An introduction
is our agreed-on intention. We want to get to know our animal
brothers in those respects that make up the stuff of the commonest
questions about them, not the far and intricate questions of the
already erudite. Never mind the rare gallinule. We can get to him
later, in some other book, if we want to become recondite gallinu-
lists. Here we're just animalizers. We're just standing in a spring
meadow, or looking out our window into the green depths of
a tree, and contemplating here and now our living brother, that
bird out there, and wondering to ourselves: Is that bird song an
instinctive thing or does the bird have to learn it? Didn't we read
somewhere once that when the birds go south, the big birds carry
little ones on their backs? Is that really true? "Scarce as hen's teeth"

. . . . Hmmmm; come to think of it, *do* birds ever have teeth? Here we go, in this mood and intention, into the world of birds.

Do all birds have feathers?

When they are grown up, yes, they do. Feathers are as characteristic of birds as hair is of mammals. It's hard for us to think, when we watch swallows skittering over the sunny farm lands or listen to a veery singing its evening song in the twilit woods, that in the long slow development of the creation birds have come into being as the descendants of reptiles. But they have; and their feathers are the modified and adapted version of what once were scales. When birds are in their babyhood, of course, their feathers are often no more than a little downy fuzz. Are there any birds' babies that have *no* covering? A few. An infant flicker, for example, is perfectly fuzzless. So is a newly hatched baby kingfisher.

Can all birds except penguins and ostriches fly?

No. Emus, cassowaries, and rheas can't fly either, nor can a kiwi, which is the emblematic bird of New Zealand. With such infrequent exceptions as these, though, birds are all a flying company.

What's the biggest bird in the world?

Omitting the consideration of wingspread, and just going by bulk and weight, the biggest bird now alive on our earth is an ostrich. Ostriches can run to a weight of something over 300 pounds, and they often stand more than 8 feet tall on their two-toed feet.

We may as well take up a parcel of ostrich questions here, while we're about it. Do ostriches hide their heads in the sand? No. It seems to be an undying legend; but they don't. Is it true that ostriches are fast runners? They're almost incredibly fleet. An ostrich can achieve, and maintain, a running speed of 50 miles per hour, which is just about as fast as a race horse can go. How big is an ostrich egg? Roughly speaking, it weighs around 3 pounds, and holds about the contents of a dozen and a half eggs of our domestic chickens. Is it true that ostriches are formidable fighters? Very. An ostrich lashes out in "rabbit kicks" with its powerful legs, and can easily disembowel even a big animal in a fight.

How long does it take a mother ostrich to hatch her enormous eggs? I suppose every living naturalist must have gone through a phase when he discovered the wonderful "trick" answer to this, and went about with it bedazzling inquirers. The "trick" answer is: no time at all. Among a great many birds, as we shall presently be seeing, the male takes turns with the female in incubating the eggs. In the tribe of flightless birds, extraordinarily, the male often takes over the whole incubatory role. A female ostrich's duties are sometimes ended with the laying of her eggs. It may be the father ostrich that broods them. So, now—putting our question another way around, to be prepared against the awful wisdom of any young ornithologists we may encounter—how long does it take her or *him* to hatch the enormous eggs? It takes forty to fifty days.

What's the smallest bird in the world?

A hummingbird: the Cuban one called Helena's hummingbird or, more informally, the fairy hummer. This tiniest of the birds is only about 2 ¼ inches long, with a wing length measuring just over an inch.

Our world's littlest birds, like its biggest, are the subject of several ever-recurring questions. Do hummingbirds live entirely on the nectar of flowers? There's a general supposition that they do; but No. When hummingbirds probe into the corollas of flowers, they are extracting not merely nectar but also quantities of small flies, bees, and spiders. How fast does a hummingbird beat its wings? Unbelievably enough, about seventy-five times a second. And how fast can hummingbirds fly? As best naturalists have been able to time it—it isn't easy, for hummingbirds are as darting and erratic as hornets—they seem to be able to zoom along comfortably at about 50 miles per hour, which curiously enough is about the speed, as we have just been seeing, that the biggest living birds achieve by running. Can a hummingbird fly far without stopping to rest? The vitality of animals, the thrust and drive of them, are a perpetual astonishment and tonic to all of us who go animalizing. The little ruby-throated hummingbirds that summer in the United States spend their winters southward to Central America and Yucatán. Is it possible that these almost bee-tiny beings, their wings so furiously a-whirr, can really manage 500 nonstop flying miles across the Gulf of Mexico? They do.

Hummingbirds provide the answer to one particularly popular bird question that logically comes up next:

Can any bird fly backward?

Yes. Though this answer usually produces astonishment, it really shouldn't surprise any of us who have ever paid more than casual attention to hummingbirds. A hummingbird flies deep into flower tubes, poises there on beating wings while it feeds, and then slips backward out of the flower in a straight reverse flight. What makes a hummingbird so fantastically maneuverable? It can turn its wings over.

Do all birds lay eggs?

All of them do, without exception. How many eggs? Well, any-where from just a single egg, which is what several kinds of sea birds lay, to upwards of twenty eggs in a clutch, which happens fairly often among some of the ducks and game birds. Why this disparity? As we keep finding out, everything in the world of the animals goes with everything else. Nothing stands alone. No event is isolated. The web of being is in a universal seamlessness, so that nothing ever "just happens," whether the length of a meadow mouse's tail or the curve in the eye of a cottontail rabbit. The nests of waterfowl and game birds, mostly on the ground, are subject to a great deal of pillaging. In being fitted to survival, these birds have been bred for fecundity. The sea birds that bring up their families on lonely and remote oceanside crags are scarcely attacked by enemies at all. They can afford small families.

Do female birds of a given species always lay the same number of eggs?

Circumstances being normal, the number of eggs doesn't vary a great deal. That is, a robin usually lays three to five eggs in a clutch, a phoebe five or six, and so on. But if it happens that some of the eggs are removed, a bird may lay replacements. When that happens, she can call on a reserve of fecundity that makes it easier to understand how our domestic chickens have been bred to their prodigies of production. The classic case concerns a flicker (golden-winged woodpecker), and was first described in the ornithological magazine *The Auk* over fifty years ago. All the eggs, except one, were removed from this flicker's nest; and the theft was repeated daily to see how long she would go on laying replacements. The baffled but determined flicker laid seventy-one eggs in seventy-three days.

Why are some birds' eggs plain-colored and others speckled?

We'd need nearly a bookful of evolutionary oölogy to explore this fully; but, putting it in the briefest and simplest sort of way, it goes like this: Originally, we can take it, birds' eggs were all just a yellowy-white like the eggs of their reptile forebears. With birds' development of the nesting habit as a protective device, the coloring of their eggs also became protectively adapted. Take birds

that nest in holes and dark, protected crannies of one sort and
another . . . birds like kingfishers and woodpeckers. They lay
white eggs. After all, their eggs are invisible by virtue of the nest
environment; it doesn't matter how gleamingly plain they are. But
take the eggs of, say, killdeer plovers, which are laid on the ground.
They're streaked and mottled in such semblance of pebbly soil that
they are almost invisible even when we are staring straight at
them. Pretty clearly, it's a protective coloring developed over the
long ages, just as the speckled coats of fawns have developed or
any of the other animal "trickeries" we were talking about a while
ago.

Clear enough. But then: What about all the solid blue and solid
green and variously blotched eggs that we find among the birds
that nest neither on the ground nor in holes but in trees? These,
as the evolutionists put it, are probably degenerations. Meaning
this: that whereas the pigmenting of eggs presumably started in the
first place as a protection when all bird eggs were laid on the
ground, the pigmenting is now in the process of dying away again
among those birds that have taken to nesting in places where the
eggs don't need it. If we do much nest exploring, we soon find out
that the eggs of a great many birds vary a lot in their coloring and
markings. Phoebes' eggs are sometimes quite heavily speckled, and
sometimes they have almost no speckles at all. Sparrows' eggs vary
immensely, all the way from nearly white to so densely spotted as
to be almost solid brown. All this is the blurry instability, which is
also the repose in progress, of evolution going on.

No more than anything else are birds' eggs "fixed." All life, as
we've been seeing in so many ways, is a changing, altering, adapting
thing. The creation isn't a set scene, but a flow. Life, in short, to put
it a little absurdly, is *alive*. You aren't, today, what you were
yesterday; nor am I; nor is any existing part or particle of all there
is. Things are "fixed," to be sure, as far as *our* terms of reference are
concerned. The mountain we look at this morning isn't going to
have disappeared tomorrow afternoon, and thrush eggs aren't go-

ing to turn from blue to something else until all books about animal life have long since turned to dust. Still, the fact of change is there. It never stops. It's just that the long, slow sweeps of change are so hugely long, so vastly slow, that we can't see them happening. It's just, as the old religious writers used to remark, that it's very difficult to think God's thoughts after Him. What color are sandpipers' eggs? Browny-spotted. What color are crows' eggs? Greenish, with black and purply streakings. Will they be the same when our grandchildren and our great-grandchildren go out animalizing along the familiar shore and up in the familiar oak woods on the knoll? They will, assuredly. Will they be the same forever and forever and forever? Why, no.

But to return to our discussion about animals and Now, there's still this last question: If birds that nest in holes are supposed to lay plain white eggs, what are we to make of the hole-deposited eggs of such birds as wrens and bluebirds? Wrens lay densely brown-speckled eggs, the speckles applied in such a fine powdering that sometimes the eggs look almost pink, and bluebirds lay blue eggs. What about that? We can guess the answer when we notice that these birds always carry a lot of nesting material into their nest holes. Inside their cavities they still make—in a rude, diminished sort of way—true nests. That means that they haven't been laying their eggs in cavities for very long. ("Very long," that is, in the enormous terms to which we have to get used to thinking in such matters.) They used to build nests in the open. Something of the habit remains, as something of the pigmenting remains on their eggs. The eggs carry pigment, we may put it, as we carry our vermiform appendix. A little while from now—a few tens of thousands, a few millions of years—and both things will be gone.

Do all birds build nests?

No. There are quite a few that don't. Sea birds such as auks and murres make no nests, and neither do such commoner and closer-to-home birds as nighthawks and whippoorwills. Killdeers, the plovers we were just speaking about, merely scrape together a few pebbles before they lay their speckled eggs in a furrow of a plowed field. Then, too, there are birds that make no nests because they live as parasites on other members of bird society.

"Parasitism" is an emotional sort of word, with overtones of nastiness and disapproval. We don't go devotedly animalizing on this good earth for many years without realizing that there isn't any "nastiness" in animaldom except as we read it there. So let's put it, then, just this way: The fact is simply that all living things are interdependent; and sometimes the relations take this form and sometimes that one. For instance? In symbiosis, each creature in the relation derives a benefit from the other. In commensalism, the creatures are common partakers of one food supply. In inquilinism (from the Latin for a tenant), one creature lodges in the nest or burrow of another. In simple parasitism, only one of the creatures in the relationship derives benefit. This life-way is not at all uncommon, and is as natural under the sun as the thrift of squirrels, the neatness of a vireo's nest, or the disposition of buzzards to throw up their most recent meal when startled or angry.

We need to have a look at parasitism, and we can conveniently do so here in terms of one of the commonest parasitic birds, the one called cowbird. (There are other parasitic birds, of course, notably Old World cuckoos; but cowbirds are perhaps the easiest for most of us to watch.) We said something about cowbirds back when we were talking about animals' courtship and sexuality. Now let's look a little more fully into their life story:

A cowbird may be found in nearly any summer field in the eastern part of the United States. It's a dull, dingy blackbird, somewhat speckled and semi-iridescent in the manner of starlings, with a browner head and a short, gross bill. It has a waddling, bobbing, assertive sort of gait, and a "song" that's a variety of creaky-voiced ejaculations and whistles. Other birds may pair for long periods

E*

and show considerable devotion. Cowbirds don't pair at all. They are always more or less flock-spirited; now and again a male and female of the company are moved briefly to sexual intercourse; that's all there is to it. Other birds may range over great distances, and surmount great difficulties, to secure food. Cowbirds are satisfied to go waddling and bobbing around the fields at the heels of cattle, gobbling what insects the big beasts' feet stir up for them. Other birds build intricate nests and are prodigies of faithfulness to their young. Cowbirds never build any nests at all, and for the issue of their brief, casual unions they decline responsibility.

As the time when she must lay an egg comes upon her, the female cowbird sets forth in investigation of the pastures and hedgerows. What she is looking for is any small bird's nest, preferably unguarded, preferably with some eggs in it. When she has found such a nest—and it doesn't ordinarily take long, for a watchful-eyed bird that can slip anywhere among the leaves, looking—she settles herself upon it, deposits her egg, and flits furtively away. Occasionally, if she must, she deposits her egg in a nest in which no other eggs have yet been laid; but obviously this makes her act of intrusion more evident, and she avoids it if she can. Sometimes, if she can find no unguarded nest, she hides quietly in the foliage waiting for the bird brooding on an occupied nest to leave it briefly. On rare occasions, of course, the cowbird may not be able to void her egg in any nest by the time when she can no longer contain it. If that happens, she just drops it on the ground and abandons it.

The egg foisted by the cowbird upon a foster parent is usually considerably larger than the eggs already in the clutch. Cowbirds impose upon nearly 200 species of other birds, but most of them are the littler species: warblers, sparrows, and the like. Sometimes robins are victimized, and phoebes are fairly frequent choices; but obviously there is an advantage in insinuating the egg into a nest where the baby cowbird will be a much bigger and stronger baby than any of the legitimate nestlings in it.

Let's suppose that the nest into which the cowbird has chosen to smuggle her egg is that of a little chipping sparrow.

The chipping sparrow comes back after her absence from her nest and finds one more egg in it than when she left. Birds aren't mathematicians. They go by feel. Were all her eggs or even half of them missing, or were three or four alien eggs added, the sparrow might be quite sure to feel something amiss. But as between three eggs and four, or four and five, she rarely detects the difference. She settles down to brood her family. When presently the eggs have hatched, her sparrow mind is incapable of noting that one of the infants is a somewhat bigger infant than the others. A devoted baby feeding begins.

At feeding trip after feeding trip, now, one beak towers hungrily above the others, and into it go the morsels brought by the chipping sparrow mother. Hourly the smaller nestlings grow weaker from underfeeding, and less and less able to raise an effective clamor. Hourly the cowbird baby waxes fatter and lustier. Presently, kicking and squirming in the small nest, he manages to heave the weak little legitimate babies out over the rim, and that is the end of them. Sole occupant now, the young cowbird thrives, strengthens, and presently flies. Almost all of us who are bird watchers may have the experience of seeing a pair of devoted "parent" chipping sparrows—hardly half or a third the size of their monstrous "child" —still carefully following him and watching over him and feeding him several days after he has flown heavily out of their little nest and has become robustly able to take care of himself. The whole drive of their instinct of parental devotion, after all, has been concentrated upon this one lubberly bird.

It isn't surprising that cowbirds survive to throng the summer fields in numbers, whistling their irresponsible whistle, waddling lazily among the hoofs that stir up their provender. They have evolved a life-way of successful vagabondage. Just how this may have come about, ornithologists aren't sure. Maybe the pattern evolved as a necessity because of cowbirds' long gypsying trips in the days when bison roamed the plains. The birds, then as now, were cattle-followers. Keeping up with the wandering bison may have made it impossible for them to settle in one place long enough to build nests and raise families. That's one possible theory. At any rate, the cowbirds are settled now in their role of shiftlessness and crafty imposition upon the rest of avian society.

Those are silly words for us to be using, of course. A cowbird is no more shiftless than an ant is industrious. Animals are the creatures of their natures. The sky smiles with the same enthusiasm upon them all. Still, since we're human, there does come a certain irresistible satisfaction when we find a cowbird's plans for its tribe's perpetuity going awry. Every now and then a robin comes back to its nest, finds a speckled egg among the blue ones, and pitches it out immediately with an outraged squawk. (Detection appears to be a matter of the egg's color, not size. Birds that lay speckled eggs are likeliest to accept the addition of a cowbird's speckled egg, even when the size discrepancy is enormous.) Every now and then some phoebe or song sparrow finds a cowbird's egg among its own and instantly skewers the strange egg with its beak. Most satisfying of all, perhaps, is what often happens when a cowbird lays her egg in the nest of a little yellow warbler. The warbler simply roofs over the whole nest, closes off the entire batch of eggs, builds a second-story nest on top of the first one, and starts all over again. It has occasionally occurred that a little yellow warbler has been victimized by a cowbird more than once. So it happens that if our animalizing takes us a great deal among birds, we may sometimes find yellow warbler nests that make an extraordinarily touching demonstration of how far a small bird's fierce determination can go. These nests are three stories high.

Are all birds' eggs hatched by brooding?

No. The overwhelming majority are, of course, but there are a few birds that follow a practice much more like that of their reptilian ancestors. Pacific mound-building birds (or megapodes, which of course means simply big-footed) lay their eggs in heaped-up piles of vegetation and mixed dirt and scratchings, and never go near them again. The heat generated by the vegetable decay in the mound hatches the eggs. Crocodile birds bury their eggs in the sand, much after the fashion of a turtle, and the warmth of the African sun does all the incubating.

While we're speaking of brooding: What makes a mother bird brood her eggs? She becomes, as we say, "broody," when a nearly featherless area near the middle of her breast becomes swollen with blood. There's an increase of temperature, too, in this brood-spot, and doubtless other bird feelings in which we can't very well imaginatively participate. At any rate, pressing the brood-spot against the rounded contours of her eggs gives the bird an assuaging and fulfillment. Why do geese, ducks, pelicans, and some other birds pull out their breast-down at brooding time? It's because their breasts are heavily feathered, with scarcely any bare area, and they yank out beakfuls of feathers so they can put the skin of their brood-spot directly against the eggs.

Does a mother bird lay all her eggs at one time, in a quick succession? No. Most birds lay one egg a day. At least, most of the common little close-to-home birds that arouse our first questionings do. The big predatory birds, hawks and owls, generally lay an egg every other day. And why, since birds lay their eggs in this staggered system that may cover quite a long series of days, don't the eggs also hatch at irregular intervals? That's an animal-introductory question that used to send me poring through bird book after bird book without success, as a boy; and evidently it still arouses a lot of unsatisfied curiosity, for it's asked particularly often. The answer is this: A bird doesn't start brooding until the last egg of the clutch has been laid. Only when the complement of eggs is complete is the bird's brood-spot applied to them with the continuousness that starts their incubation. (Like almost everything else about animaldom, as we find out, this isn't invariable. Some owls' eggs, for instance, do hatch at irregular intervals. But by and large there's an all-at-once hatching.)

We were talking a few pages ago about the colors of birds' eggs. What about their shapes? Why are some of them much rounder than others? What about the ones that are long and sharp-pointed? An ordinary oval, of course, is about the best shape for most eggs in most nests. It keeps the eggs more or less massed together, easily rollable, and fits them conveniently into a group under the brooding bird. But lots of sea birds' eggs, laid on bare rocks, would roll away if they were this commonest shape. They're sharply pointed. The eggs fit toegther like a set of wedges or triangles, forming a firm circle. Again, in the case of relatively small birds that lay relatively big eggs, the eggs have to be shaped for compactness or the bird couldn't cover the clutch. Which brings up, reasonably enough, the frequent question: Why should birds of about the same size lay eggs of such very different sizes? A plover, scarcely bigger than a robin, lays eggs almost twice as big as the robin's. Why? It's because some baby birds are what ornithologists call altricial, which is to say, naked and helpless, and others are precocial, which is to say, downy-feathered and bright-eyed and fairly well able to take care of themselves from the minute of hatching. It takes a much bigger egg to hold the developing precocial chick of a killdeer than the helpless little mite as which a baby robin comes into the world.

How long does it take birds' eggs to hatch? For a very rough and ready answer, applicable approximately to most of the commoner small birds, we can put it at two weeks. Sparrows take a little less than that: twelve or thirteen days. Hummingbirds, surprisingly enough, sometimes take a little overtime: fifteen days. But there aren't any extremely wide variations. What, by the way, about the eggs of the cowbird we were recently discussing . . . the ones deposited in other birds' nests to be hatched by foster parents? Those, to the advantage of the baby cowbird, hatch in the extraordinarily short time of ten days. The longest incubation times, understandably, are taken by the eggs of big birds with precocial babies. Our familiar chickens' eggs are incubated for three weeks. Duck eggs? Anywhere from three weeks to a month. The eggs of the biggest geese? Nearly a month and a week.

Is it just mother birds that brood the eggs, or do the father birds help? That depends pretty much on how vividly the father bird is colored in comparison with his mate. Where male and female have fairly similar feathering, they usually take turns at incubation. But where the female's much the more inconspicuous bird (as in the case, say, of scarlet tanagers; she's a dull olive drab), the female ordinarily does all the incubating and the flaming male stays away from the nest.

Do father birds bring food to their incubating mates? Usually, yes. A male bird's helpfulness includes not only feeding, but standing guard at or near the nest when his female leaves on brief necessary absences. The arrangements between mother and father birds during incubation time are of a good many different kinds, and we can get to know them in detail only by going out into birddom and watching at firsthand. Among some of the warier hawks, for instance, the male fetches food for the brooding female but doesn't go near the nest. He halts at a distance from it and calls softly. She slips from the nest and flies out to meet him. Or at the other extreme, there's the case of hornbills. Hornbills must have furnished the text for a thousand lively pieces of journalism, and the story of their domesticity is as odd a story as any animalizer is likely to encounter. A female hornbill doesn't leave her nest at all right up until the time the young hornbills are grown up. The male hornbill walls her up inside a tree hollow, closing the hollow with mud until there is only a sufficient aperture for his mate to stick out her beak. He feeds her through this while she broods and hatches the eggs, and then he feeds the hornbill youngsters too, in the same imprisonment.

(Do big birds carry little birds on their backs when they're migrating? It's a picturesque and popular belief, but they don't. As we saw in talking of hummingbirds, even these tiniest flyers are powerfully competent. Is it true that mimicking sorts of birds, such as crows and mynahs, will learn to talk more proficiently if their tongues are slit? They won't; that's a barbarous myth. Do eagles carry off children at play? There are a hundred lurid stories of that, but if we care to go following them up we discover that the facts have a way of dissolving. The greatest weight a big eagle can lift off the ground is about 15 pounds. As we go wandering through the primary facts of animaldom, we have to keep saying no, and yet again no, to so many notions about our various brother creatures that it's a particular satisfaction when we light, as in the matter of hornbills, upon something that's as bizarre as any mythical whopper but that's in fact as true as sunrise. We are reminded that animaldom, among other things, is the original and unimprovable curiosity shop. When we take to animalizing, we find a good many kinds of pleasures and restorations: a rekindled awareness of the look of the woods in the early morning, the smells of earth and rain and green growing things, a reintroduction to the whole estate of primal wonder. We find out, or we re-find out, the creation's excitement and its loveliness. And not least, while we're at it, we find out that the truth of the creation is a very *entertaining* truth, full of piquancies and queernesses, the animals of reality as capable of being astonishing as any basilisk or griffon. Animalizing, when we're being solemn about it, as we all should sometimes be, can be a very healing thing, and a thought-starting thing, and it can deeply touch our spirits. But likewise, when we're feeling a little lighter-minded, it can provide us with just the simple fun of the fantastical. There's nothing like it for making our eyes pop. See *Bucorvus*, the improbable hornbill, in the handiest jungle or the nearest zoological garden.)

But to return to the question at hand: Few father birds give much help in nest building. Their role is mostly limited to encouragement, guarding the neighborhood and now and then fetching a few token twigs or wisps of grass. (We're likely to see male wrens, often enough, bustling about with sticks in what looks like major assistance. Isn't it? Actually what male wrens do is build partial or complete nests, sometimes several of them, all by themselves; but these aren't the nests in which the eggs are going to be laid. Rather, they're dummy nests—*hints* of nests, if you like—built suggestively as part of the wren's ritual of courtship.) With the onset of brooding time, however, as we've seen, a great many male birds do enter into full partnership; and after the eggs have hatched they become busier than ever.

How does a baby bird get out of the egg?

It raps and taps its way out by means of an egg tooth. A baby bird's beak is a soft little structure, and would be incapable of smashing through a sturdy eggshell. As hatching time approaches, the infant develops a hard bony bump on its upper mandible, and with this temporary tooth breaks its way out. How long does the tooth last? Only a few days after hatching. We ought to answer a couple of other egg questions, too, before we go along. Is it true that a brooding bird keeps turning over her eggs so that they will be evenly warmed? Indeed she does. Deftly using their beaks or feet, most birds take pains to turn their eggs at least once a day. Some turn them twice every day. Why is there an air space

at the big end of a bird's egg? It's what furnishes the baby bird
with air to breathe during the interval between the time its lungs
start working and the time it can chip its way free. Do baby birds
always come out of the same end of the egg? Virtually always,
yes. They face toward the large end, and that's where the air space
is. After baby birds have hatched, why don't we find a litter of
eggshell in the nest or on the ground beneath it? Parent birds
are careful to get rid of eggshell just as fast as the babies emerge.
Small shell fragments are usually eaten. Bigger pieces are taken
far away from the nest and dropped where they won't furnish
a clue to an enemy.

We have to say so much in these pages about animals' "knowing,"
that here perhaps it will be a sufficient further comment on the
instinct and intelligence theme if we just insert a thoughtful sentence of Henri Bergson's. It's not a bad sentence for us to have
in mind whether we're investigating birds or any other part of
animaldom. It goes like this: "There is no intelligence in which
some traces of instinct are not to be discovered, more especially no instinct which is not surrounded with a fringe of intelligence."

So. By this and that kind of bird wisdom, now, the youngsters
have been brought to hatching. They're hungry.

How much do birds eat?

The food requirements of birds are tremendous. Most birds eat
at least half their own weight in food every day. Growing fledglings need even more than that. In a twenty-four-hour period they
often consume *more* than their own weight in food. This keeps
the parent birds hugely busy, fetching such a vast volume of
nourishment for the youngsters. How often do they have to bring
food to the nest? Dr. Arthur A. Allen of Cornell recorded a mother
wren whose feeding trips to her fledglings were carefully observed
and counted between sunrise and sunset of one day. In that period,
she fed the fledglings 1,217 times.

How do birds make sure their nestlings share equally in the food? Do they feed them in rotation?

When a mother bird is feeding a brood, the youngsters all open their beaks and all raise a clamor each time she comes to the nest with a tidbit. Which baby shall get the food? To try to feed the nestlings by rotation would be an impossibly difficult memory feat for the busy parent. What really happens is this: Baby birds have a nervous mechanism in their throats which slows down the speed of their swallowing as they become progressively fuller. When the mother bird brings food to the nest, she simply pokes it at random into one of the open beaks and then watches sharply to see what happens. If the morsel doesn't go down immediately, she plucks it out and pops it into the next open beak. The youngster that swallows it promptly is established as having a really needy stomach. Parent birds' feeding trips are so frequent, as we've just been seeing, that no nestling has time to become desperately hungry before its turn is reached in this foolproof system of feeding by trial.

Why don't birds' nests become fouled by the babies' droppings?

Most parent birds carry away their young ones' dung as scrupulously as they carry away and hide the fragments of eggshell. At virtually every parental feeding trip to the nest, one or another of the youngsters (commonly the one that's just been fed) raises itself up in the nest and voids its dropping, which is instantly caught by the watchful parent before the excretion touches the nest at all and is immediately carried away. Young birds' metabolism being what it is, and parental foraging trips sometimes requiring prolonged absences, we do often find a certain amount of droppings under the site of a nest; but it's only a small fraction of what would accumulate if parent birds didn't have this schedule of sanitation.

How long do baby birds stay in the nest before they fly?

The youngsters of common small birds usually spend from a week to two weeks in their nest. The babies of bigger birds need longer, so that if we have a chance to watch the home life of enormous birds like condors, for instance, we find the young ones remaining in the nest for the greater part of a year. Are there any birds that are ready to fly right away after hatching? There are, yes. They're the same birds we mentioned in talking of eggs that are hatched without brooding: the big-footed megapodes, the mound-building birds of the South Pacific. A young mound-builder is ready to fly and take care of itself within minutes after it hatches. Getting back to commoner birds that we're likelier to meet in our around-home animalizings: Between the time baby birds hatch and the time they fly, do their feathers develop gradually? In most cases, yes; there's a gradual pushing out of the babyhood down by the incoming true feathers, which start unfurling from their sheaths as soon as they're a quarter grown or less. But we don't investigate many birds' nests before we find a startling exception in the case of baby cuckoos and baby kingfishers. The feathers on these youngsters stay tightly rolled up in sheathings until they are just about fully grown. The baby stays nearly naked-looking, except for clusters of what seem to be blue-gray little rods, until suddenly the close-furled little rods pop open and there bursts into being, all within a few hours, a full feathering. One last common question about bird babies: Why is it that fledgling birds sometimes seem to be bigger than their parents? The answer here, astonishingly enough, is that many baby birds look bigger than their parents because, in fact, they are. It comes naturally to us to think of all animals as in a continual growth from infancy to maturity; but actually a young bird is often larger than its parents by a quarter or more, and after it has been launched into independence, instead of growing, it shrinks. The reason? Parent birds, up until they stop feeding a youngster, feed it enormously. When the time comes for it to start its own feeding, it faces the difficulties and uncertainties of self-maintenance with a reserve of overweight on which it can draw until it has become expertly competent, bird-wise, in the ways of the world. A bird baby has usually subsided to what will be its unchanging adult size by the time its first autumn comes.

So much for our questions about birds' beginnings and development. Now that we've got the fledgling out of the nest, so to speak, we can go along to other questions about the quality of its bird life in general.

How fast can birds fly?

The speed, the aerial expertness of birds is, of course, one of the first things about them to enchant us. We stand on an autumn hilltop and watch the migrant hawks flash by, or we see swallows skimming across the farm lands almost like darts of light, and in an instant we are caught up, in empathy, in the bird's world of rush and buoyance. How fast, really, do these winged brothers of ours go, up in their world of air and sunlight and the whistling wind?

Most of the commoner small birds have a flying speed of about 45 or 50 miles per hour. (They often go much more slowly, of course; we're speaking of maximums.) Doves and pigeons can go arrowing along at 65. If the guesses of some nineteenth-century animalizers were right, back in the days when there were still passenger pigeons thronging the American sky, those may have been able to fly even more swiftly. The wild geese? They are able to touch 70; and that's about the record speed, too, for ducks.

What's the fastest bird in the world? It's not easy to say with certainty, for several birds reach just about the same top speeds. Of the littler birds, swifts are probably the fastest. They can achieve 170 miles per hour. Among hawks, which as a group are of course the fastest of all our sky brothers, the most powerful flyer is very likely a peregrine falcon or a duck hawk. These, in their pursuit of prey, reach somewhere between 170 and 200 miles per hour.

While we're speaking of flight: Is it true that swifts beat their wings alternately?

It isn't, no. I used to think it was, when I was a boy, staring at these strangely erratic speedsters streaking across the sunsets; and almost any of us may reasonably believe the thing, swifts' flight pattern being so queerly wobbly. But, no; swifts beat their wings in unison just like other birds. (Likewise, to take care of another popular swift question while we're about it, they don't bring bedbugs to our houses when they nest in the chimney.)

How about the silent flight of owls? The wings of most birds in flight make a rushing murmur. How can an owl be so soundless as it whisks close to us in the dark woods? Owls' feathers are extraordinarily soft, and the ends of them are equipped with "mufflers." They are tipped with down.

One other flight question, quickly:

Is it true that some birds can fly underwater? I suppose there could be some quibbling over this, since flying, by strict dictionary definition, means passing through the *air* with wings; but if we use the flying term in a little more spacious and popular way, the surprising answer is Yes. Several small sea birds (murres, for instance) flap their wings underwater in about the same way other birds use their wings in the air. For underwater flyers easier to observe, take the little dipper birds called ouzels. They're haunters of streams and waterfalls, and were the beloved bird of that grand old animalizer, "mountainizer," and jack-of-all-wilderness, John Muir. An ouzel dives to the bottom of a stream and walks about on it, as another bird might walk about a pasture. From time to time an ouzel, underwater, opens its wings and "flies" to a new underwater location, beating its wings exactly as in the air. (. . . "A little dusky, dainty bird that sings deliciously all winter. No matter how frosty or stormy, go to the riverside and you will hear him. No icy, chittering cheeping, but rich, whole-souled enthusiastic music that, despite the cutting wind about your ears, will make you fancy you are in a flowery grove." Thus John Muir, in his Sierra journal, wrote of ouzels.)

Birds' feathers are so fragile, and take such hard use, why don't they get broken more often?

Feathers just *look* fragile. Their appearance is not confirmed by the facts. A feather is extraordinarily elaborate in construction. On each of the feathery fibers attached to a feather's central shaft are two rows of smaller fibers called barbules. On a single feather these delicate barbules may number more than a million. Actually, for its size and weight, a bird's feather is one of the strongest structures we can find in all animaldom.

Do any birds have teeth?

Rightly speaking, no. The beaks and tongues of some birds do have spininesses and serrations (a flamingo's tongue, for instance, is spine-fringed to act as a strainer; the flamingo takes a beakful of muddy water and strains out everything except the sea food), but no birds have any true teeth. They "chew" their food in the grinding part of their stomachs, their gizzards. The effectiveness of birds' gizzards, working in conjunction with their powerful gastric juices, can be impressive. It is not true, as some zoo visitors perhaps suppose when they feed glass and metal to ostriches, that birds can digest everything; but it is remarkably nearly true. Eider ducks swallow whole mollusks and crustaceans, and reduce the shells to fine sand. Lazaro Spallanzani, an eighteenth-century Italian anatomist, to find out just what a gizzard can do, once fed a turkey a lead ball studded with small lancets. Eighteen hours later he killed the turkey. The armature of the lead ball had been destroyed.

Why don't sleeping birds fall off their perches?

Keeping its toes curled firmly around a twig doesn't require a bird's conscious effort. The tendons that cause toe curling pass around over the back of a bird's ankle joint. The instant the weight of a bird's body bends this joint, as the bird takes its perching position, the tendons pull the toes into a tight curve, clamping the perch firmly and automatically.

Do birds have the same temperature we do?

They have much higher temperature. Their temperatures are regularly as high as 105° to 110°.

Birds live their lives with an intensity as extreme as their brilliant colors and vivid songs. If we watch a bird at close range we can sometimes see its whole body shaken and vibrated by the furious pounding of its pulse. Such an engine of aliveness must operate at forced draft; and that is what a bird does. Is a bird's breathing like ours? It is a far more intensive thing. A bird's lungs aren't the terminus of its air tubes, as are our human lungs and those of other mammals. The bird's indrawn breath fills not only its lungs, but also passes on through myriads of tiny tubules from the lungs into air sacs that fill every space in the bird's body that isn't occupied by its vital organs. Furthermore, the air sacs connect with many of the bird's bones, which aren't filled with marrow as mammals' bones are, but are hollow. When a bird breathes, it aerates its whole system, so that the bright fire of its intensive life is maintained as by a bellows.

Speaking of the drive and intensity of a bird's life: How fast does its heart beat? The general rule throughout animaldom is that heartbeat varies inversely with the size of the animal. We human creatures, in our adulthood, have a pulse of around 70 to 85 beats a minute, give or take some 20 beats. But when we're babies?

During our first year of life, our pulse is way up between 110 and 130. While we're still foetal, the beat of life trips along in us at a racing 140 to 150. But then, going in the other size-direction, how about the pulse of an elephant? That thumps along at a leisurely 25 or so. We can reasonably expect to find a small songbird's pulse furiously fast. It's almost unbelievably so. How fast? Roughly, about 1,000 beats a minute.

Do all birds migrate?

No, they don't. Some bird books of my boyhood used to categorize species with neat finality as either "R" or "M," for "resident" or "migrant"; but when we begin to know birds with first-hand intimacy we find that this sort of stiffly exact division is as inappropriate here as in most other matters concerning the fluid reality of animal life as it is in fact lived. Some birds regularly and almost invariably migrate, making tremendous travels in autumn and spring. Others are "resident," in the sense that members of the species are always present in a given countryside; but we find out, if we take up bird banding, that the summer individuals and the winter individuals aren't the same ones. Again, some birds are true residents. The same individual bird (a chickadee, for instance) may live out its whole life, the year round, in the same place. Finally, there are birds of still a fourth life-way. They migrate, but erratically. Except in their breeding season, they are almost continual travelers, wandering now here, now there, at irregular speeds and for visits of various duration, depending on food supply and the weather.

Birddom has no huger and more complex matter for a lifetime's investigating than the matter of migration. We can't do more in this book of ours than bring up the commonest questions about it; and we can't do a wiser thing, in considering some even of those, than keep a certain spirit of tentativeness and the provisional. Why do birds migrate at all? Well, probably because of long-ago ice sheets and glaciation. When migrant birds take off southward in the fall, they're probably making a return to their ancient home lands, in a behavior pattern established a very long time ago when glaciers were receding. What about a nonmigrant American bird like that chickadee we were just mentioning? Well, chickadees probably originated in the Old World, instead of having come northward, as most migrant birds of the United States probably did, from South and Central America, in long-ago times when patterns were being established; so a chickadee hasn't the southward pull, so to speak, that tugs in September and October at catbirds, warblers, and robins. How do migrating birds find their way? Well, "instinct," partly. A directional sense that may involve response to the earth's magnetic currents. Partly, a following of landmarks: rivers, mountain chains. Partly, some following the leader . . . inexperienced feathered travelers guided by more seasoned migrants. And when we've said all these things, with however cautious a murmuring of "Well . . ." and however thick a peppering of "probablys," there remain to be uttered also the four ultimate words of any wisdom and humility: We don't entirely know.

Mystery making for its own sake, of course, is an obscurative sort of nonsense. A sound animalizing should forbid us this romantic indulgence. But it must forbid us, too, the kind of brisk, pretentious scientism into which we are perhaps even more easily seduced: that temper which gets to mistaking theories, however probable and useful as hypotheses, for certain knowledge, and which confuses explaining, however informed and shrewd as far as it goes, with explaining away. Why are the trees green? In our untouched initial ignorance, the right answer is: No idea. When we learn some botany, the right answer is: Chlorophyll. And when we have studied and thought and examined into things for another thirty or forty or fifty years or so, the right answer becomes, in a certain most profound and beautiful and awful sense: We don't entirely know. Why do birds migrate as they do, and just how is this harmony tied with all the other harmonies of earth; and when we say "engorgement of the sexual areas" have we in fact explained away the whole story of the northward-rushing wings and heartbreaking bird songs of the spring? Animalizing can do a lot of things for us. One of the best of the things it can do for us, I shouldn't wonder, is keep us a little childlike. Childhood has its large credulities. But also it has a fine healthy dissatisfaction with what it senses to be an emptiness and inadequacy in some of our complacent Becauses.

Now back to our plain straightforward facts of animaldom, verifiable and not sending us off on these asides. The commonest bird-migration questions, happily, mostly fall into this province.

Since birds migrate in such myriads, why don't we see them thronging the sky every day in migration time in such numbers as nearly to darken it? That's because by far the greater number of kinds of birds do their migration flying at night. The tremendous company of warblers, for instance, are all night flyers. So are thrushes, small flycatchers, woodcock, and many more. There's another reason, too. If we're outdoors watching sharply, do we see all of even the day-flying migrants passing overhead? By no means, no. Why? Lots of traveling birds fly at such tremendous heights that they're invisible to us. Out animalizing in migration time, we may often hear the far, faint, ringing music of snipe or plover drifting down when we can see no birds in the sky.

How fast do migrating birds travel? We find out, surprisingly enough, that most of them are quite leisurely. When they must do so—traveling over expanses of water, for instance—even very small birds can fly hundreds of miles nonstop. But often a flock of songbirds may travel only a dozen miles or so in a day, if the feeding is good. When the robins return to our spring dooryard, it's natural for us to think of their having rushed here "with the sun of the south still on their wings," as a poem has it. Actually, they have come along in an unhurrying, hedge-hopping sort of way, idling and tarrying, rarely covering more than 75 miles or so in any day. (We remind ourselves how leisurely that pace is when we reflect that 75 miles is no more than a couple of hours of flying time.)

When in autumn the birds are getting ready for their great southward trip, what preparations do they make? Most notably, they make two. They put on a surplus of fat; and they molt. Some birds put on relatively little extra fat, for they can almost always feed fairly regularly along the way. The night-flying warblers we were speaking about, for instance, feed by day, when they're traveling, on insects that are nearly always available. But other birds—some plovers, for instance—must go great distances over water and may have to fast protractedly during migration. As summer deepens into fall, they become as plump as woodchucks getting ready for hibernation. The molting, which generally takes place during the dull, drowsy days of late summer, needs a little further talking about, for it involves several very common bird questions.

When birds are molting, do they lose their ability to fly? This is a very general notion, and enters into several myths and folk tales we're likely to have heard; but when we get to know bird ways we find it isn't so. (That is, it isn't *generally* so. We'll be getting, as usual, to some exceptions in a minute.) A bird loses and replaces its feathers with extreme gradualness, virtually feather by feather. When one feather has been shed, the second one isn't lost until the replacement for the first one has grown in at least partially. Further, feathers are shed symmetrically. The bird's flight pattern is never thrown off balance. The exceptions to this subtle graduality in molting are diving birds, ducks, and the like. They molt great numbers of feathers at once. They can afford to. They aren't dependent entirely on flight for safety.

How does it happen that in the latter part of the summer so many of our most vivid birds—the strikingly colored warblers, glittering buntings, flaming-scarlet tanagers—seem to disappear? It isn't migration time yet. Where have they gone? They haven't gone anywhere. What they've done is, like the other birds, molt; but in their case the replacing plumage is a drab, inconspicuous one, entirely unlike the brilliant feathering of the males in the nesting season. We don't see any fire-red tanagers migrating, for the good reason that by migration time a male tanager is protectively concealed in the same dull olive-greenish covering as the female. The post-molt autumn feathering even of our common robins is a dulled, grayed-over dress.

Do birds have another molt in the spring, then? Most of them don't, no. The general rule is only one molt a year. But very vivid birds like the tanager we've been speaking about do have a spring molt, restoring their blazing loveliness. Also, in the spring, there's another kind of color restoration, even among the great majority of birds that don't have a second molting then. We were saying that robins in autumn have a sort of grayed-over look. So do most of the migrant birds. What gives them that? It's because the extreme tips of their winter feathers actually *are* gray. But underneath this brief tipping the feathers have their full brightness. By the time the spring breeding season comes, the gray or brownish feather-tippings simply become worn away; and there is then revealed, almost as though the bird had undergone an actual molt, the fresh bright coloring beneath.

When we go inquiring, even in an introductory way, into the facts of birds' migration, we are bound to bring up a question that is immediately associated with it and that's one of the commonest of all bird queries to occur to us. It's this one:

Do birds ever hibernate?

No question in this animal-ful book of ours could better illustrate the wisdom—continually brought home to us more and more vividly, the longer and deeper we push our explorations—of remembering that animal lore isn't an absolute. The more we get to know about our creaturely brothers, the surer we are (or ought to be) that the known doesn't come anywhere remotely near exhausting the entirety of truth and, further, that what we do know—even about a titmouse, a gnat, a familiar sparrow in the homely dust—isn't a knowledge to be held with any fierce, ironminded resistance against the possibility that it may turn out to need a little modifying or even a nullifying or reversal.

Do birds ever hibernate? Back in the days of ancient ignorance, a good many quaint books of natural history (the sort of books that were serious about unicorns, and that gave instructions for making love potions out of bats' blood) used to assert that they do. The notion went on right up into the eighteenth century, when Dr. Johnson (or was it Oliver Goldsmith?) made a wonderfully absurd reference to the way swallows were supposed to retire in winter into swamp mud and river bottoms and "conglobulate together." In the eighteenth century, after all, many learned men were still accepting, without verifying, bits of nature lore that dated back to Aristotle; and Aristotle had thought, among other whimsical nonsenses, that storks hibernate in hollow trees and caves.

As ornithology became more and more a true science, hosts of picturesque old myths were discarded. Migration became a better understood thing, and so did birds' physiology. Do birds ever hibernate? Why, of course not. Whatever else in this green sunlit world a naturalist might be hesitant or doubtful about, he needn't have any reservations about *that*.

For generations of naturalists, the fact that no bird ever hibernates has subsequently been as familiar and reiterated as the fact that the sun doesn't circle around our earth or the fact that horsehairs left in water don't turn into snakes. It has been set forth in a thousand supercilious books of the sneeringly skeptical sort; it has widened the superior smiles of all instructed animalizers, magnanimously disabusing the ignorant. And then—so nearly just the other day that animal lore may take a few more centuries to readjust to it—a very careful and cautious and scientific ornithologist happened upon a poorwill in a cave. Having rubbed his eyes with a certain stupefaction over the bird's queerly torpid behavior, he addressed himself to studying the bird over a long period, applied tests to it, and considered it with extreme closeness and all his scientific might. He established, not alone to his own satisfaction but presently to that of the world of scientific ornithology, what his poorwill was unmistakably doing. It was hibernating.

Do birds ever hibernate? We can now answer—with all the easy airiness and settled conviction of Aristotle—Yes.

Now suppose we return to the more usual and accustomed birds that go migrating, and get along to the question:

When migrant birds return in spring, do the males and females travel together?

As a rule, no. Among most of our birds, the males return to the North well in advance of the females. Among red-winged blackbirds, those early spring-comers whose throaty, gleeful musics are for many of us the very voice of springtime in the marshes, the male birds commonly arrive as much as six weeks ahead of the females. Robins and song sparrows follow a similar schedule, and so do a great many of the other common songbirds that are likely to enlist our earliest interest. In the case of some kinds of birds, it's true, the males and females do travel together; but earlier arrival of the males is very general. It falls to a male bird to select and reserve the "territory" in which nesting will take place.

"Territory"? This isn't the merely "popular" word it sounds. It's the term scientific ornithology uses. Virtually all birds make claim to a particular portion of earth and establish it against other birds as "theirs." (It's not just birds that do this; we find out in our outdoors prowlings that other animals do too. A white-footed mouse, for instance, claims its particular range of woods, and announces proprietorship in its mouse way, by a pitter-patter drumming with its paws.) A male bird fights off other males from his chosen territory; he takes up a proprietary residence in it; and he utters his possession in singing.

How big are birds' territories? That depends on the bird, and on what sort of food it eats. A bird that gets most of its food in the area around where the nest's built—a robin, say, that does nearly all its worm hunting fairly close to home—lays claim to a good-sized area. An extensive patch of lawn is needed to furnish worm supply for one robin family. A male robin doesn't want another nest of robins competing for the worms in the same patch of earth. Or again, a kingfisher may claim three-quarters of a mile of brook. (Male kingfishers that stake their claim on my own crookedly meandering brook often take title to the whole of it, from boundary to boundary, through the woods and all across the pastures.) But a barn swallow makes only a small claim, and there may be half a dozen swallow nests on the rafters of one old barn. Why? Why, because the feeding range of swallows is the whole sweep of the arching sky. There are enough insects there for as many myriads of swallows as may want to throng it.

Is every bit of earth claimed by a particular bird family as its exclusive territory? No. There are neutral grounds. If we have a fancy for this sort of animalizing, we can entertain ourselves in the spring with some cartography. When we have two or three families of robins and perhaps two or three families of song sparrows and wrens under our observation, we can draw, after we've watched them carefully for a while, an exact map of their sovereignties and of, as it were, the areas of no-bird's-land. Over yonder —from that cedar tree to that oak stump to the edge of the woods —is the territory of Family One. To this side of it, similarly demarkable, is the territory of Family Two; and over there by the side of the creek are the domains, split by the barn in the middle, of Families Three and Four. Now how about this irregular piece of tansy-bright meadow that lies pretty much in among all four of them? We can mark that neutral. We discover that that's where, by bird understanding, access is free and unargued.

Why do birds sing?

As we have just been seeing, the tumult of bird song in early spring is in the nature of a territory-proclamation. A little later, when the female birds have come, there is, of course, singing that is expressly sexual. It must be a rare naturalist who hasn't gone through a youthful stage of liking to say that bird song is "only" these things, as a young chemist may delight to announce that a human being is only sixty-nine cents' worth of water and salts (or whatever it is), and a young doctor may take pride in troubling the faith of the simplehearted by saying that life is only the mechanical twitch of muscle and nerve. In time, however, we manage to grow back to the sophistication of simplicity. Some old religious writers used to say that birds sing for the glory of God. Perhaps we won't put it in quite those words; but after we have been animalizing long enough—listening to the songs of thrushes in the cool midsummer-evening woods, going out in August and September dawns to hear robins caroling and meadow larks fluting and whistling as tumultuously as ever they did in the April of the year—we do come to know that a great deal of bird song is rightly enough to be thought of, and without any sentimentality, as lauds. Our brotherly animals on this earth are glad of it. Bird songs, a lot of the time, are like rabbit caperings in the moonlight or a deer's kicking up its heels when the sunrise comes over the hemlocks. They're just a spontaneous rejoicing, animal-spirited, in the excellence of being.

Does a bird do its singing with its larynx, the way we do? No,

F

it doesn't. A bird's windpipe, connecting with its lungs, is forked; a branch goes to each lung. Just at the point where the windpipe divides, there occurs a considerable enlargement. This is the bird's syrinx; and it's the organ of its singing. There is a valve in the syrinx, a valve that flutters and vibrates when air is forced from the lungs. There are muscles by which the bird can tighten the syrinx valve, and can accordingly regulate the number of vibrations. As the number of vibrations is controlled, the pitch of the issuing sound is regulated.

Do all birds sing? This is a little hard to say, since a bird's idea (if it had any) of what constitutes a song might be quite different from ours. Humanly speaking, however, it's only the more highly developed birds that have true songs. From about the flycatchers on downward, there are only call notes, croaks, squeaks, chipperings, and limited bird speech of that sort. In the birds we consider "songbirds," utterance elaborates into two distinct kinds: the call notes, which are, so to speak, conversational and communicative, and the full-throated distinctive songs that the birds utter for such reasons as we were just discussing.

How about those call notes . . . do birds have much of a variety of them? Yes; bird vocabulary is surprisingly large. We have had enough to say in this book about the minds of our various animal brothers to run no risk, by now, of supposing that birds "talk" just as people do. (We might have a look back, here, at our investigation of the language of animals in general on pages 85–88.) But, remembering the limitations of the minds behind the calls, we do find birds flexibly expressive. We find calls meaning "hawk!" (or "shrike!" or "snake!" or whatever), and calls meaning young ones in distress, and a broad variety of parent-to-baby calls meaning "keep quiet!" or "sudden danger!" There remains to be made, one of these days, a really detailed and careful study of the language, for instance, of crows. Crows are continually saying things to one another, and in such a variety of curious and changing sounds that even after we have been animalizing for years we may every now and then be baffled by some never-before-heard woods sound which turns out, when we track it down, to be the enigmatic commenting of a crow.

Are such birds as crows, parrots, and mynahs the only ones that can learn to imitate human speech? Not by any means. In the nature of things, it hasn't been possible to find out how teachable all kinds of birds are; but there are remarkable cases of learnings by mockingbirds, catbirds, starlings, blue jays, and a great many others. A few years ago an ornithologist friend of mine, working patiently with a brown thrasher that had been found injured as a fledgling and raised as a household pet, taught it a vocabulary of 125 words.

Is the song of a bird an instinctive thing? Not in anything like its full form, no. A bird must learn its song from the heard songs of others of its species. What are spontaneous—"instinctive," if we like—are the call notes, which are simply the native sounds, as it were, of animal urgency. The distinctive song, like so much else in animal life that may at first look to us automatic and preformed, is an ability the bird acquires in living experience.

Before we get away from this matter of songs, there's this last question:

Do birds ever sing from the ground, or do they always launch their melody from a high twig or treetop? Mostly, of course, they sing from high places; and there are textbooks that lay this down as a rule, entering no exceptions. When we have gone birding a while in the outdoors, however, we find that it isn't so. Some birds do sing from the ground. Several sorts of sparrows do: grasshopper sparrows, savanna sparrows, common field sparrows occasionally. Ovenbirds often send their lyrical "Teacher!-Teacher!-Teacher!" ringing through the green woods while they crouch motionless and almost invisible among the dead leaves that layer the forest floor. Wood thrushes, too, sometimes sing their song of earth

while they are in immediate contact with it. In the evening,
especially, a thrush that has been foraging over the lawn may
suddenly halt its little pattering runs, tilt up its head to the sunset
sky, and pour out its cascading, heart-shaking music of bell-clear
notes.

Do birds ever carry their babies from place to place?

With this question we encounter the first of a rather miscellaneous
lot of common inquiries about birds. Do birds ever carry their
babies? It sounds like rather a whopper; but it's true. An alarmed
mother woodcock often tucks her chick between her thighs,
clamps her legs together, and flies off with the youngster to a
new place of safety. Isn't there some fantastic tale or other about
a mother duck carrying her duckling in her beak? There is; and
though fantastic enough, that one's true too. The ducks called
hooded mergansers make their nests in hollow trees. Sometimes
the tree may be at the water's edge, in which case the ducklings,
when the time comes for them to leave the nest, may just be pushed
out of the nest hole and plopped straight into the water. Fairly
often, though, the nest tree may be a long way from the nearest
water. How does the mother merganser get her ducklings there
for their first swim? She nips a duckling in her beak, rather
after the fashion of a mother cat carrying a kitten, and flies
with it.

(But how about the story, everlastingly recurring, of birds
moving their jeopardized nest from one tree to another, or moving
their eggs from the endangered nest to a new and safer nest they
have built? No. It won't do at all. We're not to think of birds, any
more than of any other of our creaturely brothers, as having no
gleam of mind at all, no glint of consciousness. But bird mind, in
the limitations of what it can know, learn, and understand of the
world it considers, doesn't go breaking straight across the patterns
of set instinct in any such deep-insighted ways as this.)

How do sea birds manage to get fresh water to drink?

Almost any of us who have ever crossed an ocean must have had this query pop into mind. Here are these slim-winged terns, wheeling and crying hundreds of miles from shore. How often must they have to travel to land to get their drinking water? The answer is brief and likely to surprise us. They don't. Such sea birds are able to drink salt water and thrive on it. As a matter of fact, many birds of the ocean are as unable to drink fresh water as we are unable to drink salt water.

Why do night birds like whippoorwills have bristles around their mouths?

Most of us who go prowling the night woods are likely to hear a good many thousands of whippoorwills before we have the chance, if we ever do, to get close enough to one in daylight to see in detail what the bird looks like. If we have that luck, we're pretty certain to be astonished by the bird's beak. It's a stubby little beak, lengthwise; but when it opens we find it presents an amazing cavern, running right from ear to ear. Further, it's fringed with this curious tufting of bristly feathers. Why? To make a kind of cage or trap for catching insects.

When a "bullbat," which is our popular name for all birds of the goatsucker sort, goes whisking through the darkness after flying insects, it can scarcely strike at them with the nice precision of a phoebe snapping at a gnat in the brilliant clarity of sunlit daytime. Even with good nocturnal vision, night hunting amid the checkered shadows has to be a little hit-or-miss. The huge mouth, extended still huger by catchall side whiskers, provides the bird's margin for error. If it misses the fluttering moth by half an inch or so, it's still got it.

Speaking of goatsuckers: do they suck goats? No; that's a hardy fancy, but no truer than the notion, which we'll be getting to before so very long, that milk snakes suck cows. And of course a whippoorwill's queer calling in the darkness, however insistent it may be (insistent? John Burroughs once counted while a whippoorwill repeated its call, without a pause, 1,087 times), doesn't carry any implication of dooms and disasters. This garden of our earth has its grave events in it; but they don't go casting the eerie shadows that a good many animal superstitions would persuade us to imagine. Whippoorwills don't cry doom. It might perhaps be mentioned, while we're at it, that animalizing likewise brings the cheerful discoveries that earwigs don't creep into our ears; wolf packs don't make a practice of attacking even the loneliest man in even the most wolf-ravenous countryside; tarantulas, for all the terrible tales about them, aren't particularly dangerous; and the ominous knocking of the "death watch," that we may hear in the walls of the old haunted house, is made by an inoffensive little anobiid beetle that lives in ancient wood. The beetle makes its doomful rapping by bobbing its head up and down. Why? Why, to call its mate. All of which has nothing to do with birds, but does answer a cluster of common questions that we're bound to get around to somewhere in this book and may contribute to our animalizing merriments.

When birds "drum,"
do they beat
their wings together?

The wild, primitive "boomp-boomp-boomp" drumming of such a bird as a ruffed grouse is one of the most exciting sounds any of us can hear in our exploring of outdoors; and it's not surprising that hearers of it should be curious about how it's made or should have formulated theories that are continually being put forth in hot arguments. A good many woodsmen are positive that the bird bangs its wings together over its back. (Henry Thoreau thought so, and he was a sharp-eyed woods-watcher.) The old hunter who first answered the question for me in my boyhood was sure that the bird strikes its wings against the fallen log on which it usually takes its stand for the performance. We may hear from others that the bird beats its wings against its sides. All these theories, as it turns out, are wrong. What a drumming bird beats its wings against is simply the air. We might never have known it, for sure, because the wings vibrate so fast that our eyes' testimony isn't reliable; but motion pictures have settled it. A drumming grouse just flails the air close beside its body.

Are snake-killing birds immune to venom?

We have nearly all heard that they are; but, no. Perhaps the best known of the snake killers is the one called a road runner or chaparral cock in the American Southwest. This slim, long-tailed

bird regularly kills small snakes, not excepting rattlers; and road
runners have sometimes tackled a rattlesnake a yard or more in
length and killed it. It's very natural to suppose that only an immunity to snake venom can make such victories possible. Actually,
a road runner relies on agility, on fluffing out its feathers to make a
protective covering, and on a delicate feinting with its outstretched
wings. Darting in and out, weaving, bobbing, feinting, teasing . . .
the bird tires the snake to exhaustion and then slips in and kills
with hammering pecks at the reptile's head.

While on this subject of snake killers, it seems appropriate to
bring up a question which might have been considered in discussing mammals: the matter of whether a mongoose is immune to the
venom of the cobras it so often fights. No, a mongoose isn't immune. Like our road-running chaparral cock, it depends for its
safety on speed and nimbleness.

This is a book of animals, not of English. Still, how can we
possibly mention a mongoose and not stop a second to find out
what the plural of that animal's name is? After all, it's a question
that comes up to vex every animalizer, and there's no reason why
we should slide by it in a skittish superiority to such problems. So:
What's the plural of "mongoose"? It's "mongooses." The word's
Marathi Indian, and has nothing to do with our goose that turns,
in the plural, into geese.

When a ground-foraging robin halts and cocks its head, is it listening for worms?

With this question, which must rank easily among the top ten of
all inquiries about the lives of birds, we come to the final part of
our consideration of these brothers of ours that wear feathers:
the consideration of what it's like to *be* a bird, how birdness is
experienced by the living bird itself, in terms of its sensory and
psychic life adventure under the general sun that warms us all.

Does the robin hear the worm? Almost certainly, it does. Why
the caution of the "almost"? We have to put that in, and keep it

at the back of our mind as a just-possible reservation, because of a confusing factor. Because we ourselves have binocular vision, and are accustomed to looking with both eyes at once at the world as it lies before us, we may not realize until we have been animalizing quite a while that a good many of our animal brothers don't see their world in this way at all. Most birds don't. Owls have two frontward-placed eyes, more or less on the order of our own, but birds in general have their eyes far around at the sides of their heads. When a bird studies anything close at hand, it can look at it only monocularly; and the inevitable gesture accompanying such a scrutiny is a cocking of its head. When our head-tilting robin pauses on the lawn and considers, is it listening for the tiny stir in the soil or just watching for it? There's room for both opinions. If most bird-specializing animalizers incline to the former, it's for two reasons. First, if we have an opportunity to study the way blinded birds act, we may find them still alertly cocking their heads in what would seem a pointless gesture if it's to be understood as "looking." Second, there is our certain knowledge of the innumerable special sensory keennesses that animals do have—we keep encountering, from one end to the other of this book, the vivid evidences of animals' delicate perceptions, nice awarenesses, their quiveringly acute responsiveness, and animal aliveness—and this makes it at least reasonable to credit in a bird such acuity of hearing. (How does the sightless mole know when an insect has tumbled into some distant part of its tunnel? It hears that tiny commotion. How is a common catfish informed as it glides through the murky water? Partly, it "feels" life, with its exquisitely delicate cat whiskers; partly, it "tastes" its way, for it has taste cells all over its body. A catfish taste-tests its eggs, after a fashion altogether unimaginable to us both in nature and in vividness, by passing its fins over them. When a wood tick has remained motionless for weeks or months on a twig, what moves it to transfer to our passing dog? A tick is fantastically responsive to slight changes in temperature; it can recognize blood heat when our pup comes near. It is equally

F

delicately responsive to the acid of animal sweat.) An earthworm, squirming through the sod, makes a tiny, tiny sound of passage. Can our robin hear it? It probably can.

Are birds "eagle-eyed"? They are, extraordinarily. Vision is perhaps a bird's most meaningful sense, in its world of flight and in the need—as among birds of prey—to locate small ground creatures far, far below. Who of us, even when our interest in our animal brothers is still at the most casual stage, has not watched with enchanted eyes the beautiful preciseness of a wheeling flock of pigeons, and reveled in their expertness in negotiating a landing on a narrow cornice? Scientific investigation has shown that at least a part of their lovely skill is due to their delicate visual sense of spatial relationships. We can put the thing into figures. The widening or narrowing of an angle is detectable to us human observers only when it reaches a variation of about 50 seconds. But in the wild world of a bird, awareness of the spatial qualities of the creation is far, far more keenly alive. A pigeon, by scientific tests, has been determined to have so nice a sense of visual judgment that it can discriminate lines subtending an angle of only 29 seconds.

Eagle-eyed? Just how eagle-eyed *is* an eagle? The ornithologist E. H. Eaton had an experience that lets us know in a brief, memorable way. He was standing on a lake shore, and saw directly over him an eagle soaring at tremendous height. Suddenly the eagle plunged diagonally downward, in an unswerving glide-dive for a distant area of the shore where it seized a fish it had detected. When the eagle made its catch it was so far away that the scientist could scarcely make out the fish in its talons even with the aid of powerful binoculars. A careful measurement revealed that the distance from where the eagle seized its prey to the spot over which it had been soaring when it first saw it was just about 3 miles.

There comes up here inevitably an old, old question: Do vultures detect carcasses on the ground by sight or by scent? This is one of those animal issues that are continually being hotly disputed, like the matter of whether cougars scream and the matter of whether otters catch trout. (We've looked into the cougar matter; they do scream. As for otters . . . well, yes, they catch some trout, but not regularly and not many. The worst mistake we can make in looking for the truth about animals is to have the sort of either-or minds that snap shut too impetuously. A comfortable nine-tenths, at least, of arguments about animals can stop being arguments at all if we'll just relax a little and be as composedly tentative as a squirrel inspecting a nut which may or may not prove just right for storing.) Now then: vultures.

Vultures, we find out, if we watch them long and equably enough, make use of both sight *and* scent in locating their prey, depending on the circumstances. The sense of smell in most birds isn't keen. In vultures, it's considerably keener than in most, but still not comparable to the superb olfaction of mammals, which inhabit a world primarily of smell experience. Vultures, soaring high over the earth in their usual fashion, rely on eyesight to find the still bodies of the dead below. (We can test the matter readily enough, if we like. I've tested it in more than one upland field of my own laboratory-land, when there have been vultures about. All we need do is lie down, and stay put. A half hour of immobility is generally enough to bring a gathering of dark specks in the high sky over us; and then presently the specks enlarge and become dark, spread-winged forms, as the vultures come spiraling down hopefully to have a look at our corpse.) On the other hand, when vultures aren't too high up—when they have settled in a tree for the night, for instance—they often locate a pungent bit of carrion by what must be scent, for they can find it even when it's entirely hidden from view or under cover of a moonless darkness. Sight or scent? As so often happens, in the comfortable course of a long experience in animalizing, we can watch the argument fade away.

There remain two frequent questions about birds' world of sight. Does a bird see colors? It does, Yes; but with a difference from our own color vision. A bird sees reds, greens, and yellows sharply; but it has a very imperfect perception of blues, and worse of

violet. Several animal investigators of the elaborately thoroughgoing sort have gone so far as to try equipping homing pigeons with
blue and violet spectacles to see what effect this might have. The
effect turns out to amount to a blinding of the birds. With red,
green, or yellow lenses a pigeon can still see its world; but through
blue glasses it is unable to see its landmarks at all. Any of us who
may care to fashion a purple spotlight can carry out a simpler and
less fantastic experiment to let us see this same fact about the nature
of birds' visual experience. All we need do is train our violet light
on one area of a grain-scattered chicken-house floor. We find our
hens gobbling enthusiastically all around the edge of the violet
area, but not within it. They can't see the grain there.

(Are there any exceptions to this blue-violet blindness among
birds? Yes: owls. Owls not only can see blues well; they can see
them better than we human animals can.)

If you and I stand on a windy hilltop, or ride a fast open vehicle,
the rush of the air bothers our eyes. Why doesn't it bother the
eyes of our brother birds as they go skimming and wheeling
through the sky? Birds have a third eyelid, a transparent nictitating
membrane that can move out from the inner corner of each eye and
form, as it were, a pair of windscreen wipers.

If you and I dive underwater with our eyes open, we experience
an immediate severe distortion of vision. When a kingfisher plum-
mets from its dead-branch lookout over the creek and plunges
underwater in pursuit of a shining minnow, how can it see well
enough to make its catch? A full answer to this would be enormously technical, but, putting it very simply, the thing goes like
this: The bird's eye has a peculiarly shaped lens, rather bulbous
toward the front, that can be adapted instantly to either of two
entirely different sorts of vision. While our kingfisher sits on its
twig, watching and waiting, it peers at its world monocularly. But
when it makes its dive, the moment it enters the water it begins
seeing through the forward ends of its lenses, which now operate
to give the bird a straight-ahead binocular look at its darting prey.
The water vision is virtually useless in air, the air vision virtually

useless in water. As the bird goes back and forth from element
to element, its visual mechanics shift accordingly.

It's possible, I suppose, though hardly likely, that we might go
animalizing for some years and never happen to come across a
kingfisher. But *any* bird that we notice sufficiently to begin to feel
even the first stir of curiosity about it is likely to bring to our
mind one immediate question about its eyes. It's such a very simple
and elementary query that, as usually turns out to be the way
in such matters, learned textbooks don't usually dignify it by
bringing it up at all. In this book of ours we're not standing on such
dignity. The question's this: Does a bird move its eyes freely in
their sockets the way we do? Does it follow us with its eyes as we
pass by? The answer: No. A bird can move its eyes only very
slightly. For a bird to watch the course of a moving object for
any distance, it must keep turning its head.

This about brings to an end our investigation into what birds'
sensory experience is like. We've found bird life to be an adventure in sharp awareness of colors, shapes, distances; a response to
the thrusts and drives of "instinct," such biddings as the warmth
of a brood-spot or the tug of old migrational pulls. Put together
all the kinds of things we have been finding out about these brothers
of ours that go in feathers, and what do we say, finally, of bird
personality? We're led into that by our next and last question, a
very popular one:

Can birds count?

Most often this question comes up in connection with crows. Is
it true that if three hunters enter a "blind" or similar shelter, under

the watchful eye of crows, and if two of the hunters then make a conspicuous departure, the crows will still warily keep their distance, understanding very well the difference between three and two? Well, it's true enough that the crows will usually continue wary. Where we run into difficulty is in the key word "understanding," and here we are at once carried again into the enormous and intricate business of trying to reach a right understanding of the animal mind. We made one long reckoning back near the beginning of our book; and now, before we leave birds, it looks as though we'd better take our bearings again. There could hardly be a better bird for our considering than a crow. It's a nearly universal bird; it highlights bird canniness; it can stand as an example of bird *anima* in general. It may seem a little tedious, I suppose, the way we have to keep coming back and back to animal mind, considering and reconsidering; but there is no more important theme in all animalizing, and really there's no other way in which we can properly grow into understanding of it, as distinguished from just learning some glib psychological catchwords.

Every interpreter of the lives of animals must walk a difficult trail between two besetting errors. On the one hand, there's our danger of ascribing to creatures a psychic content too closely like our human own, so that we read into the occurrences of meadow and hedgerow a degree of mental elaborateness which isn't, in fact, operative. This is the fallacy of anthropomorphism; and any scrupulous mind must detest it. But on the other hand—and for philosophers estranged from woods living and simplicity, and loving to think in an ordered kind of syllogistic logic which is sometimes falser to life than is the most primitive poetry, this is perhaps the more seductive mistake—there is the danger of assuming between the animals and ourselves a difference too total and comprehensive. It's easy to think that we are set apart from the rest of creation absolutely. This is the fallacy of exclusiveness; and the instructed mind, like the primitive heart, must reject it.

Between the two extremes of mistake, an animalizer must look, as usual, somewhere about in the middle to find the truth and the trail. Mental complexity has certainly, in a rabbit or a raccoon, not attained to a degree capable of constructs of theory, intricate self-reflection, or artful juggleries of concept and idea. But it won't do to say that when a rabbit comes out from its form on a summer morning, and contemplates the universe, its experience is nothing akin to ours. It won't do to say that the nature of the midnight coon, fishing for crayfish along the sedgy brookside, is unrelated to the nature of the midnight human fisherman. We are the brother of rabbits. We are the brother of coons. All that major part of our life experience which is emotional, impulsive, sensory and, as it were, animally spontaneous, we share with the rest of nature's creaturely brotherhood. We share a kind of primal intelligence which is a sensorimotor thing. We are distinguished by an extension to intellectuality: to the abstraction of principles. That addendum does indeed transform our world of experience. It makes us, in a valid sense, a new and unique species of being under the sun. But it does not abolish the fact that an enormous, indeed major, area of the life experience, below the level of intellectuality, is common to ourselves, coons, rabbits, and all the rest of animaldom.

Nothing more effectively corrects exaggerated anthropomorphism than to see an animal, confronted by circumstances unfamiliar in its world of habitual experience, responding with actions densely inappropriate. There is at once borne in on us the truth that, great as are these beings' gifts and graces, the kind of apprehension properly to be called insighted reasoning or rational understanding occurs as only, if in fact at all, an uncertain flickering and glimmering. On the other hand, in correction of the opposite interpretive error which would divide the community of creation, nothing is more effective than a familiarity with crows.

Do we human beings love to play at pranks and rascality? So do crows. Do we sometimes seek our ends with slyness and stratagem? The crows do, too. We play games; and crows play them.

We feel merriment; and crows feel it. Are we dismayed when one of our community suffers injury or death? That dismay isn't unknown in the crow world. As moral beings, do we practice a certain samaritanism? We didn't invent it. Enduring ingredients in human morality are not products, happily, of our conjecturing minds. They are in us animally: out of a mammal, by way of a bird, by way of a reptile, by way of a fish, and back to when two cells first conjoined in the gesture of alliance and cooperation. A crow, in its crow way, is in moral bond with its fellows.

The dusky bird cawing over the corn lot isn't some kind of creature completely alien and apart from us. It is our feathered, smaller, and not equivalent, but undeniable brother.

The mischief and merriment of crows are very like the healthy rascality of small boys. The appreciation of elaborate humor, obviously, is reserved for instructed and elaborately conceptual minds; for it is only by thinking in patterns that there can be awareness of the pattern disruptions, the incongruities, that are the essence of the funny. But a boy can be a very small boy and still have a sufficient degree of obscure pattern-awareness to perceive at least, with shouts of delight, a sudden and uproarious amissness in the pattern when a walking man trips and falls down. A baby will grin and giggle over the glorious disruption of the normal which is sensed when he is swung by his heels. And so with crows. In their nesting season, in the very early spring, crow steals from crow; dark forms go gliding surreptitiously to nests not their own; twigs and rootlets are slyly pilfered; presently they are slyly stolen back again. There are raucously shouted cawings of hilarious triumph. There are uproars of outrage. It is impossible not to see, in this delirious game of wits and exuberant animal pranksomeness, precisely the spirit that is in a tussling, laughing, teasing gathering of human youngsters. As the human youngsters grow, their simple glee will become a complicated glee, refined by the ever clearer perception of principles and patterns. The crows can't attain to that. But the crows, within the limitations of their world of sub-idea, are capable of enormous entertainment.

They demonstrate it in countless ways. They play a game of Waking the Sleepers: stealing up on a dozing rabbit and rapping him sharply on the skull, settling surreptitiously on a drowsy cow and suddenly setting up a tumult, rousing our farm dog to startled ki-yiking and then flapping off across the fields with a wheezy cawing and hawing of boisterous glee. No animal can appreciate a joke that requires understanding of principles; but crows can, in a precisely accurate phrase, *see* a joke. They can relish the upsetting of the sense-familiar world. A Cornell ornithologist has recorded the huge and raucous delight of his pet crow when the children's seesaw would suddenly get out of balance, tumbling one of the teeterers to the ground.

The guile and the cleverness of crows are constantly evident. The feeding flock posts a sentinel; the sentinel distinguishes between a man carrying a walking stick or a fish pole and a man carrying a gun. A dog with a tidbit is spied; three crows fly down and undertake to obtain the tidbit by strategy, one crow luring the dog's attention this way, one crow luring it that way, and the third crow—vigilant, patient, and beautifully adroit—waiting his turn to dart in and seize the morsel when the dog's attention is properly engrossed. A crow finds a hard, dry crust of bread. He flies with it to the nearest brook, dunks it, and softens it to edibility. A crow finds a clam or oyster, and cannot open the shell to get at the soft, sweet meat inside. He picks up his find and flies high in the air with it and drops it on the rocks or on a macadam highway, and flies down and feasts.

Should all this be called intelligence? It cannot possibly be called anything else. If we find ourselves falling into the fallacy of exclusiveness—the supposition that only human beings are intelligent —we need only make the acquaintance of crows and we will be disabused. Intelligence runs all through creation; here sharp, here dim, but omnipresent. At its best it becomes, as in crows, an indisputable canniness of high degree.

Anthropomorphic error occurs when, as popularly happens, intelligence is equated with reason. The two are not the same. The difference is a subtle one, not easily put briefly. We've tried earlier in our book. Here, tersely, let's try again: Intelligently effective action can be achieved by the synthesis of units of sensory and motor experience. Reason, even at its rudest, requires the recognition of principles abstracted from the sensorimotor experience of the here and now.

Three crows may fool a dog a thousand times by their triangular strategy; but they cannot grasp triangularity, and apply that concept to their understanding and mastery of the world. A crow can learn the effectively intelligent act of dropping oysters. It can't learn the principle, or crows would have developed a science of physics. A crow can recognize the difference between four eggs and three eggs, or between three and four huntsmen; but it cannot count. Counting requires the concept of number; and even the concept of the number "one," though we entertain it, as we imagine, so easily, is in fact a flying leap almost into metaphysics.

Crows have humor. Crows have intelligence. They have emotions: anger, alarm, love, excitement, curiosity, relaxed contentment. Crows have also moral impulse. What lies behind the so-called "trials" that crows conduct—those occasions when a flock gathers around one singled-out member, and, after a deal of cawing and parleying, swoops en masse upon him and pecks and buffets him to death—is doubtless not equivalent to human judiciary understanding. It may be questioned whether crows execute a sentinel crow that has been derelict in duty. But it is certain fact that crows are moved to mutual aid. Let a crow be injured, and his dark fellows gather in distress around him. They feed him. They try to lift him. When crows tumble into a river, or get caught in a snare, or suffer any other catastrophe, the sounding of the trouble call brings immediate helpers, who strive to the limit of their corvine wits to give assistance. As the sense of fun is not exclusively ours, nor the gift of intelligence, neither is the moral law. What is exclusively ours is that we can elect to break it.

Of all the animals of outdoors, none is much better qualified than a crow to keep sensible our understanding of our nonhuman fellows in this world, and of ourself in relation to them. If we suppose that there is no psychic difference between the dark bird and ourself, our whole interpretation of the natural world is at once shot through with error. But if we suppose that there is not a vast and deep community between bird self and human self, our misunderstanding severs nothing less than the taproot of the tree of life, wherefrom ourselves and crows alike—with anthropoids and amoebas and the beings between—are all of us commonly grown and all of us thereby made inseparably brothers.

That is a rather heavy-going lot of words with which to be concluding our investigation into the light, bright, refreshing world of birds. We can comfort ourselves, however, with the thought that at any rate we won't again have to be pondering on our fellow animals' minds in any quite such solemn way or at such length. Insects, snakes, and fish don't confuse us into mis-reading their behaviors as readily as birds or mammals may. To augment what briefer comments we may be making on their dim little psyches in the remaining pages of our book, we can just flip back and reread these words about bird mind, and our extended earlier words about the inner life of animals in general, and that ought pretty well to keep us straight.

So now we leave Birds, and make our introductory acquaintance with Insects. Do the veins on a butterfly's wings have blood in them? What becomes of flies in the wintertime? What does a moth use its "feelers" for, as it explores its twilit moth-world of experi-ence? Let's see.

Insects

When we select even ten or twenty of the commonest questions about such animals as mammals or birds, and answer them in a leisurely sort of way with the kind of meandering side excursions that have been occurring in this book, it's possible for us to get a pretty fair picture of what life in that department of animaldom is like. Not an elaborately detailed picture, of course, nor anything like a complete one; but at least an introductory one, a block-out, a serviceable primary sketch. When we come to the insects, however, we are up against a sort of animals so vastly numerous and diverse that we might easily select and answer a thousand questions, or ten thousand, and still have done not much more than begin.

This grass-green and blue-skied earth of ours, as we were finding out in the early part of this book, is inhabited by four or five thousand kinds of mammals and perhaps fifteen thousand kinds of birds. But insects? We frankly can't guess how many kinds there are; but at least we can be certain the answer is in millions. Further, there is this consideration: All the mammals, however much they differ, also have a great deal in common, and the commonness runs right from shrews to whales. They all have hair. They all suckle their young. Birds all have feathers, and all lay eggs, and so on. But insects? Well, what *is* an insect? Insects are animals that most commonly (though not always) have three pairs of legs, and that never in any case have more than three pairs. Insects have bodies consisting of three parts: a head, a thorax, and an abdomen. When we have said that, we have said almost the last word that we can say in any big, broad, general way.

Can all insects fly? No; lots of them can't. Are all insects' eggs more or less round or oval, the way birds' eggs and reptiles' eggs are? Far from it. Some moths' eggs, fantastically enough, are rectangular; the moth deposits them in rows that look like a miniature experiment in bricklaying. Walking-stick insects' eggs look like seeds, and sometimes like flasks; and they have a sort of pop-uppable lid on top. How many eggs do insects lay? Well, fifty; a hundred; a thousand; it all depends on the sort of insect. Are male and female insects usually the same size and shape? Sometimes yes, sometimes no. There isn't any "usually" about it. A male cabbage butterfly and a female cabbage butterfly are very much of a muchness. A male glowworm is a winged beetle. His female is a grublike-looking animal, with a longer, plumper body and no wings at all. How long do insects live? There are May flies that exhaust their whole span of adulthood between a naturalist's lunchtime and his supper; and a queen termite may thrive and go right on egg-producing while the same naturalist grows from boyhood into manhood and gets married and has children. Do insects eat much? We can consider that effectively in terms of the same two sorts of insects we just mentioned. Some May flies don't eat at all. A termite munches up solid wood.

(We'd better stop right here, for a minute, and take up this termite matter a little more carefully. It's a very popular insect question: Can termites really digest wood? The answer involves a distinction so nice as to be almost metaphysical. It isn't the *termite*, exactly, that does the digesting; a termite carries inside it colonies of tiny unicellular animals—along with the standard content, of course, of bacteria—and it's *these* that effect the digestion of cellulose. What happens if these little animals are removed from their host, the termite? The termite goes right on hungrily eating wood . . . and it starves to death. It can't, "on its own," extract any nourishment from the sawdust it swallows. Do the cellulose-digesting animalcules live anywhere but in termites' insides? Nowhere at all.)

Well. It becomes pretty plain that in answering our selection of the commonest insect questions we shall have to be leaving a great, great many other insect questions undiscussed. Even more than usual, we shall have to be sticking to primer questions, foundational questions, the First Things of this teeming, teeming world of our insect brothers. Henri Fabre did most of his insect watching on one tiny little acreage (which he called, in the best of naturalists' perennial metaphors, his Eden) at the edge of the village of Serignan. His *Souvenirs entomologiques* runs to ten volumes. On my own country acreage—Eden, workshop, and living laboratory—I don't know how many kinds of insects there are, but there are certainly thousands. There are enough insects just in my alder-thicketed swamp to need a shelf of books and a battery of entomologists. There are enough aquatic insects in just 50 feet of the winding brook to need a lifetime.

Well, and well again. Our start into insectdom may not be able to carry us very far, but at any rate we'd better get under way if we're to make a start at all. Here we go with it, then, as best we can, in terms of the insect questions that most commonly come along.

Are spiders insects?

No. They are like them in being backboneless animals with jointed legs; but this is simply to say that they belong in the same big phylum—the arthropods—with crabs and lobsters. Insects typically have three pairs of legs. Spiders have four. An insect's head and thorax are distinct. In a spider they form one continuous part, the spider's cephalothorax. Spiders have the sort of eyes that entomologists call "simple"—that is, they're not compound—and usually eight of them. Spiders have spinnerets on their abdomens for spinning silk. What's the right name for the class of animals to which spiders and their relatives (such as scorpions) belong? They are arachnids. There are something like 30,000 different kinds of them; and they never, by the way, have wings.

What's the difference between an insect and a bug?

That is the form in which this perennial question most often comes up, so it's phrased that way here; but actually, in that form, it's an impossible sort of question. It is a good deal like asking, What's the difference between a musical instrument and a violin? All bugs are insects, but not all insects are bugs. Bugs are a rather flattened-out group of insects with beaky mouths adapted for piercing and sucking. For example, chinch bugs, bedbugs, and the big water bugs are true bugs. (Query: Are there really such things as "kissing bugs"? Not, perhaps, to the frostier formal entomologists; but, practically speaking, yes. Several of the true bugs are particularly likely to bite us on our faces, and especially on the lips. They can cause a good deal of discomfort and swelling.) Now and then, in a pond or stream, we may see what seems to be a true bug that seems to be swimming upside down. Why does it give that funny appearance? It *is* upside down. These bugs are the back-swimmers, and they regularly assume the position of an overturned canoe.

Are most insects injurious?

Offhand, we may be likely to think of insects, other than the lovely big moths and the butterflies that brighten our meadows and gardens, as simply something to swat, spray, or otherwise combat. The word "insect" may go almost automatically in our minds with the word "pest." When we take to animalizing, however, we find that insects, no less than all the other beings in the great general brotherhood of the creation, are participants in such a complex immensity of interdependences, cofunctionings, and subtly interwoven patterns of vital relationship, that an ecological philosopher might keep his hand poised practically forever in indecision whether to slap even the gnat on his wrist. (In practice, of course, we aren't paralyzed by these nice problems; but if our animalizing is to have any real depth of insight to it, it ought at least to make us see that these deeps within deeps, these infinite intricacies of the tissue of total being, are indeed the stuff of reality.)

Obviously the doings of many insects compete or interfere directly with what *we* are doing. Insects eat the vegetations we want to eat. They damage innumerable kinds of goods we want to cherish. Insects feed on us, directly or indirectly. All that's plain enough. But now we look a little further into insectdom, and the problem of these six-legged fellow creatures of ours begins to become less clear-cut. We have said, speaking loosely, that "insects" are inimical to us. How *many* of the insects? If we make even an elementary exploration of insectdom, we find out that the damage done to our interests is actually done by about 1 per cent of the insects. The other 99 per cent have to be exculpated.

Or, come to think of it now, is exculpation really a strong enough sort of term? The legions of insects that carry pollen from blossom to blossom . . . these little animals aren't anything so merely negative as "harmless." What they are, exactly speaking, is vital. They are the very secret and sustainment of this flowering and fruitful garden. Take a look at that small fly hovering among the cabbage plants. Harmless? A good deal more than that. This fly's life-way is parasitic, and what it is doing is laying its eggs among the cutworms. It is doing damage to a kind of insect that would otherwise damage in greater numbers our cabbage crop. Or consider that dragonfly, darting and shimmering along the brook. Will it sting us? No. That shining "needle" is as stingless as a spear of grass. Will a dragonfly "sew up your lips"? Or does it kill horses? Or does it somehow have a queer partnership with snakes, as its popular name, "snake doctor," would persuade us? A dragonfly doesn't do any of these things. What it does do, though, is eat mosquitoes.

We come to realize that a great many insects don't feed on

leaves and saps and the like, but on other insects. If we investigate a bit further into the life-ways of these myriads of lives around us, we turn up the surprising truth of the matter. How many insects are primarily destroyers of other insects? Just about half of all the insects there are.

When we have realized this, we confront, of course, a new problem-intricacy. Because an insect is an insect-destroyer, does *that* make it beneficial or injurious to us? In short, of insect-destroyed insects, how many are themselves insect-destroyers? And of those that aren't, how many make one kind of contribution to the life-whole and how many another? Obviously, these are the questions that could keep our reflective entomologist or philosopher meditating and analyzing and charting for a lifetime, just to be sure whether he really ought to slap that gnat or not. We can't go further with the thing in this book; but at least all of us who go animalizing, even a little, must enter the realization that even the tiger beetle exploring an old stump, even the harlequin caterpillar undergoing its dim little life experience on a milkweed stalk, is no trivially dismissable being, nor an isolated one, but like every other fellow animal of ours is a linked part of the creation's total texture, and thereby big with consequence and implication.

That's enough of that. We could go exploring insect ecology forever. Let's get to particulars of our insect itself, our living and immediate brother animal.

Do all insects have voices?

As a matter of fact, insects don't have voices at all. When we listen to all the chirps, squeaks, trillings, and murmurings of insectdom around us, it is almost inevitable that we think of these sounds as issuing from the insects' mouths, as mammals' or birds' cries and comments do. But they don't. An insect, though altogether our brother, is constituted very differently from us; and we have to get a clear picture of the differences if we are to make anything

like an accurate imaginative entry into the insect's world of being.

Does an insect breathe with lungs and throat, the way we do?
No insect does. An insect doesn't have lungs. It takes in its oxygen
directly through little spiracle openings along its body. The air
travels throughout its system by a network of fine tracheal passage-
ways. So an insect's mouth isn't a breathing apparatus at all, and
the animal can't force air along the air tube of its throat to "speak"
as other animals do. What an insect does, to utter its reactions to
the life experience, is to make mechanical noises with its wings,
legs, and various other sound organs.

Most of us, long before we begin to look intimately into insect
life, have gathered somewhere a notion that crickets make their
crickety little music by rubbing their hind legs together. Is that
true? Not exactly, no; but it's a step in the direction of a right
understanding. What male crickets do is to rub together the bases
of their wing covers. Katydids make their far-carrying calls in the
late summer nights by the same sort of stridulation. Grasshoppers?
This is a slightly different sort of voice. A grasshopper rubs a
roughened part of its long jumping-legs against the upper surface
of its wing covers. How about cicadas, the "locusts" that we hear
droning and buzzing away in the dust-whitened greenery of hot
summer afternoons? A cicada is one of those insects that are
equipped with, so to speak, a natural drum. On each side of the
base of a cicada's massive abdomen there's a panel of thin, tough
membrane, stretched tight over a sound box like the skin over
a drumhead. Inside the cicada's body the membrane is attached
to powerful muscles. Tightening or relaxing them, the cicada
can make its tympanum vibrate. When we hear the dry, rasping
drumming sounding from tree to tree, is it the talking back and
forth of males and females? No; these cicadas we hear are all males.
A female cicada has no drum equipment. Nearly all insect voices
we hear, as a matter of fact, are those of males.

Though we're talking here about insects' world of sense and experience, it's impossible to mention cicadas without bringing up a very common question of another sort about them. Do these "seventeen-year locusts" really appear every seventeen years? Yes, that's true. There are several species of cicadas, of course, and not all of them have the same life tempo. But a common *Cicada septendecim* really does take seventeen years to develop from egg to adult. We'll be considering the life pattern of insects in more detail a few pages from now, in connection with questions about houseflies and about butterflies and moths. Right here it's enough to say that an immature cicada, having hatched from its egg after about six weeks' incubation by the summer sun, burrows down into the soil and remains there, immature, puncturing and sucking at roots, while sixteen rounds of seasons go by. Not until its seventeenth spring is it moved to come tunneling up into the outer air, clamber up a tree, and leave behind it, presently, one of those queer split cicada husks that we're continually finding and wondering about. The husk is the discarded shell from which the finally matured insect has flown away.

Not all cicadas start or finish their long-drawn life cycles, of course, in any given year. There is a degree of "staggering" about it. Still, there is sometimes enough coinciding throughout cicadadom to give us a "peak" or "wave" year. When that happens, we have an impressive look at the enormousness of the insect company. How many cicadas may come tunneling up under just one tree? There have been several counts made of that. The tally runs to around thirty thousand.

An insect-investigating animalizer is constantly being astounded by the hugeness of this part of the animal creation. Our talk about species running into the millions involves such vast figures that they may not have a very vivid meaning for us. The reality gets home to us more effectively when we go out in a peak year for cicadas—which are *one* kind of insect among those multimillions—and just make a count for ourselves of the cicada holes under the one familiar tree. Or we might try something else. We might try going out on a late autumn day, before the ground has frozen too hard, and turning over a few spadefuls of earth and making a count of those insects (only a small portion, after all, of all the insects in a territory) that do their wintering in the topsoil. I must have been about eleven years old, I think, when a passage in some kindling "insect book" first set me to making one of these counts. The result seemed to me so exciting—such an enlargement of imaginative awareness of the enormous throng of fellow lives going on hiddenly all around us—that even in later years, when I know well enough what the answer will be, I've still gone on making a count now and then, in a spadeful of woods loam, a basket of pasture earth. How many wintering insects in one ordinary acre? At a rough but cautious computation, there are around 700,000.

Can an insect hear?

The insect drummings and stridulations we have been speaking about are made to be heard. But how? Does an insect have ears? Again we have to remind ourselves how very different the whole structure of an insect is from ours. These fellow animals do have ears, yes; but unexpectedly located.

How does a common grasshopper hear the sounds in its sunny meadow-world, and the dronings and clatterings of other grasshoppers? It hears by a pair of "ears" on the first segment of its abdomen. They're tympana, drumheads—whatever we like to call them—like our cicada's sound organ. Each ear, that is, is just an area of thin, tight-stretched skin. But inside this eardrum there's a little auditory sac, a nerve connection to a bigger ganglion, and then a larger nerve running from there to one of the major nerve bunches in the lower part of the grasshopper's thorax. We think of hearing as head-hearing. A grasshopper listens to life, as it were, through its stomach. It receives auditory informations in its chest.

Where's a cricket's ear, or a katydid's? On the insect's foreleg.

It's rather as though, listening alertly, we were to hold up our arm, and were to cock, instead of our heads, our wrists. How about the ears of gnats and mosquitoes? These insects hear with their antennae, their "feelers." Their antennae are covered with countless tiny hairs, so delicately responsive that they are set vibrating by even very slight sounds; and down in the bottom of each antenna there is a bunched intricacy of nervework for transmitting the heard sounds to the small brain that is to register them.

An insect, of course, like every other living animal, chiefly hears the sounds that are meaningful to it. "Hearing" is only partly in any auditory apparatus, and very largely in what the receiving consciousness does with the sensory message. As you and I go through life, we move through a constant tumult of sounds; but we are aware of hearing only the ones that have a significance for us and so enlist our attention. When we're listening to the talk of a friend, we hear his words and we don't hear the competitive sounds of rustling grass, bird song, a distant train. We hear what we want to hear; we hear what concerns us. What greatly concerns a good many insects, of course, is the sound of humming. A certain sort of humming means, to a bee, another bee; to a mosquito, another mosquito. Why does it happen every now and then that such hordes of mosquitoes come swarming around a piece of outdoor electrical apparatus? It's the whining hum of the thing. The machine has happened to hit just the right pitch to sound, to listening mosquitoes, like the summoning voice of a mosquito giant.

Speaking of humming: How fast do insects beat their wings to make these dronings and buzzings of theirs? When a bee sounds its standard buzzing noise, it's beating its wings about 430 times a second. When it makes its low rumble-bumble buzz, the rate's rather less, but when it makes its high, furious *zeeeeee*, the wingbeats quicken to over 500 a second. Not all flying insects, of course, are such notable buzzers and hummers, and some fly soundlessly. Their wingbeat rates? Well, our ordinary housefly makes about 350 beats a second. The glittering dragonfly we were talking about a few pages ago makes around 30. Most moths and butterflies make somewhere between 7 and 10.

Can insects see behind them?

If we give to our small brothers the insects even the minimal attention involved in trying to swat a fly, we perforce learn, in an exasperated sort of way, some animal lore. It begins to look very much, after the third or fourth ineffective swat, as though our intended victim must be able to see what's going on behind its back. Can it really do that? Yes.

Some arthropods have only simple eyes—what are called ocelli—and a few have only a single one of those; but the eyes of the common insects likeliest to be subjects for our animalizings are multiplied into the fantastic aggregates called compound eyes. The enormous curved eyes of a common housefly or bee or dragonfly are compounded of, so to speak, packed bundles of visual rods or columns, each one of which gives the insect an image of one section of the world it contemplates. We were finding out, when we were talking about mammals, that the bulging eyes of a rabbit let it see virtually full-circle. Our insect's compound eye has an even more sweeping convexity, so that it sees not only to the side but straight ahead and straight backward.

As the insect regards this spread of universe, does it see the same world we look upon? It sees something very different. As insects hear the sounds of earth, and utter their responses to the life adventure, in ways so different from ours that it's extremely difficult for us to partake imaginatively of their experience, so does their seen world require a considerable effort for us to imagine. It presents itself to the insect as a mosaic. Each eye facet perceives a kind of little jigsaw "piece" of the scene, and these "pieces"—glimpses in all directions, at all sorts of angles—can't be fused together into a smooth continuum by the insect's rolling its eyes or making any of the small eye movements which we make with our own eyes almost continually. Why not? The insect's eye is fixed stationary. Further, each fragment of its mosaic view, though very clear, is separated from each other fragment; for each of the compound eye's visual rods or columns is cut off from the others by a coat of pigment. It's as though we had numbers of individual eyes, clustered together, but each looking out through a shaft— like the shaft of a telescope—aimed in a slightly different direction. We think of the scene as unitary. To an insect, it's a multiplicity of scenes, each one limited in area and only revealed at all when there's bright enough light to penetrate that particular column-shaft to the sensory cell at its base.

If there must be such bright illumination to reveal to the insect its jigsaw world, how can it see at night? It can't. All our common diurnal insects are night-blind. Only moths, fireflies, and similar insects of the darkness have eyes adapted for night-seeing. In the eyes of these ones, each columnar element isn't isolated from the others by pigment. The pigment is distributed so that light can go from one element to another, letting the insect utilize very faint light to the maximum.

How many "pieces" in the insect's world-picture? The number of single eyes making up a compound eye varies among different insects; but suppose we take, for a common and sufficiently stunning example, our common dragonfly we were just mentioning. It sees its world in about 25,000 views.

If an insect's compound eye provides it with no very integrated impression, in our human sense, it does give it an extremely keen awareness of movements and of the play of light and shadow. Now how about colors?

We watch a honeybee traveling from a white flower to a yellow one to a blue one as it investigates our garden on a summer afternoon. . . . Does it see these differences of tint? Yes, it does. It does, that is, with the exception of reds. There have been a lot of tests made of bees' color-sensings, and the results indicate pretty surely that red, to our bee, doesn't appear as a color at all but only as a shade on the scale of grays and blacks. With this exception, the insect sees all the blaze of flower colors that we see ourselves; and it turns out that it sees more than that. It sees ultra-violet. Our insect moves through a world bright with a color that to our human eyes is entirely invisible. It's not just bees that see ultraviolet. Other insects do too. Ants have a particularly subtle and acute responsiveness to it.

The attempt to get inside an insect's life experience and share something of its quality is difficult enough even in this matter of its mosaic world-view and its awareness of colors about which we know nothing. It becomes harder still when we find out about insects' other sensory adaptations and acuities. Take taste. How delicately aware is our insect of the sweetness of the flower nectars on which we see it feeding? Well, we can put it this way:

You and I generally use at least a spoonful of sugar in our coffee. If we used much less than half a spoonful we could scarcely taste the sweetening. As a matter of statistical exactness, the fact is that the extreme limit at which our human taste can detect sweet-ness is in a solution of 1 part sugar to about 200 parts of mixer. But flies? There are a good many flies that can detect sweetness in a mixture when the sugar is present only at the rate of 1 part in 40,000. When a butterfly flits from thistle-top to vervain to yarrow, tasting, tasting, it's exercising a taste faculty so fabulously subtle that we can have no imagination of the experience. This little light-winged brother of ours, fluttering around the sunlit summer meadow, has small equipment for mind-knowing its world. But for feeling it . . . for *tasting* it? A butterfly can detect sugar in a mixture of 1 part to 300,000.

Or take scent. When I was a boy I used to gather in winter the cocoons of big moths—Luna, Cecropia, Polyphemus—and keep them in cages until the great moths hatched in the spring. ("When I was a boy," do I say? That's true, but it contains a concealment. Actually I still go right on doing the same thing today, prowling around my snow-swept fields on cocoon hunts every winter, and I hope I shall still be doing it in an old age devoted to such childish

G

enthusiasms.) Well, anyway, one of the delights of this cocooning, of course, is watching the moths hatch. It is as exciting an animal event as any of us can ever see, even if our animalizings take us around the globe. But there is a special fascination in what happens when our hatched moth is a female and we put her on the window screen:

Does a moth have a scent? If we hold our big female moth an inch from our noses, you and I could swear that she hasn't. But now we try putting her on the inside of the screen of our window, open in the earth-smelling spring dusk, and we wait a little while. Presently, out of the twilight, there comes a clustering of male moths on the outside of the screen. Very likely we've never seen one of these moths in our neighborhood before. But now here they are, drawn from the countryside all around by the female's scent. From how far away may they have detected the animal odor of her? Henri Fabre found that out, experimenting with peacock moths. The males can detect the female's scent, which our human nostrils can't catch at an inch, from a distance of nearly a mile. And finally: Male moths can tell, by scent, whether a female has been mated.

Can insects see behind them? In answering that, we seem to have been led on into a good many other questions about insects' sense-world and the quality of their inner experience. We'll get along now, a little delayed, to some common insect questions of other sorts.

Why don't insects get bigger than they do? Why aren't there butterflies the size of eagles?

There has been a good deal of fantastic fiction in which writers have imagined insects becoming larger than human beings; and there are plenty of tall tales about supposedly enormous insects actually existing now in far places of the world. But insects don't get very big. The huge Indian Atlas moth, that we're likely to hear cited as the biggest flying insect in the world, actually has a wingspread of about a foot. What's the very biggest insect that has ever existed? It was probably a now-vanished dragonfly that had a wing span of about 18 inches. Why this limitation of insects' sizes? It becomes plain enough if we just think about it for a minute. It's a matter of the way insects breathe. As we were seeing a while ago, an insect doesn't have a "pumping" respiration, such as can furnish oxygen to an animal's whole system. Air is merely let into its body via admitting apertures and set flowing in only very feeble little currents by its body's expandings and contractings. With such a breathing as this, any part of an insect's body that was much more than a quarter of an inch or so from the nearest air intake could never get enough oxygen.

Which leads to the very common question:

Do the veins in an insect's wings carry blood as our veins do?

No. These veins in a mature insect are veins in not much more than the sense in which we speak, for instance, of the veins in rocks. They don't function as blood vessels. They are simply structural framework giving the wings stiffness and strength.

We have constantly to be remembering, in getting to know the world of the insects, that familiar terms, meaning one thing when we use them of ourselves or of our brother animals closely related to us, may mean something surprisingly different when used of the insect's life-ways. We speak of our veins, and of the veins on the tawny wings of a monarch butterfly; but the two sorts of veins have not the same function. We speak of our jaws, and of insects' jaws; but whereas jaws, to us, mean jaws that work up and down, the jaws of insects generally operate sideways. Chewing, so to speak, isn't done with uppers and lowers but with rights and lefts. Our skeleton? That's an interior structure of bones. But does an insect have bones, and a skeleton in that sense? No. An insect's skeleton is what's technically called an exoskeleton. That is to say, it's on the insect's exterior. When we look at a butterfly resting on a flower top, or a fly that has alighted on our hand, we are looking at its skeleton. The soft flesh of the insect is all on the inside of that. It's putting it only a little fancifully to say that an insect, in our terms of being, lives its life inside out. Or, finally, we speak of our bodily color, and we speak of the color of a butterfly's wings; but in the one case the color is truly something part of the flesh, and in the other it's something applied . . . a dusting of scale particles. What color is a butterfly's wing? Rub off the powdering of scales, and the answer is: transparent.

The veins in our insect's wings, to make a little clearer the facts about them, do *start* as something like veins in our human sense. Each vein is a sort of double tube, one tube carrying air and the other blood. But the circulation occurs only for a short time after the insect has emerged into adulthood, while its wings are opening out and assuming their final flatness and rigidity. Presently circulation virtually ceases, and the venation becomes what we were describing: just a dry, brittle, structural framework.

We ought to have a very brief word or two more here about scales. Does a butterfly or moth have the color-giving scales just on its wings? No. Scales cover and color its whole body too. And why "scales" for these microscopic varicolored particles? Because, as we can readily find out by looking at them through a lens, they are flattened out—generally in a sort of shield shape, but sometimes in more feathery structures, or like tufts of fine hairs—and applied to the insect's wing in precisely the way of shingles to a roof, in row upon overlapping row.

Can insects tell the weather?

None of our brother beings, whether insects or any other kind of animal, can *fore*tell the weather, in the way a good many old folk notions about animals would persuade us, as though animals had some mysterious intuition of far events to come. (We'll be coming back to this in another connection.) But it is true that many insects do have a very subtle sensitivity to existing weather conditions, and particularly to temperature. Take the case of a common cricket:

"The crickets chirp faster when the temperature goes up." Almost any of us who ever had an old grandmother, or listened spellbound in childhood to the lores of a country nurse, is likely to have heard that ancient popular notion. Unscientific folk for ages have fancied that, just by listening at the window to the crickets' chirping, they could tell before venturing outside what temperature to expect to encounter.

It sounds a preposterous sort of fancy. If we care to try some very simple observings and experimentings, we find out that it is perfectly true. Count the number of chirps a cricket makes in 14 seconds. Add 40. The total is the temperature. Ninety per cent of the time it's accurate to within about 2°.

Why do houseflies bite more in muggy weather?

They don't. The flies that bite us are flies of other kinds: horseflies, deer flies, black flies, and so on. When the air is light and windy, all flies have trouble navigating, and these bloodthirsty ones aren't likely to bother us. On still, heavy days their hunting conditions are perfect, and they may hover around us in clouds. Common houseflies aren't able to bite at all. A housefly's mouth parts are a pair of soft fleshy lobes at the end of its proboscis. There is no chewing mechanism. Which brings up the answer to another of the commonest housefly questions: What makes flyspecks?

A housefly can feed on, say, a lump of sugar only by first softening it. To do so, the fly regurgitates on the sugar a drop of fluid from its last-digested meal. This is what a fly is doing at our dinner table when it seems to be leisurely "exploring" the sugar bowl; and it is these regurgitated droplets, together with the fly's dung, that make up the familiar "flyspecks."

Houseflies are such common and nearly universal animals that they are the subject of a number of the most frequent of all insect questions. We may as well take them up in a clump.

Are the little flies around fruit and vegetables baby houseflies? No. They are other sorts of creatures entirely, perhaps *Drosophila*, "banana flies." (These, by the way, are favorite animals for the experiments of evolutionary scientists, because generations can be bred so fast in the laboratory. Testing this and that evolutionary process, experimenters have bred *Drosophila* into dwarf flies, short-winged flies, hairless flies, and flies with red eyes. To watch the changings of *Drosophila* over the generations, as environment and other factors are carefully altered under controlled conditions, is to see—over a matter of months and years—a speeded-up reproduction of exactly the sort of thing that has given greater and slower-breeding beasts their diversity of shapes, habits, and adaptations over the millenniums. Back when we were talking about evolution in general, we were saying that no naturalist can seriously doubt the broad general truth of evolution in the main. Anyone who does entertain lingering doubt may be invited to breed *Drosophila*. He can see the very shape and flow of the creation shifting and taking new directions, so to speak, under his creative hand.)

How can a housefly walk upside down on the ceiling? Each of its feet is equipped with an adhesive pad of sticky hairs. Why doesn't a housefly drown if you hold it under water? It will, if you hold it there long enough; but a fly's entire body is covered with a dense tangle of fine, close-growing hairs, and similar hairs grow on its wings, legs, and feet. The supply of air in the interstices of this dense and almost water-impervious pile can last a fly a long, long time. How long does a housefly live? Well, at a rough and generalized estimate, it lives three or four months. Spring- and summer-born houseflies mostly die in the autumn, if by any chance they have avoided, as few do, a violent death long before that. Do all of them die? No; and that brings up the very grandpa and champion of all the animal questions that keep coming a naturalist's way: What becomes of the flies in the wintertime?

Great numbers of flies die when the cold weather comes; a lesser number withdraw into sheltered places—under bark, under fallen leaves, into barns and the attics of houses—and winter in variable states of activity, depending on the temperature. Houseflies grow torpid and seek shelter when the temperature falls to 55° or so. In the attic of a heated house, they may remain active all winter if there is food available. Dr. R. H. Hutchinson, who did a study of the over-wintering of houseflies for the *Journal of Agricultural Research* a number of years ago, and who performed the delicate task of dissecting uncountable flies taken in winter in attics, found that most of the wintering flies were fertilized females. Of all the females he examined, 78 per cent contained active sperm cells. Flies aren't strongly cold-resistant. A temperature of 15° or 20° for two or three days is fatal to them. They undoubtedly die by millions and billions every autumn, so that only a tiny remnant, relatively speaking, of fertilized females survives in warm places to carry on the race over the winter.

How do flies get themselves born, and how do there come to be such myriads of them? Their life cycle is the egg-larva-pupa-adult cycle, common to thousands of other insects, of which we shall be talking some more presently.

Our housefly starts its life as a tiny egg, much smaller than a pinhead, deposited by a female fly in a manure pile or in any rotting refuse. Within twenty-four hours it hatches forth as a transparent, legless grub. Before a day has passed its size has so tremendously increased that its inelastic skin can no longer contain the body. The skin therefore splits and the grub crawls out growing a new one. Three times within as many days this splitting and shedding of old skins occurs, and then on the fourth day, its translucent color changed to a dull white, it crawls away from its feeding place and burrows into the ground.

Now then. During this underground burial of about three days, there form inside the pupal jacket the striped body, the six legs, the two veined wings, the multifaceted eyes. Then the pupa bursts and the adult fly emerges. Tunneling upward, it comes out into the sunlight, ready, when its wings have dried and stiffened, for those two or three or four months of adult life we were talking about.

From egg to adult has taken less than ten days. And this adult fly is ready immediately for breeding. If it is a female, in less than a week it will probably lay its first batch of a hundred or more eggs, and it can repeat at ten-day intervals. Why are there so many flies? We begin to see plainly enough. Nine generations is a comfortable average in the season, say, from mid-April to September. The result is a statistic that naturalists love to bring up. The offspring of one pair of houseflies in that time, if all of them lived, would amount to 335,923,200,000,000 flies.

Though a housefly's life cycle is a very typical one for common insects, it is not typical, of course, in speed. Some mosquitoes can match it. But from egg to adult for most of our moths and butterflies takes a whole autumn, winter, and spring. Other insects take longer than that, as we find out in the answers to other questions. But the basic pattern holds.

All of which perhaps seems a somewhat overcopious answer to a question about flies biting in muggy weather. But animal life is all a continuum, and fact is linked with fact; and every now and then, for us to have the general feel and pattern and texture of the thing, it's just about unavoidable for us to slow down a bit like this, and take a lot of related questions in a clump, and give them some cohesiveness.

Do all insects have the same sort of life cycle?

No. Broadly speaking, and omitting for the sake of simplicity such life-ways as aphids', insects go through their lives by two routes. Common flies, or mosquitoes, or moths and butterflies, develop like this: First there is the egg; and then the larva (a grub or caterpillar, that is) hatches from it; and then this larva lives and feeds and undergoes molts for a while; and then—sometimes first wrapping itself in a cocoon, sometimes not—it becomes a pupa, during which stage it metamorphoses from a "worm" into an adult-formed insect; and then finally it comes forth in its perfected maturity. That is the pattern of one insect life-way. For the other one, take the life of a common grasshopper. It develops like this: First there is the egg; but then from the egg hatches not a larva—not a creature seeming entirely different from the final form of adulthood—but an unmistakable little grasshopper, only without wings. This is called a nymph. The nymph sheds its skin periodically, just as caterpillars or larvae do, but with each molt it becomes more and more like a full-formed adult; and after (in most species) some four molts, it has the full-sized wings of adulthood and is completely mature.

Do caterpillars mate?

No, never. No sexual activity occurs among insects except when they have taken on their fully mature form.

Do moths and butterflies grow?

Not a bit. It's the most natural thing in the world for us to suppose, when we begin to look at the world of the animals and wonder about it, that the little butterflies we see are the youngsters of the big ones, the small bees are the children of big bees, and so on. But no. Moths, butterflies, and other insects don't appear in their winged insecthood until they are in the final phase of their development, and when they reach that they do no more growing or changing.

Do all insects lay eggs?

As far as most of us need to know, we could probably say, "Yes," and let it go at that. But it isn't really true. There do exist a few insects in which the eggs hatch inside the mother's body and the mother insect brings forth her young alive. Having learned this,

G*

most of us, unless we intend becoming technical entomologists, may profitably forget it; for egg laying is by and large a characteristic of the insects' world.

What's the difference between butterflies and moths?

Mostly, of course, butterflies fly by day and moths in the darkness or dusk; but this is not an invariable distinction. A few butterflies are active in twilight. A good many moths are active in full sun. (Which brings up a frequent question that may just as well be answered here as anywhere else. Are hummingbirds related to insects? No; there is no relation at all. Hummingbirds are all bird, in every respect. The insects which often frequent the same flowers visited by hummingbirds, and which look enough like the birds, at a quick glance, to keep the confusion alive, are clear-winged hawk moths. They are sometimes called hummingbird moths. They are active in the daytime.)

For more serviceable distinctions, of a rough and ready sort, there are these: Most butterflies, when at rest, fold their wings up vertically over their backs. (Except, of course, when they are fanning them.) Most moths at rest spread their wings out horizontally, or hold them slopingly out from their bodies like the pitch of a roof. Butterflies' antennae (their "feelers") are mostly smooth and thready, and they have a swelling or bulb at the end. The antennae of most moths are feathery, and there is virtually never a swelling at the tip. The caterpillars of most moths spin cocoons; the cater-

pillars of most butterflies pass their pupation as cocoonless chrysalids.

There are a lot of "mosts" in that. "Most," in fact, has to be a
wearisomely familiar word in all these pages. For the things that
are generally true about animals—the truths that hold for just
about all practical purposes, and that provide comfortably the sort
of introductory acquaintance with animaldom that is what in this
book we want to secure—have a way of being flawed by exceptions, and marred by a lot of "yes buts," when the farther reaches
of scientific technicality are reached. It would be immensely more
readable, and simpler, if we could just say, "Moth caterpillars make
cocoons; butterfly caterpillars don't." That would be *nearly* true.
It would be true, probably, as far as most of us are likely to want
to go exploring into entomology. But it would not be truth to an
entomologist. "What," he would demand to know, "about the
Hesperiidae?" The Hesperiidae are the stout-bodied little butterflies popularly called skippers. Their caterpillars build rather make-
shift little cocoons by drawing together bits of leaves and so on
with silk. Or there might come the challenge, "How do you propose to fit some of the Geometridae moths into this?" The geom-
eters' caterpillars are our familiar "inchworms." Some of them,
pupating in burrows in the ground, don't wrap themselves in
cocoons.

And so all these cautious and qualifying "mosts," all the "nearlys"
and "pretty muches" and "so to speaks" and "as it weres" in this
book. Moths positively and definitely do not have club-tipped
antennae. Range up to Greenland and they don't. Travel to Tierra
del Fuego and they don't. Only down in certain parts of the tropics,
to spoil the whole scheme of simplicity, there are some moths
that do.

As any reader of these pages will have noticed long before this,
the answers to animal questions tend every now and then to wander
around a good deal. A naturalist who has devoted himself from
boyhood to watching animals, studying animals, meditating on

animals, and getting to find out everything he possibly can about these brotherly beings of ours, cannot always just answer an animal question and stop short. One question irresistibly reminds him of another that equally often gets asked. Or one problem brings to mind a similar problem. Which is why (speaking of moths) a reptile question is insinuated here:

How many orders of living reptiles are there? The common-sense answer ought to be three. There are the snakes and lizards, which are called the squamates. There are the crocodiles and alligators: crocodilians. There are the turtles and tortoises: the chelonians. There is nothing left to be covered, is there? Unhappily, there is. There is an order resoundingly called the rhynchocephalians. It continues to clog reptile study, and make the whole reptile class of living animals unwieldier than it ought to be, because of the survival in New Zealand of one lone iguanalike creature called a tuatara. The sum total of living rhynchocephalians is the tuatara and nothing else.

Do butterflies ever migrate?

Remarkably enough, some do. Most butterflies and moths, of course, spend their winters dormant: a few as adults, most of them as eggs or pupae. But there are a few of the fragile-winged creatures that undertake to fly away from cold climates in autumn, as migrant birds do. Monarchs, the big red-brown butterflies with black-veined wings, are familiar to American watchers of the summer fields as far north as Canada. In fall they gather in great flocks and migrate southward. They travel hundreds of miles, probably thousands. Within the last fifty years or so, monarchs have been turning up increasingly often in England. How do they get there? So far, a naturalist can only guess; but the guess is a pretty sure one. They fly.

Some of the butterflies called "painted ladies" spend their winters in the North African desert. In spring they cross the Mediterranean and set out northward across Europe. How far do they succeed in traveling? A few of them, almost incredibly, reach Iceland.

Do insects have red blood?

Never. The red blood that may come from a squashed insect is always some other animal's. Insects' blood is just about colorless, or faintly yellow.

How do moths and butterflies winter?

They may spend the cold season in any of the four stages of their development: as eggs, larvae, pupae, or adults. Every now and then, on some mild midwinter day as we're exploring the woods, we may be astonished to see a dark butterfly with creamy wing-edgings flitting from tree trunk to tree trunk across the snow. What's that? That's a mourning-cloak butterfly (in the Old World, a Camberwell beauty), one of the butterflies called angle-wings. They winter as adults, hiding in bark crannies and similar sheltered places and venturing into flight whenever a mild spell comes along. Or again: On a winter day we may turn over a stone or a log and find there, stirring feebly, a very fuzzy caterpillar with broad transverse markings of black and brown. What's this? A "woolly bear," to use its country name. More exactly, the caterpillar of an Isabella tiger moth. To find winter *eggs* of innumerable small moths, we need only examine the leafless twigs of the handiest tree.

(We can't very well omit here the question that always comes up in autumn about that woolly-bear caterpillar. Do the relative widths of its black and brown bands foretell the severity of the coming winter? No; no more than the thickness of deer coats or the fatness of autumn woodchucks or the extent of squirrels' nut storings forecast it. There is nothing about animals' lives to make absurd or contemptible the view that they are in the care of Providence. It was men who were very close and comradely to animals, after all, in whom dawned irresistibly the sense of *anima* at the back-of-beyond, in fatherhood to all the creation of particular things and lesser spirits. But there is no indication that animals, however guided and guarded in their Now, are also forewarned about the To-Come. There isn't any conflict between religion and science. But foolishnesses of religion, and foolishnesses of science, lead of course to all sorts of scrappings, as is the way of foolishness.)

Though wintering may be in any of these modes, most of the higher moths and butterflies spend the winter in pupation. We go out on a bitter February day, and we may think to ourselves that not much seems to be happening in animaldom. But plenty is happening, of course. After all, it is in winter that tens of billions of little particles of matter are in process of changing from the dry brown object called a seed into what will next spring be the living green thing called a flowering plant. In winter, the birds may not be many; but the drabbest little snowbird is as extraordinary as the flamingest scarlet tanager. We have only to look a little closer at things, and think a little, and alert ourselves out of our dull drowse. The splendor still lies at the heart of events. We need only brush aside the snow a little, and there is the green moss. We need only have our facts about us, and in the grayest blizzard we can "see," with the eye of our mind, the mole still active as ever in his runways down underneath the frost line and the woodchuck sleeping his fabulous sleep in his grass-lined den deep under the snow-covered meadow. There are no bright wings of moths and butterflies to catch at our attention in the white, cold world of February. No. But in cocoon and chrysalis, those wings are in the making. What were "worms" the preceding fall—caterpillars—are in the metamorphic sleep of pupation.

What does "pupa" mean? It means a girl. By extension from that meaning, it designates any kind of little childish figure, a doll, a puppet. Linnaeus gave the name to this instar of the insects' lives because most pupae have something of the look of feminine figurines. In their millions, in winter, they are to be found throughout the cold countryside, small, inconspicuous, and miraculous.

There are innumerable kinds of them, for the life histories of moths and butterflies are of many sorts. There are butterfly chrysalids, spangled as Egyptian sarcophagi, hanging by tiny hooks in sheltered crannies around houses and under the protective, shaggy bark of trees. There are pupae (of common sphinx moths, for instance) lying quiet in small hollowed-out chambers under the frozen earth. Most easily found, there are the pupae that are encased in cocoons: silk-woven capsules attached to twigs, to the old siding of buildings, to tree trunks. This little ovoid gray bump on a willow twig . . . what's that? It's the cocoon containing a pupa of Cecropia, the great tawny moth that makes magical our summer gardens. This stubbier, fatter cocoon . . . ? This holds a pupa of the huge, yellow, eye-winged Polyphemus. Everywhere in the wintry woods and fields, the flowerless gardens, there are wings in the making.

Let's take a look inside the process. We have already briefly done so in talking about houseflies, but moths and butterflies give us the chance for a further look.

As a caterpillar goes about its feeding it periodically sheds its skin. It goes through these ecdyses—the periods between them being called stadia, and the insect's form in each stadium being called its instar—all through the span of its larval life. That larval life may not come to an end in autumn, but most commonly among our moths and butterflies it does. The waning of summer means the waning of caterpillarhood. With the coming of autumn the caterpillar grows lethargic, ceases its feeding, and creeps to the place of its pupation. Its life as a larva is about to close.

(There is a great deal more poetry in scientific terminology than we may suspect. *Larva* is Latin for a mask. It was the charming and accurate fancy of old-time naturalists to think of a caterpillar as simply the masked presence of winged beauty to come.)

In the last larval stadium, now, the caterpillar has been developing the first, faint secret hints of wings inside its worm-body. The pre-wings have been forming in saclike formations within the body wall. The larva is about to enter the prepupal instar.

If it's the larva of a butterfly, it may spin now a little silken disk from which, as pupa, it can suspend itself by means of a pupal hook called its cremaster. Or if the larva is that of, say, a great Cecropia moth or a Promethea, it sets to spinning around itself a tapering silken case of extraordinary construction. Spinning, spinning, it makes a case of great toughness and strength; but at the end of the case it builds a kind of conical valve. When in the spring the adult moth will be ready for emergence, this valvelike construction— virtually impregnable from the outside—will open readily to inside pressure to set the big moth free. Or again, the larva may burrow in the soil and round out a little chamber in which to pupate; or, yet again, it may hang head downward and sling around its body a thin, tough, silken girdle—a kind of guy wire or strut—that will keep it from being whipped and blown down by the winter wind during the oblivion of pupation.

In its cocoon, now, or whichever other situation, the larva has become prepupal. The forming wings are thinly covered now only by the last layer of larval cuticle. The prepupal animal stirs and wriggles; the larval skin breaks and is sloughed off for the last time; and what lies ready for winter sleep is the pupa.

The pupa looks rather like a foetal mummy of the winged creature to be formed. Wings within the case are discernible, but tiny, crumpled, and folded upon the breast like a baby Pharaoh's withered hands. In the crinkly brown outline of the pupa, we can make out legs; but they are packed into very small compass and glued to the body. The pupa lies in incompleteness and sleep, without ability to do more than twitch and squirm a little, as an unborn baby will, upon the application of pressure.

We say that the pupa sleeps? Well, yes, it does; but its body is a tumult of physiological activity. Actually, as the grand old entomologist of my boyhood, Dr. John Henry Comstock, used to insist, the pupal stadium is the most furiously active period of the creature's whole postembryonic existence. Nothing happening outdoors, out in the frozen February woods? No wonderful animal events, to keep a naturalist from boredom? It isn't so. The pupae are developing; and if that's not quite as noticeable a wonder, for most of us, as the blossom-burst and bird song of summertime, it's no less a one.

The February winds whistle; the March winds roar; the April "robin snows" come drifting down. Then, in cocoon case and chrysalis and underground chamber, there is a stir, and we are let know what has been happening. We're let see what prodigious chemistries have been occurring. The instar of last autumn was a crawling worm. The pupa case splits and opens now; the valve-door of the cocoon is pushed apart, or perhaps a hole is worked in the tough silken case by the filelike tool with which some pupae are equipped; and now there creeps unsteadily into the pale spring sunshine the final insect that scientific language terms imaginal.

(More poetry of earth. The larva was the mask, the obscuration of things to come and not yet seen. And now there is the final perfect moth or butterfly, so vivid in identity, so perfect in revelation, that it is, as we may say, the very image of itself.)

The long body is heavy, pendulous, carrying its biological memory of the worm-body of the caterpillar. The wings are crumpled and damp, the antennae limp and not yet tuned to test the texture of the world. The insect's blood and vital fluids are mostly in its thorax and abdomen. It stirs, stretches its crumpled wings, begins fanning them rhythmically. The effort brings quickening of circulation. As distribution of fluid becomes more even, the wings expand and smooth out; the antennae are raised and begin their delicate searching of the air; the long, heavy abdomen shrinks and hardens. Into the spring sky flutters a moth or butterfly, riotous in color, exquisite in grace, ready to entrance us.

Why do some ants have wings?

There were few more frustrating puzzlements in my life as an entomologist of ten or twelve or so, than occurred on the day when I looked up "Ant" in a dictionary I had come across and found an illustration depicting an insect with wings. Wings? I had put in a good many solemn hours of ant watching, and never had seen any sign of wings. The dictionary's dense little paragraph of erudite fine print telling me that ants were properly to be called Formicidae gave no help. It was unilluminating to learn that another name for an ant was an emmet. All very well, but . . . why those *wings?*

It's a very reasonable question, and not merely in our childhood. Ants, as far as the casual observations of most of us go, are obviously wingless little beings. If suddenly we come across a throng of wing-bearing ants, we're likely to suppose they must be those rare and mysterious creatures, "flying" ants, to which we may perhaps have heard obscure allusions. Or if we happen upon "Ant" in a dictionary, and find a vignette of a creature with gauzy wings, it's a very likely and altogether natural thing for us to be entirely puzzled.

The commonest of all insect questions, not surprisingly, are those about houseflies, moths and butterflies, and ants and bees. We have been finding out some answers about the first three; and now it looks as though we'd better devote what space remains to us for insect considerations to taking up the host of most popular ant queries and bee queries. There are a fearful lot of them. We'll start out with ants, and get along to bees presently.

First now, those ant wings: Sexually developed male ants and sexually developed female ants both do have wings. There was no deceit in the little dictionary picture. But the ants called workers— sexually undeveloped and infertile—are wingless. It's not unless we take up animalizing to the point where we go poking into the galleried labyrinths of ants' nests that we're likely ever to see any kinds of ants but workers. Ant queens and their winged males stay sequestered in their chambers deep inside the earth-mound or the old stump.

"Workers?" What work do they do? The answer to any ant question has to be only a partial and simplified answer. There are rather more than 6,000 different species of ants going about their intricate little insect-rounds on this earth of ours. No two of them have quite the same life-way. The life-way of any one of them can preoccupy a naturalist all his days and leave him ignorant. However, putting it broadly: Worker ants perform the labor of building the nest; they attend to gathering the food, and to storing it; they look after the larval baby ants; they protect the nest; they wage war; they carry forward the whole life of the formicary, save for the laying and fertilizing of the eggs.

Are all these workers alike? No. In most ant colonies there are big workers and smaller ones, and they split up their duties. Nurse ants, soldier ants, foraging ants—there are ants to carry out every imaginable need of a society that has its center in the egg-producing queen.

Can we tell a queen ant from a male? Very easily. She's a much bigger ant, often twice as big (frequently four or five times bigger than the active workers), with a long, heavy, massive-abdomened body. Furthermore—to throw into confusion now what had seemed to be getting so easily set straight a few minutes ago—if we unearth a queen from her underground chamber we find her wingless. Why? The queen has wings only until her nuptial flight. That flight is what is taking place when all of a sudden we see, for perhaps the first time in our life, one of those swarms of "flying ants" we were talking about. The swarm is a group of winged male ants clustering around the winged female. When she has mated, and the flight ends and she drops back to earth, the queen ant twists around and bites off her wings. She will not again seek the light. She is pulled now by a drive toward darkness. She initiates an ant colony, and becomes from now on only an invisible producer—hidden away in the dark depths of the formicary—of the eggs that will produce more generations of queens, males, workers, and soldiers.

Do the queen ant and her males live the same life span? No. Male and female generations in an ant colony go forward at very different paces. Male ants live only a short time. Their function is the brief one of fertilization. The worker ants live much longer, and queens generally longer still. How long? Lives of six or seven years for workers aren't uncommon. A queen may still be egg-laying, down in the darkness, when she's ten. (Is it a continual day-to-day production, then? No; it's cyclic. She has a rhythm of alternation: ovulation and rest, ovulation and rest.)

When first we hear a female ant called a "queen," it may strike us as an overimaginative sort of name. Actually it's a sober enough name for her role. Among such social insects as the ants (by the way, are all ants social? They are, yes; there are no solitary species as among the bees and wasps), the big fecund female is in an exact sense the ruling spirit of the colony. She is its very center and reason; she empowers it. What happens when a queen ant dies? Worker ants, of course, are continually dying. The other workers just throw out their bodies and get rid of them. But when something happens to the queen? The ants keep her body. They carry it from place to place in the nest, in funereal ceremony. They keep coming back and back and back to it, in distracted little scurrying visitings. How long do they keep up these special attentions? Why, just as long, sometimes, as anything remains of their queen's body. She continues their queen until she has crumbled into dust. And then? Then, little by little, the ant colony disintegrates. The workers' activities become no less, but their pattern falls into futility. Unproductive, its central spirit gone, the colony dwindles as the workers die off and are unreplaced. Presently the rounded earth-mound in the meadow, that was lately so teeming, has become only a mound of earth. It is a vanished city.

Often enough, when we turn over a stone and disclose a formicary, or when we watch a file of ants hurrying across our lawn, we see the ants carrying pale tan or whitish oval pellets almost as big as themselves. We have probably been accustomed to hearing them called "ant eggs." Is that really what they are? No. Those are the ants' pupae or cocoons. Ants have a special concern for them, and when a colony is disturbed their first impulse is usually to rush the cocoons away to safety.

We are almost sure to have heard or read allusions to some ant ways that sound so fantastic that we may have assumed them to be only scraps of myth preserved in metaphor. But ant society is so intricately developed a working of instincts, special senses, special responses, and insect-wise "knowings" of the sort we have undertaken so often in this book to explore, that in fact a good many of even the most whoppery bits of folk-notion about ants turn out, as we find, to be quite true.

Is it true that ants keep cattle? They often do. The colony's livestock are little sap-feeding insects: scale insects and aphids. Worker ants "milk" these charges, patting and stroking them until they void a droplet of their processed nectar. Is it true that ants sometimes have special chambers in their formicaries as "stables" for these minute insect-cows? Oh yes, that's quite true. It's also true that bands of worker ants often set up guard around groups that they come across in their wanderings away from the nest, in the fashion of cowboys guarding a herd of cattle out on the range.

Is it true that ants keep slaves? Many ants do. The colony sends out raiding packs; the eggs of another species are seized and carried to the home nest; the young ants that hatch become laborers for their captors.

Or again: Are there really ants that cultivate gardens? Indeed. Parasol ants bring millions of leaf bits to their underground chambers, and prepare a rotted mulch in which they raise mushrooms. Every step of the operation, from the cutting and transportation of the leaf bits to the maintenance of the fungus crop, which involves a constant and careful weeding by the smallest worker ants that virtually never leave the nest, is of such a precision, such an expertness and apparent purposefulness, that if we have a chance to observe it happening we can scarcely avoid feeling we are watching something as intelligently integrated as the life of a human community. For such ages have gardening ants raised and tended their special fungus, as a matter of fact, so completely have they acclimated it to ant domestication, that in a wild state it has become extinct.

We might go on about ants forever. Any animalizer who takes ants as his special province is undertaking to investigate what amounts to a whole animal universe in itself. There must be a comfortable ten thousand books about nothing but ants; and the last word in the ten-thousandth of them is an infinite distance from being the last word about ants. However, we've put the commonest questions behind us now, and we have to be turning from ants to the chief questions about bees.

It doesn't make much difference, I should think, which question we select as our lead question. Suppose we use the ever-recurring one:

Does a bee die
after it stings?

Generally speaking, yes. A bee's sting is equipped with backward-pointing barbs, and after it has been plunged into a victim it is almost as inextricable as a fishhook or a porcupine's quill. As the stinging bee struggles to get away, its embedded sting is pulled out of its body and the bee generally suffers irreparable injury. It does, that is, if it's a worker bee; and unless we have an experience that is rare even among beekeepers we are not likely to be stung by a queen. A queen bee can sting repeatedly. She has a formidably long curved sting, with the barbs on it much less developed, and this needle is attached inside her body much more firmly than a worker's sting is.

(Is it true, by the way, that bees, mosquitoes, and similar stinging insects can't manage to sting us if we hold our breaths? This is the sort of question that no high-minded scientific treatise ever seems to dream of taking up; but it involves a belief that's been popular for ages all around the world, and what good is an introduction if it's afraid to be introductory? No; holding our breaths won't make it impossible for insects to sting us. The notion perhaps rests on a fancy that insects introduce their stings into us through our pores and that a deep breath makes the pores close tight. But an insect doesn't insert its sting into a pore, except by chance; and no sort of breathing could close our pores tightly enough to trap it if it did. An insect can sting us though we stay resolutely breathless till we're black in the face.)

If queen bees almost never have occasion to sting human beings, what do they sting? They sting other queens. In a sprawling ant colony there may be several queens; but a community of bees has just one. She is violently hostile to other queens . . . so conditioned to this enmity, in fact, that she will sting even their dead bodies if she should come upon them. A queen bee must remain central and unique in her community.

What composes that community and how does its life go forward? A difficulty about textbooks and encyclopedias, as we've had occasion to complain before, is that when we turn to them for information we're often dismayed by finding a great deal too much of it. A simplehearted question about animals comes to our mind, and we'd like a simple answer; so we look up the subject and lo! here are fifty-seven pages of fine print. This is particularly and painfully true in the matter of bees. Books with titles like *The ABC of Bees* turn out to be almost too heavy to lift. It's true that bee ways are immensely complicated. It's true that there are something over 10,000 varieties of bees whirring and buzzing in a golden throng around this garden of the creation and fertilizing its flowers. But let's see if we can't bring a little ordered simplicity out of all this. By "bees" let's just mean plain, ordinary, everyday honeybees (after all, if we need to know about leaf-cutting bees or carpenter bees or the hosts of others, we can turn to the sources of specialized information), and let's just take up their ways in terms of the most universal and popular questions about them. Our remaining space is very little. Let's try to get to the heart of the hive.

Now: How is a bee community made up? It contains one fertile queen, a number—say some hundreds—of males (which are called the drones), and anywhere from around ten thousand to twenty or thirty thousand infertile females which are the workers.

Can we tell these apart, as in the case of ants? Readily. A worker bee is the littlest bee. It's the bee of our familiar experience, the one we see droning from flower to flower or shouldering its way through the long meadow grass. A male bee, the drone, is a good bit bigger and bulkier; and the queen bee, finally, has a very much long and narrower abdomen than a male has.

Our queen bee is the egg layer. As we found in investigating ants, she is tremendously productive and also long-lived. A queen bee may live fifteen years. On the other hand, the worker bees are almost ephemeral. That bee droning around our flower bed in the summer sunshine . . . how long will it live? If it has emerged as part of the spring brood, its life is generally not more than two or three months. If it's an autumn-born bee it may have a rather longer life experience, but not often more, even so, than seven or eight months.

We watch our worker bee going from flower to flower, and then disappearing to seek its hive or its community nest in a "bee tree," and perhaps we have some mental picture of the honeycomb inside the nest and some notion of the nature of our bee's errands. But what, exactly, are the facts of the thing? What's honeycomb? Does our bee gather honey from flowers? Where does the wax for the honeycomb come from?

Beeswax is something worker bees exude in little drops on the undersides of their abdomens. As the liquid drops issue from the bee's wax-plates, they spread and harden like the molten drippings of a candle until presently they have coated the bee's underside with a flattened layer of waxy exudate. The worker bee cuts and scrapes off the wax with a sort of pincer-cutters on its hind legs and goes to work with it.

Bees' jaws are specially developed for use in the way of a sculptor's spatula or a mason's trowel. Chewing, patting, smoothing, legions of workers construct hexagonal cells of honeycomb. Meanwhile other workers, and the queen, are putting the finished cells to their uses. The queen, fulfilling her one destiny, moves from place to place in the hive, depositing eggs. (How many? In a year she may lay as many as a million eggs; but she puts just one egg in each cell of honeycomb.) The workers labor at filling other cells with honey and pollen.

Does a bee find honey in flowers? No; what it finds is simply the thin, watery flower nectar. It sucks this up, swallows it, then flies to the hive and regurgitates it as a processed honey. It's a thin, rather bodiless stuff when the bee first empties it into the cell. It needs to be dried out to give it thickening. How do the bees manage that? They hover over the cells, buzzing and fanning. We were finding out a while ago how tremendously fast insects can vibrate their wings. It sets up a rushing flow of air currents over the cells, and dries the watery honey to the thick, syrupy honey consistency familiar to us.

What about the pollen? Our worker bee gathers that in pollen baskets on its hind legs, "baskets" that are in fact simply concavities on the outer surface of one of the legs' segments.

Honey, pollen, bee eggs . . . the cells of the honeycomb are variously filled with these deposits. We take a look now at what happens to the bee egg:

How long does it take to hatch? It takes about three days. What issues is a little white larval grub, and it is (of course) hungry. Most insects, as we have found out, take little or no care of their young; but our young bee is immediately taken in charge by nurse bees. These are simply worker bees that assume this special duty. What determines which workers assume it? Well, by and large, nursing bees are the youngest ones in the community. They are worker bees in the first phase of their lives, and they haven't yet gone forth from the hive to take up pollen gathering and honey making. Before their first foraging flights into the outdoors, they have a week or so of nursing function.

For two or three days the baby bee—the larva—is fed by the nurses on bee jelly. That's a regurgitated substance of extraordinary food value and easy assimilability. Then the bee baby is weaned to honey and pollen, and then presently the workers stuff a small food supply into a cell, pop the baby bee into it, and place a wax cap over the top. For a few days the immured larva feeds on its provisions. Then, in the standard insect pattern we've been finding out about in talking of other insects, it becomes a pupa. It stays one for thirteen days. At the end of that time it metamorphoses into adult beehood, chews its way through the cell's wax cap and comes creeping forth, and is ready as soon as its wings have dried to take up its role as a member of the bee community.

That's our bee story, in its simplified essentials. The last part of it brings up one of the commonest of all wonderings about bees: What destines a bee to grow up to become a queen? The answer lies in a very special handling and feeding beginning at infancy:

A queen starts its life as a regular bee egg in a regular little hexagonal cell indistinguishable from any of the other throng of cells that make up the honeycomb. But the worker bees, when they are moved to create a queen, begin giving this selected cell special attention. They tear down the cells that are clumped pressingly around it, and enlarge this nuclear cell into one great big one. When the egg inside it hatches into a larva, the workers begin feeding it bee jelly in massive concentrates, and they never switch its diet over to pollen and honey at all. The infant gets nothing but an assiduous feeding of bee jelly all the while it remains a larva. Walled up at last in its special outsize cell, it hatches out a queen.

Are all bee eggs exactly alike at the start, then? There's one important factor of variability. The eggs a queen lays are sometimes fertilized and sometimes not. The fertilized ones produce either workers or—in the case of the special treatment and diet we've been talking about—a queen. The unfertilized eggs produce drones.

Doesn't a new queen ever appear in a hive while the old queen is still presiding? Yes; new queens appear from time to time. That's when the queen fights we were speaking about occur, the bees lancing at each other with their curved stings until only one of the new queens remains alive. What commonly happens then is that the old queen—what most bee-fancying animalizers call the mother queen—quits the hive and takes off across country with a horde of followers. The bees, as we say, are "swarming" then. They gather in a dense mass around their queen at the newly selected nest site, and presently the cell making and food gathering of a new colony are under way.

Do bees fly in a beeline? They do, pretty much, when they are on their way back to the hive from foraging expeditions, though not, of course, when they are just exploring from flower to flower. A beeline, by the way, is a good deal shorter distance between two points than the distance "as the crow flies." We don't have to go out animalizing in many a fall or winter dusk, watching the crows straggle back across the sunset-streaked sky to their roost in the dark hemlock woods, to find out what a feeble piece of language the old phrase is. Crows love to flap along in wide, random deviations.

There remains one question about bees that brings up such a different kind of consideration that I think perhaps we'd better give it a separate heading. It will make a thoughtful sort of matter, now, with which to bring the insect part of our book to a close. In coming to that close, of course, we leave a multitude of insect questions unanswered. It can't be otherwise. The earth age in which we live, as a naturalist thinks of it, is the Age of Insects; and a library full of books would answer all the questions about them only a little less incompletely than this one part of our one informal and introductory book is able to do. We can't answer all the questions. We must rest content with having answered the commonest. Of these, now, there is this final one for us to take up:

Can bees tell time?

They can indeed, in their fashion, and it's worth talking about more than briefly. It involves, as so many of our questions about animals must, the whole matter of their minds, their instincts, their intuitions. "Intuition" is a vague word, if you like, not a scientific one. True. Still, it stands for a reality.

Intuition is older than the analytical mind. We have in us a great many kinds of knowings prior to the intellect—instincts, subtle physiological sensings, perceivings by means of the great subrational part of us which until a little while ago, evolutionarily speaking, was our major psychic equipment as it is still the major psychic equipment of our brother animals. There are many unconscious understandings and prelogical awarenesses in us, some of them lulled and dulled by neglect, some of them still quite active, all of them very old and very deep.

Most of us may simply accept, spontaneously and without further notice to the matter, these intuitional knowings. Science, however, is forever trying to find their how and why. It's a difficult task. In some respects it's an impossible one. For science deals in things like facts and measurements and mathematical analyses; and who is to measure with calipers the feelings in a human heart on a spring morning, or precipitate in a test tube a chemical combination to account for the knowledge that *Numen inest?* It isn't always possible to see, through a laboratory lens, the things that are plain enough to the eye of the spirit; and it's not always possible to find out, with the analytical mind, the how and why of the happenings that occur in the older and deeper regions of us. But it is sometimes possible. Our "deep-knowings" are sometimes translatable into the scientific idiom, and their nature made plain in the light of the laboratory. A piquant case of this involves scientific researches into the problem of The Clock of the Bees.

Do we have the fancy, as we look back in memory to the days when we were children, that an hour somehow lasted longer in those days than it does now? Of course we do. All men have always had the feeling—one of those unrational, intuitional knowings that are so many and so potent in our lives—that in adulthood time flies past with tragically greater speed than in the days of youth. Once upon a time—remember?—a golden summer afternoon was a very long while. A vacation, stretching ahead at the close of school term, was infinity. And now today the hours and days and months and years rush by so fast that we can scarcely seize them.

Or so it convincingly seems to us, "in our bones." In a whimsical-enough fashion, science has found a mode of exploring the matter, and confirming the intuition, and learning the why of it. The experiments have been mostly made in Britain. The subjects of the experiments have been bees. The story of the undertaking has been scientifically set down by Professor H. Munro Fox of the University of Birmingham. Acknowledging a debt to his records, suppose we have a look now at our question: Can bees tell time?

For ages beekeepers have insisted that their small, winged charges have an extraordinary sense of time. Bees, many a countryman has said, know exactly at what times of day to visit those flowers that periodically open and close; and their visitings are as punctual as clocks. When we are long intimate with animals, we are almost certain to become convinced that there are many curious "deep-knowings" and baffling intuitional insights in the psyches of these brotherly beings. Science, as best its tools will allow, periodically has a look at the matter. But the investigations aren't by any means always satisfactory. A wild hare is subtly cunning in a thousand ways in its wilderness home; but science's laboratory mazes and puzzle boxes can't, in the nature of things, provide an appropriate test of that cunning. The prankish and preposterous guile of a crow, to which any naturalist can testify, isn't susceptible of analysis in terms of Binet intelligence tests or controlled scientific experiments. The deep-knowing of animals, which is still deeper and subtler than our own, is a glimmering and elusive thing, as evasive sometimes of scientifically formal analysis as a Beethoven symphony or a poem or the sense of beauty. But this explicit question of the time sense of the bees . . . well, *that*, at any rate, mightn't be too hard to test formally, the scientists thought. They undertook it.

A little outdoor feeding table was set for the bees. For a few minutes, every day, there was put on the table a supply of sugar water. Then, as the bee guests were partaking of this sweet offering, each bee was dabbed with a tiny identifying spot of paint. When a considerable group of bees had been marked, the experimenters killed off all additional bees that came to the table. So they established, presently, a little test group of marked bees. They began, day after day, subjecting this marked group to careful scrutiny.

Informal naturalists and old-time beekeepers, it was soon made plain, hadn't exaggerated. Each day the marked bees arrived at the feeding table at almost exactly the time when the sugar water was regularly put out. Seldom were they five minutes early. Seldom were they five minutes late. And at no other hour of the day than the one brief feeding period did they come to visit the table at all.

The experiments were carried a step further. One day no sugar water was put out. The bees arrived punctually, nevertheless, at what had been the regular feeding hour. The next day again the sugar water was withheld; and again the bees paid a visit to the table exactly on time. And so for a week. Though no food was put out, the bees still came each day with punctual exactness. They had learned a feeding hour; and they were still promptly faithful to it.

The spirit of science is immensely thorough. Experiment had now confirmed that bees do possess an extraordinary and astonishingly accurate sense of time. But what is its origin? What is the clock of the bees? Could this intuitional awareness in the psyche of an insect be translated, perhaps, into an idiom scientifically acceptable? If so, there might result also some scientific understanding of the less perfect, but still functioning, sense of time in human beings. How does a man, without a timepiece, know approximately the hour of the day? His intuition in the matter is less sure and precise than a bee's; it has grown dull with neglect, perhaps; but doubtless it is the same kind of intuition. What's the nature of man's invisible and moderately serviceable clock, and of the exquisitely accurate invisible timepiece of the bees?

Was the bees' clock hunger? No, it couldn't be that. The bees weren't hungry; they did their eating in the hive; they were collecting the sugar water only to store it. Possibly, then, the bees told time by the position of the sun? To test this hypothesis, the whole experiment was now repeated indoors, in a great shedlike room electrically lighted with a constant brilliance at all hours of the day and night. The bees arrived as punctually as ever at the feeding table. Then how about changes of temperature and humidity? The experimental conditions were elaborated to test this too. The building was now air-conditioned, and an absolute stability of temperature and humidity maintained. The clock of the bees continued to function with its customary uncanny precision. At last . . . could it be possible, could it be remotely possible, that the clock of the bees might be the changing intensity of cosmic rays? There was a way to settle this; and science doesn't mind a little trouble in the effort to settle things. The experimenters took their feeding table and their bees and all their paraphernalia underground. They went down to the bottom of a mine. No cosmic rays could penetrate there.

The bees were just as phenomenally accurate as ever.

Not hunger, not light, not barometric change, not sight, or scent, not cosmic rays . . . what remains? There remained, the experimenters were made to see, one thing. Suppose that the bee *itself* were a kind of clock? That is to say, suppose the rate of chemical change in the living cells of the bee's own body furnished a subtle and silent internal tick-tock whereby the passage of time was made reckonable, intuitionally, to the bee? Was there a way to test this? There was. It was quickly and easily done, and it was an instant success.

The bees were each given a little dose of thyroid extract. Presto! They arrived for their sugar water very much too early. Now they were given each a little dose of quinine. Presto again! They arrived for their sugar water very much too late. Thyroid extract hastens chemical change in the body. Quinine slows it. The clock of the bees, plainly, was in fact the clock of the cells. The bees' intuitional knowledge, their "deep-knowing," was indeed deep. It was derivative from the foundational chemistry of life itself.

That's all there is, scientifically speaking, to the story of the experiments with the clock of the bees. But it's a story which tells a good deal more by implication. It tells, for one thing, that we are right in our feeling that a childhood hour used to last longer than an adult hour does today. Time *was* less fleeting in our childhood. In youth our bodily chemistry is quick. With age, it slows. And "time," of course, is not the thing that is ticked off by the mechanical clock on the mantel. Time is experience. In youth, our experience of time—our "cellular intuition" of time—is fast in relation to external time, horological time. In adulthood, our time-as-experience grows slow with the slowing of our chemistry; and so external time, as measured by the clocks, glides faster for us. The story of the bees suggests, as have a great many other more solemn and more elaborate experiments, that our mathematical time, like so much else in our world of constructs of the mind, is indeed but a construct and a convenience. The ancient saying had it that the heart is wiser than the schools. To put it a little differently, the living cell inhabits a realm of reality that eludes the machinery of Big Ben.

Intuition is very old. It is as old as sentience. Before there was the eye, there were obscurer seeings. Before there was the thinking brain, there were deeper and different knowings. The blood has its wisdom. The flesh has its knowledges. The living cells provide an intuition of the passing of the hours. The story of the bees is a reminder—as are so many, many other things that an animalizer encounters—that there are old and profound "knowings," keen and alive in the animals, that have grown dull in us. We need to remember that, always, if we want to understand the animals' world, even an insect's, even a bee's.

Snakes

A good many more people would probably be animal enthusiasts if the animal kingdom did not contain, as an important portion of it, the animals called snakes. We all have enough of Adam in us to love with an inalienable love the morning-fresh garden of this earth, of which we are part. Our hearts leap up to hear birds' songs. We are stirred and touched by the ways of four-footed beasts, even as we are stirred and touched—and, in the depths of us, comforted and assuaged—by hills, by running brooks, by the smell of a handful of hickory nuts and the look of the slanting sunlight across a furrowed field. In a very deep way, we are forever at *home* with all this. This is the garden into which we are born. This is where our ancestral roots are. This is our heart. But however passionately we may feel all this, however soundly and happily at home we may be with the rest of the creation, we're likely to have some trouble with one of its ingredients. We're likely to be scared of snakes.

Why? Psychiatrists have put forward tentatively some possible reasons. Theologians have guessed at some others. Perhaps some of the fear is an inheritance from a distant age when great reptiles were a major menace to us. Perhaps this . . . perhaps that . . . none of it is at all sure. A naturalist, however, can be sure of at least this much: that wherever and however the terror may have started, it has been incalculably furthered and increased by the wild, wild misinformations about snakes and complete misunderstandings of them that have flourished for a long time and that continue to persist. If we can just get rid of those, if we can just get some elementary facts straight about these brother animals of ours, we may go a long way toward abolishing a lot of unnecessary horrors.

Are small children instinctively afraid of snakes? No. A little child responds to a snake exactly as to a kitten or a puppy or a Teddy bear. But then, as we grow up, we begin to hear gasps of revulsion when snakes are mentioned; we begin to pick up eerie and awful bits of popular snake lore; we begin, naturally enough, to transfer to snakes a whole load of other fears.

What, really, are snakes like? Are some of the poisonous snakes very dangerous? Why, certainly they are. But then, so is an angry dog and so is a rusty nail and so is a falling tree limb. We don't go around with our eyes fixed in terror on the ground, watching for nails. We don't cower away from trees and shudder at a litter of puppies. What are the facts about snakes? Let's see if we can't take a straight look at them.

Snake questions, in my own experience and in that of other naturalists with whom I've talked about it, come up more frequently than animal questions of any other kind. Taking them quickly, and just as they come, let's see what we can do with them.

Are snakes slimy?

Perhaps no other single notion has been as responsible as this one for the feeling that snakes are "nasty" animals. It's altogether baseless. Snakes aren't slimy. They are as dry and inoffensive to the touch as the smooth bark of a tree. The fact is that snakes are one of the most fastidiously clean of all animals.

Do snakes go very fast?

It may look to a terrified beholder as though a snake darts across the ground with arrowy speed, but actually most snakes are not quick travelers. When a startled snake is trying to make its get-away, it often gives an illusion of speed by its rapid sideways whippings and undulatings; but in its actual coverage of distance from point to point it doesn't often proceed as fast as you and I do when we're walking. Do *no* snakes go faster than this modest 4 or 5 miles per hour? There are a few exceptions, but not many. The snakes called racers, which include common black snakes, can go at about the speed of a human run when they're in pell-mell flight. (The word for us to keep in mind here is "flight." Black snakes are mostly a timid company, and they use their exceptional powers of speed to run *away* from us. By the way, just to pause for a second over a perpetual black-snake question: are they very dangerous constrictors? They aren't constrictors at all. The idea of their alarming squeezing power is perpetuated even in their scientific name, *Coluber constrictor*; but, as we have had occasion to see in other instances, the terminology of science can be just as false to the living truth about animals as any backwoodsman's yarnings. Isn't it true, then, that a black snake can wind itself around our arm or leg and squeeze us numb? Not a chance of it. The big black chicken snake that's sometimes popularly called a mountain black snake has constrictive power, but the ordinary black snake of everyday, *Coluber constrictor*, no.)

Quickest of the exceptional speedsters among snakes are perhaps the whip snakes. They can go about as fast as a top-notch runner can run. On a down-slope they can outdistance him. But here again we need to beware against a lot of nightmare misinformation. Do whip snakes lash their victims with their tails? They don't. Will they fling themselves around our legs so that we stumble and fall? They won't do that. Does *Masticophis* hurl itself on the rattlesnake and flog it to death? It doesn't. Is the whip snake poisonous? It isn't. What a whip snake is, in short, is a snake that happens to be able to go much faster than most. Also it has an exceptional endowment of curiosity, and sometimes follows people, rearing up its head now and then to have a look at what's happening. Lynxes likewise sometimes follow people. So do foxes. So do bands of chirruping little chickadees. Our fellow experiencers of the life adventure on this surprising earth share our inclination to do some peering and pondering; and a little something of this, in a snake-dim sort of way, can go on even inside the pointed head of a whip snake.

Are most snakes poisonous?

Far from it. Now, nobody who devotes his life to animaldom, and to an exploring, as it were, of the world of The First Day, wants to see this world misrepresented in a pastel sentimentalism that would deny any dangers and harshness in it. Of course not. We want to go with our eyes open for poison ivy and stinging nettles, as well as for columbine and hepaticas, when we investigate this garden. It's required of creatures here, among other things, that they be alert to challenges. But it's at least as bad as sickly sentimentalism—in fact it's simply the other face of the same sort of wrongness—to multiply the dangers and disasters and pretend that this earth of ours is all athrong with traps and terrors. It isn't.

How many kinds of poisonous snakes are there? Of the land snakes (we may leave out some sea snakes; we're not likely to encounter them), the venomous ones total around 250. And how many kinds of snakes of all kinds are there? As we saw in the beginning, when we were talking about the numbers of animals, there are between 2,000 and 3,000. Putting it briefly, only something like 1 snake in 10 has any venomousness at all. Of this small poisonous minority, are all the species very dangerous? No. Many have hardly enough venom to affect a human being seriously; many are furtive, timid, and scarcely ever bite. Finally: If we include even the snakes that are exceedingly poisonous—big rattlesnakes and such—how do the tables of mortality from snake bite look? Quite surprising. The United States has a hundred-and-fifty-some million persons, vast tracts of wild land for hunting and picnicking, enormous farming areas where there are few facilities for medical attention, and an abundance of rattlesnakes, copperheads, coral snakes, and water moccasins, all of which are venomous. Mix those considerations together and then contemplate the statistics of snake-bite death. Only about 100 persons a year in this country are killed by snakes. In the same country in the same period, motor vehicle accidents kill about 30,000.

Do snakes have yellow blood?

No. A snake's blood is as red as a bird's or a puppy's or yours or mine. The notion about yellow blood is just one of the innumerable fancies that would impute a peculiar queerness or nastiness to snakes.

How does a snake move?

When we say that a snake "glides," we have already persuaded ourselves to shiver a little. If we say that it "slithers," we are as good as undone. Suppose we try saying, for our reassurance, what is the simple fact: a snake walks.

A snake doesn't have any breastbone. The tips of its ribs are free-moving and amount, so to speak, to feet. A snake walks along on its rib tips, pushing forward its ventral scutes at each "step," and it speeds up this mode of progress by undulating from side to side and by taking advantage of every rough "toehold" it can find in the terrain. Let's look at it this way: A man or other animal going forward on all fours is using a sort of locomotion that's familiar enough to all of us and isn't at all dismaying. Now: Suppose this walker is enclosed inside some sort of pliable encasement, like a sacking. The front "feet" will still step forward, the "hind legs" still hitch along afterward. It will still be a standard-enough sort of animal-walking, only all we'll see now is a sort of wiggling of the sacking, without visible feet. That's the snake way. A snake has its covering outside its feet, as an insect has its skeleton on its outside, with no bones on the interior. There's nothing "horrid" about the one arrangement any more than about the other.

Does a snake undulate up and down like an inchworm? No,

never; or at least only in very tiny and almost imperceptible undulations, and then only under such extraordinary circumstances as when it may be trying, for instance, to cross a sheet of glass. The up-and-down undulating is shown in lots of old prints, and is likely enough to be engraved early on our disturbed imaginations; but it isn't the way a snake goes. Does a snake ever take its tail in its mouth and roll like a hoop? Never. Can a snake stiffen its body and stand on its tail? Never, again. And when our snake, walking along through the green world, wants to hurry up suddenly, does it scrabble faster and faster with its rib-legs? No; this is when it does its lateral undulating, its whipping from side to side. These undulations are pushes. Each lateral loop of the snake's body is pressing backward against some little roughness in the terrain, sending the straightened fore part of its body speeding forward. We were speaking a minute ago of a snake trying to cross a sheet of glass. How does it make out on a smooth surface like that? Very badly indeed. On a truly smooth surface, a snake is almost immobilized. It can only flounder and make excited swimming motions. Which brings up, appropriately enough, our last question about snakes' movements: Can land snakes swim? Yes. Virtually all snakes are effective swimmers.

Are snakes "deaf as an adder"?

They are. Snakes have no ears at all, in the sense in which we think of ears, and no discoverable other auditory apparatus. It is certain, however, that they do a good deal of a kind of "hearing," in their own snake way, by feeling subtle vibrations in the ground. (We ourselves can "feel" organ notes, rumbling through a church structure, when we may not be able to "hear" them.) But what about snake charmers' flutings and incantations? Can't snakes hear those? No. What "charms" a snake is the rhythmic swaying of the charmer's body and the adroit movement of his flute or wand. Music, spoken commands, and similar incidental sounds are to charm the spectators, not the snake. They don't penetrate the snake's awareness at all.

Do snakes die in the sun?

They do if it's direct enough and hot enough. Because snakes are cold-blooded animals, with no internal regulating mechanism to maintain a steady body temperature, their heat or cold varies directly with the temperature of their surroundings. They must withdraw early in autumn or be frozen, and they must avoid the midday glare of hot sun on stones in summer. Some desert snakes can briefly stand temperatures up to about 115°. Above that, they cook to death. Nondesert snakes die of overheating at much lower temperatures. Any snake anywhere will die if it has to stay more than a short time on a sun-heated rock on a summer day.

Where does a snake's tail begin?

This used to bother me immensely when I was a naturalist of ten or twelve or so, poring earnestly over the herpetological manuals in search of elementary information. "Thus-and-such a species has a long tail. So-and-so species has a short one." *Tail?* A snake looks to be pretty much all tail from the neck backward. Actually, however, there *is* a distinction between body and tail. A snake's tail starts at the animal's anal shield, a big pair of scales covering its vent. On the underside of a snake's body the scales are usually broad ones, reaching right across from side to side. At the beginning of the tail, they start to be divided in two. It takes practice

H*

to tell tail from body, viewing a snake from above; but flip the snake on its back and we can see the demarcation clearly enough.

Do snakes sometimes sting with their tails?

No snake, anywhere in all the world, has ever done it. Sometimes mud snakes, helping to perpetuate the myth, do poke and prod at a capturer with their tails; but even a mud snake's tail isn't a stinger. It just has a horny hardened tip.

This question about tail-stinging resembles a lot of our commonest other snake questions. These are the questions that spring out of folklore, out of something we heard rumored in our childhood, out of a misunderstanding based on a whisper based on a misobservation in the first place. The answer to every one of them is No. Suppose we clear them away, here, in one massive lot, instead of laboriously bringing them up one by one under individual headings:

Does a killed snake live until sundown? No more than a killed rabbit or a killed butterfly. Reflex action may persist a long time even in a decapitated snake (as it may, familiarly enough, in a decapitated chicken), but that's all there is to the story. Is a poisonous snake's severed head dangerous until there's a thunderstorm? The origin of this popular fancy is evidently the same. A snake's severed head may persist in reflex action. It may indeed bite. It continues dangerous until the last twitching of muscle and nerve. We can forget about the thunderstorm.

Will a horsehair left in water turn into a snake? It won't, as we have stated before; but the belief illustrates vividly what a wrong deduction from observation can do to set a mythical animal lore in motion. The likeliest place for a countryman to notice a horsehair in water is in a horse trough. A horse trough, too, is just about the likeliest place to notice one of the long, fine threadworms or hairworms slowly whipping and undulating about. A hairworm looks, in a casual sort of way, like a small attenuated snake. Put two and two together to get a hasty five, and there is born the hardy supposition that snakes are hairs become animate. Snakes, of course, come into being from antecedent snakes, their birth-ways being something we shall talk about presently.

Are snakes' tongues poisonous? No more than their tails. When a snake keeps thrusting forth its flickering tongue, it isn't brandishing a weapon but using a delicate sensory organ to obtain impressions of its world. We don't know, for sure, just what a snake finds out by its tongue-testings of the air. Its experience may in any case, quite likely, be something almost humanly unimaginable, like certain sensory experiences of ants. Ants don't have, separately, a sense of smell and a sense of taste and a sense of touch. What they have is a fused "topochemical" sense. All over an ant's feelers are delicate organs giving the ant simultaneously impressions of odor-taste and of tactility. It's as though (words necessarily break down and fail us) we were to experience triangularity as acid, or were to think of sweetness as particularly circular. When a snake pulls in its quivering tongue, it thrusts the forks of the tip into a pair of pits in the roof of its mouth, called Jacobson's organ. The pits contain quantities of nerve endings. As the indrawn tongue seeks and makes contact with them, the snake experiences . . . well, it isn't certain what. Perhaps taste. Perhaps scent. Perhaps a combination of these. We have been seeing that snakes are earless, and so as "deaf as adders" as far as a hearing like ours is concerned. It's conceivable that there may be hearing of a different kind, and that a snake's tongue may be the organ of it. What a snake's tongue *isn't*, at any rate, is a poisonous weapon. And by the way: Does a snake coat its prey with slime before swallowing it? That's just another eerie dreadfulness. It isn't so.

Is a snake afraid to cross a rope on the ground, or a railroad track? Many a cowboy and camper, before settling down for the night, is still careful to lay out a protective circle of rope around him; and the curiously uneven distribution of some kinds of snakes in a countryside is still likely to be explained by the local "snake doctor" as caused by snakes' inability to cross a railroad track. If we like to do a little direct and firsthand animalizing of a simple sort, we can try loosing a snake inside a rope circle, or chasing it to a railroad track, and see what happens. Snakes, naturally enough, avoid obstacles when there's an easy way around them. When there isn't, they cross.

If we kill a venomous snake, will its mate seek out the body and lie beside it, waiting to inflict revenge? When I was in the boyhood stage of animalizing, an impressive old woodsman told me a wonderfully eye-widening story about this. In the years since then, I've heard a good many others; and so, no doubt, have most of us. The stories make exciting storytelling, but poor snake lore. All of our animal brothers, as we have been seeing again and again in these pages, have a certain quality of personality, from the inexpressibly dim and tiny *anima* in a speck of paramecium to the lively characters of the mammals that are our most immediate kindred. But the personality of a snake is a long way down this scale of consciousness, and slight and feeble even for the animal's place in the evolutionary scheme of things. Snakes don't take any elaborate care of their young. They don't leap up in play, when the sun shines bright and the birds are singing on a summer morning. They don't go grieving. The glint of being, in a snake, is a dulled and sluggish gleam. It doesn't extend to any devotion to a mate, far less to such scheming as a plan for revenge.

Is it true that all green snakes are venomous? We may be led to think so by an obscure association with the familiar phrase, "poisonous green," which perhaps derives from the color of arsenic; but greenness in snakes need not signify danger. One of the most delicately lovely snakes, our mild and harmless common grass snake, is a green one.

How about snakes skimming the cream off standing milk with their tails? They don't. And how about snakes sucking the milk from the cows? They don't do that either. The abundant American king snake called a milk snake bears that name because of its supposed proclivity for cow sucking, and various other snakes in other parts of the world go by the same popular name for the same reason. But what a milk snake is seeking, as it glides through the tall meadow grass and around the barn, isn't milk but mice. A good many snakes are effective mousers. Milk snakes are among the best of them. Is it *certain* that snakes can't milk cows? After all, there are a good many eloquent old Rattlesnake Petes and Snake-Oil Joes to swear that they have known the thing to happen. Well, yes, there are. But if we get to studying milk snakes carefully, we find the tales of cow drying a good deal hampered by the actual facts about the actual animal. As for instance: A snake can't exert the suction necessary to draw milk. Even if it could, it would have to clamp its mouth closed to do so, and in doing that it would have to bite the cow's teat savagely with its mouthful of sharp teeth. A snake doesn't have a mouth and cheeks like ours. To suck at all, it would have to get a cow's teat—now badly mangled by its teeth—well down its throat. And at last, supposing all these difficulties to have been overcome (the list of them having started, as we might have mentioned, with the impossibility of the snake's reaching up to the teat unaided and the unlikelihood of the cow's having docilely permitted it to clamber up a leg), there would remain for the snake the problem of what on earth to do with the quarts of extracted milk. How much milk can a milk snake hold? Several down-to-earth animalizers have conducted forced-feeding experiments to find out. A milk-stuffed milk snake, brimming to the chin, can hold about two teaspoonfuls.

So. Have we got to the end of this cluster of the especially whoppery snake questions? Not yet.

Is it true that snakes can't bite unless they can coil and strike? Snakes can bite in any circumstances in which they can reach the object to be bitten. The coil and strike are of course standard snake technique when there's time to arrange it; but a dangerous snake in any position is dangerous. Will a rattler always sound its rattle warningly before striking? It won't. The purpose of rattlesnakes' rattles—their evolutionary significance—is a matter considerably debated among naturalists, and unresolved. It's been guessed that rattlesnakes may have evolved on the western prairies and used their rattles to warn off bison. It's been guessed that the rattle is whirred to startle small prey into an instant's immobility, so that the rattler may strike at a stationary target. There is the possibility that the rattle evolved simply because the shape of a rattler's tail tip results in the adherence of a few fragments of old tissue each time the snake sheds its skin. Whatever the rattle's origin and significance, a rattlesnake does *not* always rattle before striking. The snake's very apt to sound its whirr when it's actually gliding away in flight; or it may lunge and strike without sounding any whirr at all.

Is a rattler's age in years the same as the number of its rattles? All of us, of course, have heard that this is so. When we carry our animalizing into a firsthand exploration of the living world of living snakes, we very shortly find out that it isn't. The number of a rattlesnake's rattles affords at best only an extremely rough means of computing the snake's age, and more often is entirely misleading. (In any case, if we make the computation at all, for what little or nothing it's worth, we ought to make it on the basis not of one year per segment but of a half year per segment.) There are a number of factors that make rattle counting an untrustworthy way for us to calculate age. An infant rattlesnake may be born— they quite often are, in fact—with two rattles. As it grows, a rattlesnake may add three or even four each year. After it has reached maturity, it may add hardly any. As a final invalidation, there is the fact that the buttons of the rattle, especially in a snake's maturity and old age, may easily break off.

Can snake venom kill a tree? Over the hill from the sprawling wild acres where I live and do my animalizing, there used to live one of those grand old back-country patriarchs whose neighbors usually call them Uncle and who are understood to be wonderfully learned in the ways of animals and the lore of the woods. Old Uncle

Charlie had seen some wonderfully exciting things in his eighty-some years. He'd seen how a fox goes fishing by artfully dangling its tail in a creek pool. He'd watched the red squirrels exterminate the gray squirrels in a territory by the ingenious device of biting off their testicles. Snakes? Why, Uncle Charlie minded like it was just yesterday the time the hoop snake come a-rollin' through his dooryard, fetched up bang against a crab-apple tree, and was so mad it stang the tree with all its might. By sundown that tree had commenced to wither, and the next morning it was leafless and dead. The evidence of the occurrence was plain to see, even now. Look—there was the dead tree right in the dooryard.

Being a naturalist wouldn't be half the fun it is if there weren't any Uncle Charlies. They really feel the magic of the outdoors, these adventurers; and if they dress things up a little in their eagerness to stir the same responsiveness to earth-excitements in their hearers . . . well, it's a much more warmhearted sort of sin than the chilly prim-lipped sins of rectitude and pride. Still, we have to learn to love the old Uncles without believing them. We've seen that there aren't any snakes with stingers. We've seen that no snakes can roll with their tails in their mouths. Also, now, snake venom can't hurt a tree.

Is it true that black snakes are the implacable enemies of rattle-snakes, so that the two can't coinhabit a territory? Can a caught snake twitch off its tail and escape to freedom to grow a new one? Is it true that the snakish eye has a hypnotic power, so that snakes are able to "charm" birds and small animals? Do poisonous snakes lose their poisoning ability if they are without water for six days? Do constrictor snakes kill people by winding around their necks and choking them? Are all water snakes poisonous? Is it a fact that water snakes have gills? We can answer these seven questions with a simple seven-part No. There is just no substance in any of the beliefs they indicate, except that most durable of substances, the magic stuff of myth.

And here, I think, we have about completed our consideration of whoppers. We have been finding out a lot of things that snakes *aren't*. We can get along, now, into investigating rather more fully what snakes' lives are like in fact. Snakes may not be able to roll like hoops or cast mesmeric spells athwart the green woods, but in the actualities of their lives they are as interesting as any others of the animal brotherhood. A bird, as we were saying a while ago, is in a real sense only a sort of reptile in feathers; and it is also the case that we ourselves, so to put it, have our share of hereditary snake blood. The creation all goes together. Nothing in it is alien, or interlopes. In animaldom we are all at home, and together.

How big do snakes get to be?

There was a generally esteemed book some years ago by an explorer who had traveled in unmapped areas of the steamy jungles of the upper Amazon. Among other remarkable adventures, he had killed an anaconda 51 feet long. The book had a badly blurred photograph (fogged, no doubt, by jungle conditions) of this colossal reptile; but as the snake was shown coiled in a pile, and might have been almost anything from a large anthill to a tangle of lianas, the plate was less than satisfactory. Unfortunately, something or other—very likely those "jungle conditions" again—prevented the giant snake's skin from being brought home. To phrase it simply, something or other always does.

We make endless jokes about the way fish grow in anglers' stories. It is as nothing compared to the way snakes grow in snake observers' stories. Nor need we ascribe this, with a sour cynicism, entirely to willful exaggeration. Snakes' sizes are very deceptive. When a 6-foot black snake slips away through the grass in its quicksilvery fashion, it looks about 10 feet long to even the coolest witness. When the snake is of some much bigger and more startling species, calculation is thrown still more completely off by the arithmetic of terror.

How big do snakes really get to be? The biggest snake on our earth is a regal or reticulated python. The longest one of these ever accurately measured was a little over 33 feet long. Give or take a foot or so, we can say that the biggest snake alive is about 35 feet long.

Though a python's the longest snake, it isn't the bulkiest. Anacondas are considerably heavier foot for foot; and as the massive anaconda is probably the second longest of all snakes, reaching somewhere between 25 and 30 feet from nose to tail tip, we need not smile too superior a smile at our Amazon explorer and his excited statistics. There is a wide difference, statistically, between 30 feet and 51; but it's all much of a muchness when the living animal comes gliding out at us from the green jungle undergrowth. A big anaconda may weigh over 500 pounds.

What's the biggest *poisonous* snake in the world? That's a king cobra. Exceptionally, cobras can be close to 20 feet long. Many have been measured at 15 and up. Rattlesnakes? The biggest diamondbacks reach about 9 feet. Here again, however, "size" involves another consideration besides length. Rattlesnakes are the heaviest poisonous snakes on our earth.

For some reason the huge size and general terribleness of big snakes are most popularly symbolized in the awful words "boa constrictor." As a matter of scientific technicality, boas are one kind of snake and constrictors are another; but even if we don't bother with this quibble the fact is that the snake we popularly call a boa constrictor (*Constrictor constrictor* to the herpetologists) is nothing like our nightmare versions of it. How big do boa constrictors get to be? At the outside, perhaps 16 feet long. Can one of them swallow a man whole? Not conceivably. A boa constrictor preys on small mammals and birds.

This is a good place to clear up an important point. Venomous snakes are dangerous. Big constricting snakes are dangerous. But we may dismiss, along with so many other popular snake-awfulnesses, the notion that any snake is *both* venomous and a constrictor. That fusion of menaces occurs nowhere in all snakedom.

Do big snakes
eat people?

If we say, "Yes," we create an unwarranted alarm. If we say, "No,"
we aren't strictly true to facts. Suppose we put it this way: Yes,
it is possible for some of the biggest snakes to engulf a small human
being, and there are a few—a very few—reliable records of the
thing's happening; but, no, big snakes aren't ordinarily eaters of
human beings, or even disposed to kill them.

How big an animal can the biggest snake swallow? It must
be a rare one of us who hasn't picked up in our childhood some
fearful tale about a great snake, in South America or the Orient,
gliding into a native village and seizing and swallowing three or
four of the inhabitants as they race around the compound. Or
perhaps the snake in the story swallows a water buffalo. That one
is perennially popular. As a boy I used to pore over a sumptuous big
book in my grandfather's library that bore the straight-faced title,
A Boy's Book of Natural History. It had a memorable full-page
illustration showing a water buffalo enwrapped in coil after coil
after coil—about 90 feet of them, I should think—of monstrous
serpent. With rolling eyes and muzzle raised in a last bellow, the
buffalo was sinking to its knees in the snake's implacable embrace;
and you could see very clearly what was going to happen in a
minute, for the snake had reared up its head and opened its mouth,
and it was a mouth that might have received not merely one
buffalo but a small herd of them.

That's the way it goes in the fanciful tales. But the real snakes of our real earth? The largest of the cold-fleshed, elongated brother creatures prowling around this planet with us can swallow a fair-sized goat or fawn, or say a wild pig weighing up to somewhere around 100 pounds. Simply as a matter of mechanics, the biggest snake under the sun couldn't engulf an animal weighing over 150 pounds or so, and that animal would have to be of extraordinarily manageable shape. The natural prey of even the most enormous pythons are relatively small animals. (By the way, just to be thoroughgoing about it, how big *is* a water buffalo? An average one stands about 5 feet high at the shoulders. From nose tip to tail root its length runs to between 9 and 10 feet. The body girth of a water buffalo that size is about 8 feet.)

A good many of our notions about the enormousness of what snakes can swallow are tied in with a wrong understanding of what a constrictor snake does to its prey. So now:

When a snake constricts its prey, does it crush it to a pulp?
It doesn't. This fracturing and mangling of a constrictor's victim belongs with that other unpleasantly vivid fancy we were mentioning a little while ago, the snake's supposed coating of the crushed victim with saliva preparatory to eating it. A constrictor doesn't crush the animal it has caught. What it does is to throw three or four coils quickly around the animal and then rapidly tighten its grip in a series of rhythmic squeezings. Rhythmic? A constricting snake responds to the breathing rhythm or heartbeat of the creature to be killed. At each exhalation or pulsing it tightens the grip of its coils in an answering pressure. What kills a constrictor's prey is not any such slow horror as the breaking of bones or bursting of flesh, but the quick process of stopped circulation and breathing. Constrictors, as a matter of fact, have an extremely subtle animal awareness of the occurrence of death in their prey. The instant the squeezing coils fail to feel the beat of life, the constrictor relaxes.

How do a poisonous snake's fangs work?

Leaving the big constrictors now for the snakes that carry venom, we find this first question easily leading the list. We have to start our answer to it by saying: It depends on the kind of snake. Don't all venomous snakes have the same fang arrangements? No.

Some snakes are back-fanged snakes. That is, their fangs are at the rear of their mouths. Other snakes have fangs in the front of their mouths, the fangs being set immovably. Finally, viperine snakes are equipped with fangs in the front of their mouths and solidly embedded in jawbone, which nevertheless can be either laid flat or erected, depending on the position of the snake's very mobile maxillary.

Probably not many of us, unless our animalizing leads us into a detailed exploration of snakedom, are likely to have much encounter with back-fanged snakes. They are largely tropical animals (including, by the way, those "flying snakes" we discussed in another section of our book), and most of them are venomous in not much more than a technical sense. Their poisonous fangs aren't hollow, but are simply enlarged back teeth with grooves along them through which venom can flow. Most of the rear-fanged snakes don't use their fangs in striking. They have a relatively weak venom, and it serves them chiefly in paralyzing frogs and similar small animals, not in the moment of the strike, but as the seized prey is worked backward toward the snake's gullet.

What ordinarily we mean by "venomous snakes" are such ones as cobras and rattlers. Now about the fangs of these:

Our ordinary harmless snakes, constituting the vast majority of our brotherly "crawly creeples," have six rows of teeth. They have four rows in their upper jaw and two rows in the lower. The teeth are small and sharp, and a couple of the upper rows stud the roof of the snake's mouth. The teeth curve inward. (We'll be speaking about this a little more shortly.) Now, what has happened in the case of snakes like cobras is that the snake's jaw has become a good deal shortened, and in the course of this process all or most of the small teeth have been lost, giving place to nothing on the maxillary bone but the big fangs. In some of these snakes the poisonous fangs are incompletely tubular—the venom-carrying groove on the fang, that is, isn't quite closed over—but in most of the ones we're likely to want to know about the fangs have become, exactly speaking, hollowed hypodermic needles.

Such fangs are formidable equipment, but they have the limitation of being stationary. They enable the snake to strike effectively only from certain angles. In viperine snakes this restriction is overcome. The fangs are retractile. The viperine snakes are by far the most generally distributed poisonous snakes of our world, and the subject of the most popular questions that come up about poisonous snakes.

What happens when one of these snakes bites? Does the snake open its mouth before it strikes? No. Old prints of rattlesnakes generally show them with their jaws agape even when still coiled; but in fact the snake's way is to complete the greater part of its thrusting lunge before it opens its mouth and throws forward its fangs into erection. When does the poison start flowing? That is synchronized with the fangs' entrance into the flesh of the struck creature. Our snake has two sacs of poison, one in each of its cheeks, and ducts from these sacs run to its fangs. In the instant the fangs strike home, the snake squeezes powerfully bunched muscles around the poison sacs and sends jets of venom spurting through its fangs.

What does snake venom look like? It's a pale yellow or almost colorless liquid, sluggish and viscous. Several especially common questions about it come up:

Is it true that venom is harmful only if it gets into our blood stream, and that we can safely swallow it? Here, as sensible animalizers, we want to exercise a nice prudence, and remember, not for the first time, that a textbook fact and a living fact aren't always exactly the same thing. It's quite true, technically and theoretically speaking, that snake venom is a harmless substance to swallow—almost as harmless, say, as the white of an egg, which innocent protein, like snake venom, would raise a deadly havoc if injected into our blood stream. The sideshow snake doctors aren't necessarily just performing a sleight of hand, then, when they toss off a phial of the stuff? No, not necessarily; but probably. Venom swallowing entails, in practice, a heavy risk. One tiny cut on our lip, one tiny abrasion anywhere throughout our whole alimentary system, and our demonstration of a superb confidence in the rightness of our animal lore may be the last demonstration we make.

Nine-tenths of horrid suppositions about snakes aren't true. It's good to get rid of morbid alarms, and come to realize that a snake is just another animal brother of ours going its reasonable way on the same good earth under the same good sun. But snake venom wants respecting. A clear-minded wariness when we're dealing with poisonous snakes is just good animal sense, not cowardice; and the better we get to know snakes the less likely is our familiarity to breed the sort of contempt that leads to silly bravadoes. If we keep our earth-wits about us as we go animalizing around this garden of the creation, are we likely to get into trouble with snake poison? There is small chance of it. Snakes and ourselves can comfortably coinhabit the same woods and fields. But if we do get into snake trouble, is it serious trouble? Very.

Is the venom of all poisonous snakes alike? No, it isn't. Putting it broadly, there are two kinds: neurotoxins and hemorrhagins. As the names make plain enough, poisons of the first kind attack the nervous system and poisons of the second kind attack the circulatory system, causing internal hemorrhages. Such snakes as cobras and mambas carry neurotoxic venom. Viperine snakes carry hemorrhagic. The latter venom is likely to cause the greater pain and the more evident local symptoms; but on the other hand neurotoxins are deadlier in their speed. How fast may a cobra bite or a mamba bite kill a man? Death sometimes occurs within a minute. What happens is that the neurotoxin almost instantly paralyzes the victim's sympathetic nervous centers; and it's our sympathetic nervous system that controls breathing. Viperine snakes, as we were seeing, are much more generally distributed than the snakes that can sometimes cause death this quickly. If we're bitten by a rattler or copperhead or cottonmouth moccasin, or any of the other viperine snakes that are the ones we're likeliest to encounter, we get immediate local pain, swelling, ugly discoloration, and very possibly a variety of other disturbing manifestations. But the progress of the poisoning is generally very, very, gradual, taking many hours before reaching its maximum. And here, surely, we'd better bring up the anxious question:

What's the best treatment for snake bite?

When we have consulted one "snake book," or listened to one old backwoodsman, we find out that treatment for snake bite is a simple matter. There are dozens of long-used folk remedies. There are half a dozen more scientific procedures. But what we find out, if our animalizing takes us into a long-enough experience with snake-bite cases, is that few of these treatments are in fact of high effectiveness and that a great many of them—including all the ones the old backwoodsman told us about—range from useless to worse than the snake bite.

There is a perfected antivenin, isn't there? Well, there is antivenin; and it has saved a good many lives; but it doesn't always save them and sometimes it ends them. There is no way of knowing how much venom a snake has injected with its bite. Sometimes it injects a massive lot, sometimes a very little. Calculation of antivenin dosage is difficult and dangerous. An overdose can kill the recipient as effectively as any snake bite. Further, though it seldom seems to bob up in the literature about antivenin, there is the fact that a great many people "react unfavorably," as the suave phrase has it, to its administration. The unfavorableness takes the form of serum-sickness or death. Antivenin, let's be clear about it, is of important value. We're not to underestimate its usefulness. There are often circumstances in which it is the only recourse. But it's a good idea for us to get rid of any notion that it's an easy treatment, or an invariably sure one, or one without real dangers.

How about a tourniquet? A tourniquet's not a bad idea, provided the snake bite's site makes it feasible, and provided we don't tie it too tight, and provided we remember to loosen it at suitable intervals, and provided we don't so bind it that it either induces gangrene or brings about our death from shock when it's released. In short, this isn't a measure to be undertaken light-mindedly either.

Incising the wound? Using suction on it? These are about the best and least risky things we can do. But if we'd be snake-wise, we mustn't put too serene a reliance even on these. Making a small sharp X-cut at the site of our snake bite may help some of the venom to be drawn off, along with our gushing blood; but if bloodletting greatly upsets us, or if we botch the job and make a nasty wound, or, especially, if our cutting tool isn't absolutely sterile, we can easily put ourselves into a worse fix than if we hadn't cut at all. As for the suction . . . well, if it's mouth suction we run the same risk we were talking about in connection with venom swallowing. And whatever kind of suction it is, it must operate against this difficulty: Snake venoms mix into our body fluids almost instantly, and once they have mixed they can't be separated again by suction or anything else.

Are big draughts of whisky helpful in counteracting snake bite? They are worse than worthless. They merely burden us with one toxicity on top of another. Will it do any good to cut a chicken in half and clap its body over the bite? It will furnish a compress of sorts; nothing else. How about putting a pinch of gunpowder over the bite and igniting it? Doesn't that "cauterize" the wound? We could put it that way, I suppose. In effect, it just doubles the danger and compounds the pain. All the folk treatments turn out to be no help to us . . . and so does what a great many texts have recommended as a "scientific" treatment: putting crystals of permanganate of potassium in the incision made at the bite site.

Potassium permanganate affects only the small amount of superficial venom with which it comes in immediate contact, and in the course of rendering that inconsequential service it destroys body tissue appallingly.

By now, perhaps, it begins to sound a little hopeless. What *are* we to do if a rattler or copperhead sinks its fangs into us . . . ? Just sit quietly on a stump with our hands folded and attune our spirits to the peace of the earth scent and the rustle of the leaves? Put that way it sounds pretty silly; but as a matter of fact it's just about the right answer.

Incising and suction are both desirable measures for us to take, with an understanding of their possible drawbacks and limitations; but the primary wisdom of all snake-bite wisdoms—the most powerful reinforcement we can have for any treatment we use— lies simply in our keeping reasonably calm and quiet. Panic can set our circulation pumping disastrously. If we fly into a hysteria and run for help, we maximize a danger into a catastrophe. A snake-bitten man in the remote woods who keeps his composure, even though he may get no treatment beyond what he can do for himself in matter-of-factly opening up the bite and encouraging its drainage, is in small danger compared to what he would incur if he rushed away on a mile sprint, even though every known medical facility might await him at the end of the run. It's no very novel philosophical discovery that fear has a way of bringing about evil things, as faith has a way of materializing good. But if we go animalizing around the outdoors we're continually encountering particularly down-to-earth instances of the way this works. If we start up a cliff with a panicky misgiving about falling, there's a first-rate chance that we'll fall. If we climb with a serene confidence, we may often look back, from the top, at a performance that was "impossible." Do we have a terrified expectation that the bees will sting us? They probably will. Bees are sensitive to the quality of fear, and it excites and arouses them. But if we go among them tranquilly, knowing them as just brother beings of ours, as fellow lives with which we may live on terms of mutual respect in this multifariously thronged world that is the given homeland for both of us . . . why, that's very much the sort of brothers they generally turn out to be.

This book of ours is to answer questions about animals; it isn't supposed to be a book of philosophy, and certainly not a book of faith healing. Still, there *is* a helping and healing in faith; and it's relevant to the everyday experience of every animalizer. That's a major reason why questions about venomous snakes and their poison have been answered at such length in these recent pages, even at the risk of our seeming to give to venomous snakes a much bigger role than they in fact play in snakedom as a whole. Get to know snakes well enough so that we lose some of our nightmare notions and dispel some of the hysteria in our aversion, and we have done something practical against the extremely remote and unlikely day when we may be bitten. Does dried venom keep its venomousness? That's true; it keeps it almost indefinitely. Are there snakes that can spit their venom? That's true. Spitting cobras can eject their venom in a fine spray for as far as 10 or 15 feet. Hardly any of us are likely to meet these snakes; still, they do exist. Do venomous snakes ever attack without provocation? Very, very rarely; but we need to be aware of the fact that it can happen. Over against disquieting facts like these, however, there are all sorts of reassurances to be set. It's high time for us to be leaving poisonous snakes, to consider a few other questions about the life-ways of the general snake brotherhood; but we may wisely do our concluding on some notes of cheerfulness.

If a snake bites us, and we notice the wound shows only two punctures, does that necessarily mean the snake was poisonous? By no means. The nip of a harmless snake often leaves only a couple of spaced toothmarks. (Every year a certain number of people die from having been bitten by snakes that turn out not to have been venomous. They die of the shock of terror. The power of mind over matter, spirit over flesh, is no mysticism. It has been proved time and again.) If a rattlesnake or copperhead should bite us and we should get *no* treatment—if we can't even open the wound, can't even employ suction—are we certain to die? We're not under any such certain doom at all. The bites of copperheads and the smaller rattlers, even when untreated, are not usually fatal if we are in good health and spirits. Are most poisonous snakes eager to strike at us? They are very reluctant to do so. Snakes, by and large, are a peaceable brotherhood. The overwhelming majority of snake bites result from snakes' having been stepped on or otherwise molested. Finally, as a source for sensible faith and a warrant for reasonable serenity: Is there a cozier and more reassuring word in our language than "home"? There hardly is. But for every one of us killed by snake bite, there are several hundred killed each year by accidents befalling us while we're staying safely at home.

Now on to remaining questions about snake ways.

Do snakes lay eggs?

Some do; some don't. There are slightly more of the kinds that do. Even snakes that bear living young aren't strictly viviparous, though that's the imposing technical adjective I was once upon a time taught must be applied to them. Exactly speaking, these snakes are ovoviviparous. Their young ones are born encased in thin membrane from which they very shortly wriggle free.

Oviparous snakes—the truly egg-laying ones—lay eggs not altogether unlike the eggs of a bird. The mother snake seeks out some sun-warmed place in the summer soil, or perhaps some sheltered spot like a hollow in an old log, deposits her clutch, and then goes on her way. Doesn't she look after her eggs? Not ordinarily, no. A few snakes do stay coiled around their eggs until they hatch; most ignore them entirely. What hatches snake eggs, of course, can't be any warmth from the parental body. It's just time and the sun.

Are snake eggs hard-shelled? Not as birds' are. Rather, they're leathery-rubbery. (If we care to try dropping a fresh snake egg, we find that it bounces.) And their size? That depends, curiously enough, on how far they have progressed toward hatching. A snake egg, after it has been laid, grows. Sometimes it grows by as much as a third or more before the snakelet comes out.

How does the baby snake get out of the egg? Just like a baby bird. That is, it has an egg tooth in its upper jaw with which it rips and pries its way out. In the course of the little snake's first week or two of free life this infant tool, like a nestling bird's, disappears.

There's a very common question that is particularly important for us to bring up here. How soon do baby poisonous snakes begin to be poisonous? A baby poisonous snake is equipped with venom from the instant of its birth. Further, it's born with a ready equipment of snake instinct, snake impulse, a hereditary instruction in its reptilian psyche. A brand-new little baby snake will coil and strike.

How does a snake shed its skin?

By an easy analogy from the skin sheddings of our familiar insects, there arises a common supposition that a snake's skin splits lengthwise, when it comes time for the snake to cast it off, and that the snake in its new skin creeps out of this long fissure rather as an adult cicada creeps out from its split pupal husk. But this isn't what happens.

As a snake grows, it has to discard its limitedly elastic skin quite often—anywhere from twice a year to as much as four or five times in one summer. When the time comes for a shedding, the old skin to be discarded takes on a milky look and the whole snake appears dulled, even its eyes. (But skin doesn't cover its *eyes*, does it? Yes. A snake has a protective transparent eye cap of skin forming part of the integument that covers all the rest of it. Snakes don't have any eyelids. Hence the "unwinking stare" that figures so balefully in snake yarns. Even when it's asleep, a snake's eyes are wide open.) Presently the snake begins rubbing its chin against a stone or a rough bit of bark or the like, until it rubs a break in the skin there. Gradually it works its entire head free. Then, catching the skin against whatever rough surface it is using, it pushes forward and pulls off the whole skin backward, inside out.

Is a snake blind during the period just preceding its skin shedding? No; but it does see very imperfectly, its vision being reduced to something like our own outlook when we peer through a fogged or frosted windowpane.

Do snakes have keen senses?

We have already spoken about snakes' tongues, and what reptilian knowings may come to a snake as it flickers out its forked instrument of inquiry and draws it back into its mouth again. Also, we were talking a while ago about snakes' earlessness, and their probable inhabitation of a world of silence. Now how about the rest of their sensory adventure?

Visually, a snake's world is a vivid one, but a little one. Our snake sees objects near it with sharp clarity, and can focus its eyes with nice adjustment on moving prey. But as far as we can tell, the snake doesn't see distant things. Or at any rate, to put it with due caution, the snake doesn't perceive them in the sense of a "seeing" that finds the seen meaningful.

Taste? Our snake doesn't experience that; at least not as "taste" strictly defined, meaning perception by taste buds. Even in ourselves, however, what we informally mean by "taste" is very largely a matter of scent; and of that sort of smell-taste our snake has lively experience. When a rattler or copperhead has struck successfully at a fair-sized animal, the animal may manage to get away a considerable distance through the woods or meadow before the effects of the venom overtake it. That doesn't mean that the prey is lost to the snake. The snake can follow the trail perfectly, by scent.

Perhaps the most specialized sensing in many snakes, and the most difficult snake experience for us to share imaginatively, is a subtle sense of temperature. The temperature of your or my surroundings has to vary several degrees before we notice a change. But any pit viper—meaning snakes, including copperheads and rattlers, that have little indentations or pits on their faces—has a temperature awareness immeasurably subtler. The organs of its knowing are the pits. The sensitivity of these tells the snake that warm-blooded prey is in the neighborhood even when the snake can neither see nor smell it.

Some experimenters of the American Museum of Natural History once subjected pit vipers to a long series of carefully controlled tests of their temperature discrimination. They found out exactly how sensitive these snakes' temperature sensitivity really is. A snake will strike at the warmer of two proffered targets. It turned out in the experiments that the snake can still tell which target is warmer when the temperature difference between the two is narrowed to less than 0.2 °C. Blindfolded, its nostrils closed, a pit viper can detect a mouse's body, by its heat, at distances at which a delicate scientific thermometer fails to record a trace of the radiated warmth.

In our brother snake, lazing away on the old stone wall, there is but small and sluggish stir of mind. But even in this cold creature, after its fashion, there is experience of the blaze of being.

Does a snake have any means of defense except biting?

Yes. Snakes have the ability to loose a stench. Way back—when I was first becoming interested in snakes, long before I had that living laboratory of country acreage on which in later years I have been able to go about inquisitively prodding the water snakes in the creek, dislodging the black snakes from their sunning place in the old spring house, and committing an endless variety of such animalizing impertinences to my heart's content—I used to be puzzled by the very varying descriptions of snake smell I came across. Sometimes it was called hideously sickening. Sometimes it was called moderately unpleasant. Now and then some writer (a snake-daft herpetologist, of course) would say that it was an agreeable aroma. (Enthusiasts of rattlesnakes are fond of insisting that an irritated rattler smells like sun-warmed cucumbers.) Eventually I found out that what a snake's stench smells like depends not so much on the snake as on the spirit of the smeller. If we have a sick fear of snakes, they smell sickening. If we feel toward them a merely wary respect and have accepted them, with all their queernesses, as brothers, they just smell comradely but queer . . . as do, say, fox urine or the fleshy green spathes of skunk cabbage along the spring brook. If we're really wholeheartedly in fellowship with snakes, I suppose, even the stench of their angry voidings is delightful.

An angry or frightened snake makes its stench by suddenly voiding its excrement, doesn't it? No. That misconception just helps along our disposition to find the musky-sweet odor revolting. A snake has a special pair of scent glands under the base of its tail. They have nothing to do with the snake's excretory processes, any more than does the sulphide-spraying apparatus of a skunk.

How can a snake eat things that look too big for it to swallow?

The very first time we see a snake in predatory action—a common garter snake, for instance, catching a frog—this question is sure to come into our minds. We were discovering some pages ago that even the biggest snakes can't swallow such colossal prey as our lurid snake myths would have it; but all the same, snakes regularly do engulf animals that are obviously much too big for them. Here is our garter snake, no bigger around than our finger, with a great fat frog in its jaws. How is it going to manage it?

Snake teeth, as we found, are sharp, numerous and, most significantly, all curved inward. This gives the snake an almost unbreakable grip, and tends to work backward whatever it grips and chews. Now furthermore: A snake can unhinge its upper and lower jaws, and it can work them independently. Forcing the disconnected jaws cavernously agape, the snake throws forward one jawbone, hooks into the victim, and pulls it inward, the recurving teeth of the other jaw offering no opposition. Then it disengages that jaw, clamps in the teeth of the other one, and pulls *that* jawbone inward. It pulls in its prey, if you like, by a series of alternating hitches.

A snake's skin has elasticity. Its ribs are very mobile. All its internal organs are capable of being pushed around to an extraordinary degree. Put all these considerations together and we find our garter snake able to engulf (though it may take it an hour or two) a fat frog that's three times its own diameter. Is it true that a snake sometimes swallows another snake longer than itself? Yes, that can happen.

We are led into our final snake question, one of the half-dozen commonest of all animal questions in the world:

Do snakes swallow their young to protect them from danger?

They almost certainly do not. We entirely retain the right spirit for animalizing, however, only as long as we retain in our answer the small and powerful word "almost."

Many herpetologists don't bother with it. They say, simply, no . . . this one-word answer being supplemented with nothing unless perhaps a harrumphing snort. And it does look as though this answer, if not the spirit of it, is pretty surely the right one. An impressive lot of good reasons, all but compelling, can be put forth to show the wild unlikeliness of snakes' doing any such thing as this.

In the first place, a snake is virtually without maternal instinct. She doesn't look after her babies. If she is an egg-laying snake, she doesn't usually even stay with the eggs until they hatch. In the second place, a snake has extremely powerful digestive juices. It can digest even the teeth of the prey it swallows. A baby snake that darted into its mother's gullet for safety would find itself in a singularly deadly sanctuary. In the third place, no snake scientist or snake keeper or trained snake watcher of whatever sort has ever seen the incident occur among the charges under his watchful care; and there have of course been thousands, tens of thousands, of snakes kept under such intimate observation. Next, there are considerations of another kind. Many snakes, when killed, are of course females with a brood of living youngsters inside them. When a host of little snakes are seen to emerge from such a victim, it's the most natural thing in the world, if we don't know about snakes, to suppose that the little snakes had been swallowed; and from that supposition it's a tiny step to persuading ourselves that in fact we saw the swallowing. Or again: Some snakes eat other smaller snakes. When such a snake-eating snake is disturbed at its dining, it's very likely to disgorge its dinner. (All snakes have a nervous readiness to eject what they're eating if anything comes along to trouble them.) It's the most natural thing in the world, if we don't know about snakes, to suppose that the small snake issuing from the big one's mouth is a baby being released by its mother from safekeeping. Finally: Some snakes, such as moccasins, have a habit of opening their jaws wide and keeping them open for long periods, while the snake is just lazing away, say, on a log in the sun. Mix all the other misleading evidences with this one, and behold, here is a mother snake holding her mouth open in readiness for her youngsters to pop into it if a danger should threaten.

Does a mother snake swallow her young to protect them? She almost certainly never does. True, Rattlesnake Pete once saw it happen . . . but then it was Rattlesnake Pete who also once saw the whip snake whipping its victim to death. True, Grandpa once saw it happen, and Grandpa is an honest man . . . but he saw it happen, we find out, when he was a lad of nine, and today he is ninety-one. True, the fellow at the next farm down the lane thinks he saw the thing happen just last week . . . but his understanding of snakes, it turns out, is such that he believes them to be a land phase of eels and is persuaded that both kinds of animals come into being from horsehairs left in water.

Do mother snakes swallow their young? It's almost surely just another fantasticality. But the wider and longer our experience the less likely we shall be to let the "surely" wholly override the "almost." Grandpa, it's true, is very old these days. But we who are naturalists and animalizers don't commit the final and fatal fault when we pay perhaps a little more courteous attention to an old gaffer than his narrative strictly deserves. We don't commit it even when in an absent-minded moment we confuse the snake we ought to call *Lampropeltis triangulum triangulum* with the one we ought to call *Lampropeltis triangulum syspila*. When we commit the really final and fatal fault—when we let ourselves be seduced into the ultimate preposterousness—is when we get to believing we know all about animals.

Fish

From the southeastern to the southwestern boundary of those
hundred-and-some acres of fields, swamp, and woods that make up
the world in which I do my day-to-day animalizings, there me-
anders a small stream. For part of its length it is a swamp-stream,
running diffusely through an area of cattails and alders. That's
where the first spring peepers start their calling, and the first male
red-winged blackbirds come in March, swaying on the reeds and
singing their creakly-croakly songs. For another part of its length,
the brook is a trout brook, running fast and clear over a stony
bottom. Elsewhere it's a heron brook, a water-snake brook, and a
muskrat brook.

Naturally enough, a great many hundreds, probably thousands,
of my animalizing hours have been spent in prowling along this
brook. I go there in the early mornings, in spring thaw-time, to see
what the red-wings are up to. I go often at midnight, for a look
at how the muskrats disport themselves, diving and cavorting in
their deep pool, under the glimmering light of the moon. I go to
see what the herons are catching, and what story the deer tracks
may tell in a fresh February snow, and whether the otters have been
frolicking on their otter slide.

(Query: It's really true, then, that otters make shoot-the-chutes,
and spend hours in delighted sliding on them, like so many children

having a coasting frolic? Oh, yes, it's quite true. Nearly all animals play. It's one of the most tonic truths we find out about this green garden of our earth, when we get to looking intimately into the lives around us. Bears love to go sliding and tumbling downhill. Deer play what amount to games of tag. Birds exuberate in a hundred kinds of group fun, and a solitary fox or coon will entertain itself by the hour pawing and tossing just a twig or a clump of moss. A spirit of play runs all through animaldom. Why not? It's a pretty grand thing to be alive on this earth, with subtle senses all fresh and alert to it, and an equipment of good powers for the exercising, and the thrust and drive of livingness in us, urging us to eager participance. We human beings, of course, can murk all that, and turn the life adventure dull and dismal, by what we do with our minds. But the mind of animaldom, as we've been seeing in a dozen ways, stops short of power to bring into the Now those shadows of misgiving that can attend self-consciousness. The sun's up, and the water's fine, and the sliding's capital today . . . and what more natural, for our exuberant brother, an otter, than to kick up its furry paws?)

At any rate, there are plenty of good reasons for a writer-naturalist like me to go frequenting the brook. I never hesitate to use them, and solemnly. Largely they're a fraud.

I go to the brook, more times than not, actually for the same reason that impels all of us to go to such places. I go there because the small boy or girl who lives inside all of us—the primitive Original, the inveterate Adamite idler and wonderer—loves nothing better than to sit beside a brook pool and stare into it and contemplate fish. We use all sorts of excuses for it. We say we're fishermen. We say we're thinking up a new chapter of a book, or composing a sonata, or meditating upon the Trinity . . . anything will do. What we're doing is just peering into the hypnotic thing that is flowing water, and speculating upon the soothing thing that is a fish.

What must it be like to be that minnow down there, resting on the gravelly bottom and gently beating its filmy fins? I wonder now: Can a fish hear anything, or is it all a perpetual silence in that strange cool world among the water weeds? Do fish see colors? Gently, gently, we go on with our brookside wonderings. . . . Would a fish, now, be needing to drink? . . . and do fish perhaps ever make a noise? . . . and what in the world can the world *look* like to these underwater sharers of the life experience with us? And now all of a sudden a whole brookside afternoon has somehow been dreamed away, and we're strangely and wonderfully refreshed by a long journey outside ourselves, and we're heading for home with our preposterous yarn about having been on a fishing trip or having been working on a book.

Once upon a time, in the very early hours, so to speak, of the creation, we were fish. We still have vestigial gill slits in our necks, just as we still bend a stump of animal tail under us every time we sit down. The brotherhood of the creation (how many thousand times do we find it out, as we go animalizing?) is indeed all an entity. Even now when we're Man, our special and unique self, the self-consciously rational and meditative one that can contemplate all the other brother animals and be their student and custodian, there is still a special sorcery for us in the old, old underwater world and those fish-brothers of ours that have never left it. A good many of us may do our first rapt animalizings when we press our noses, as children, against the magic glass of an aquarium; and a good many of us may still be finding one of our serenest pleasures, years and years later, in staring deep into the brook-pool world of minnow and pickerel.

And now it's time to be bringing up the commonest questions about the finned brother animals that inhabit that dim, strangely remote, strangely enchanting world of underwater. When the darkness comes, do fish go to sleep? How big do fish get to be? How little are the littlest? Every now and then, as we stare lazily into the world of pool or pond, we see a fish make its way to the surface and spend a few minutes there. Why does it do that?

Let's see about these things:

Can fish hear?

Yes. Fishermen have always supposed so, of course, and are careful to keep as quiet as possible so that the fish won't hear them. But then there are plenty of fishermen who are sure, too, that carp live five or ten centuries and that eels are a kind of snake; and we don't have to go very far in our animalizings before we discover that those things aren't so at all. Fish, after all, don't have any ears, do they?

No, fish don't have any external ears. They don't have any middle ear, either. But a fish does have an inner ear, inside its head, and it's not greatly unlike our own inner ear. The snail-shell-whorled structure in our inner ear that's called the cochlea is missing in a fish's inner ear, but most of the rest of the apparatus is there. It hasn't been possible, naturally, to test one by one all the 15,000 or more sorts of fish that throng the waters of this earth; but a number of experiment-minded animalizers have tested enough minnows, catfish, and several other sorts of fish to make it certain that their underwater world isn't experienced in anything like a silence. A catfish can hear almost as many vibrations a second as we can. The minnow in our brook not only can hear up to about 7,000 vibrations a second, but is able to distinguish between the sounds it hears with a subtlety that reminds us of the hearing niceties we were talking about when we were inquiring into the sensory world of mammals. A minnow can distinguish half tones.

A snake, as we said a while ago, is as "deaf as an adder" as far as ordinary ear hearing is concerned, but has a delicate awareness of ground vibrations and also, just possibly, may do some "hearing," in a way, when it thrusts out its flickering forked tongue. Not only are an animal's special senses vividly keen; we can't properly separate them into sensory "compartments," as we have a way of doing when we speak of our own sight, touch, taste, smell, and hearing. Taste, even in ourselves, is fused with smell. We orient ourselves, in a strange new set of circumstances, not by an orderly investigation with separated faculties of touch, sight, hearing, and so on, but rather by a kind of over-all sensory percipience, a totality of feeling, in which, as it were, we touch-hear, taste-see, and smell-feel, and in which also there are several other sorts of sensings and deep awarenesses which interact and co-inform us: the sense of balance, the sense of gravitational pull, the sense of temperature, and so on. In the vivid sensory world of the animals, this blending and fusion of knowings makes up a whole-knowing in which, even more than in ourselves, sense is not readily to be separated from sense. As we've seen, an ant's topochemical sense is feel and taste (at least) in one sensory cognition. Now a fish, we say, hears with its inner ear. So it does. But *only* with its inner ear? No. What it hears ear-wise is supplemented by what it hears skin-wise. Below a certain vibration rate, our minnow "hears" with its sensitive and alert flesh.

Does a fish see colors?

It does. Whether it sees them quite as you and I see them, of course, must go on remaining a secret until the last day. We can't get completely inside any brother animal that lives; we can't *be* it, by however vigorous and scrupulously instructed an act of imaginative projection. But we find out, if we try some simple tests on our brookside afternoons, that a trout or dace can distinguish, at least among strong, simple colors, as readily as we can ourselves. The fish world isn't silence, nor is it the color monotone of the mammals.

How big do fish get to be?

Were whales fish, our answer would of course be easy and immediate; but we've learned that they aren't. The largest of fish, however, are sufficiently impressive in their own enormousness.

They are jumbo sharks, generally called whale sharks. Whale sharks get to be 45 or 50 feet long, and may have a weight of some 27,000 pounds. In a way, really, some other big fish are likely to strike us as even more colossal, though in fact they are smaller. What makes them seem stunningly immense is that they appear in fresh water. In the great deeps of the sea, somehow, it isn't astonishing to find monsters; but a monster in a lake or river. . . . There are enormous Russian sturgeons that grow to be more than 25 feet long and weigh well over 3,000 pounds.

What's the littlest of all fish?

This is a goby that's been found (not very often, by the way) in some lakes in the Philippines. It's almost transparent, and a single-file line-up of four gobies would barely span an inch. But this infinitesimal goby is a true fish, for all that, backbone and all.

Do all fish lay eggs?

No. It's true that most of the common fish that may enlist our earliest interest in underwater animalizings do lay eggs; and fish eggs can be fantastic in their numbers. (How many eggs may we find in a common perch? A comfortable quarter of a million. A fair-sized cod roe? That holds about seven million eggs. A salmon, if we use a rough and ready calculation that's fairly serviceable, yields about a thousand eggs for every pound of its body weight.) But there are also a good many fish that are ovoviviparous—that is to say, their eggs break open and the youngsters hatch before the egg leaves the mother's body—and there are quite a few, too, that are really viviparous. The baby forms and develops inside the mother fish's body, and it's born very much after the fashion (speaking conversationally, of course, not with scientific technicality) of a fox cub or an infant squirrel. Some common minnows bear living babies in this way—as I found out to my overwhelming astonishment one morning when I was an aquarist of ten or twelve or so, wasting in those days almost as many happy hours staring

into the underwater world as I continue to squander thirty years
later. So do guppies.

Do fish look after their youngsters? No more so, by and large,
than snakes or insects do. Many fish have elaborate courting
rituals. Many, though not all of them, engage in sexual embrace.
(An interjection here: We were saying, when we were talking
about animals' sexuality in general, that nearly all animals engage
in specifically sexual relationships, male lying with female, sperm
fertilizing egg, and so on. Now that we're talking of fish, we need
to make something of a qualification. Among some kinds of fish
the sexual contact of male and female is very casual and slight.
The female simply looses her cells, the male simply looses his, and
the commingling of the two, in fertilization, is left to the accidents
of nearness and water current.) Many fish prepare an area of the
stream bottom or pond mud to receive their eggs, and quite a lot
of fish make nests of one sort and another and show a variety of
solicitudes in guarding the eggs until they hatch. But when a baby
fish emerges into life, it's already fully, so to speak, in its fishhood.
It is ready to be an individual animal, without training. A few fish
guard their infants for a while. Most ignore the small fry altogether.

How long does it take fish eggs to hatch? That varies tremendously. An ordinary brook trout? Say three or four months. But
a black bass? From fertilizing to hatching spans only about ten
days. For the eggs of striped bass, a scant forty-eight hours may
contain the whole process. Fish eggs, after all, aren't steadily
warmed and incubated, as a bird's are. The growth of cold-blooded
fish babies in their egg-capsules is speeded or slowed by variations
in the water temperature. That same variable factor influences
fishes' growth all their lives. (*All* their lives? Surely when a fish
reaches maturity it stops growing? As a matter of fact, No. From
birth to death a fish goes right on growing. Not, in old age, at the
same speed as when it's a youngster, of course, but the growing
never ends.)

Is it true that among some fish the fathers rather than the mothers do the nest building and also guard the eggs? That's quite true. It's a fairly common pattern in fish life; and the activities of some male fish are astonishing. Take, for instance, sea horses. Like a mother kangaroo, a male sea horse has an abdominal pouch, and in this the female deposits her 200-odd eggs. The entrance is then sealed with a sticky secretion. For the next forty-five days or so the father sea horse is a traveling incubator. When the young are due to emerge, he twists his tail around a sea fern, or similar support, sways back and forth with convulsive movements, forces the pouch open, and finally ends his "pregnancy" by expelling his tiny youngsters in swarms. Or consider some marine catfish: The male gathers the eggs in his mouth and carries them there for something like two months until they hatch. Or suppose we have a look at common fresh-water sticklebacks. These are among the most popular subjects of fish questions, and they are a fish we may encounter even if our underwater animalizing is only of the most close-to-home sort. We may find sticklebacks (along with herons, muskrats, and a beautiful lot of sunshine and idleness) in easy brook excursions.

A male stickleback nips off the leaves of the slender water weeds and builds of them a barrel-shaped nest, leaving two holes for doors, glueing the structure together with a sticky secretion from his skin. Having completed his nest, he goes forth to find and attract a mate. Coaxing and caressing, he persuades her to enter the house and lay her eggs, after which she glides away again. The male remains to deposit milt upon her eggs. There must be a continual flow of water over the stickleback's eggs if they are to be effectively fertilized and hatched. The male stickleback has provided for that. In building the nest he has placed the two doors in line with the direction of the current, so that water runs constantly over the eggs.

Intelligent foresight? Planning? No, not at the fish level in the development of consciousness. This is our familiar flesh wisdom, race wisdom, instinct wisdom, about which we've had so much to say in our animalizings. This isn't aware thinking, but mind below mind. It's none the less a significant performance for us to watch, in the cool, flowing underwater world where the sunlight dapples the shallows. It's as good a reason as any for taking us out along the brook.

Since fish have gills for underwater breathing, why do they seem now and then to "come up for air"?

What looks like "coming up for air" turns out, when we get to know fish life with some intimacy, to be precisely that. Whether an animal breathes with mammalian lungs, through insect spiracles, or by means of the gills of the underwater beings, what it needs is oxygen. And oxygen can become scarce in the underwater world just as easily as in an air-area where there are a lot of people breathing. A too-dense populace of fish can exhaust the underwater oxygen; too-big fish in a too-small body of water can exhaust it. Whenever the deeper water levels become fouled for whatever reason, a fish glides up to the top to refresh its oxygen supply. This leads us into perhaps the most popular of all fish questions.

Can a fish drown?

We're involved here in a matter of definition, like the one in our question about whether there are any birds that can fly under water. As flying, by strict definition, means passage through air, so drowning, strictly, means suffocation by the mere fact of submersion in liquid. Fish, obviously, are habitually submerged and don't drown. However, if we relax our definition a little, and are willing to let drowning mean suffocation by special circumstances connected with submersion, why then we answer, "Yes, fish do sometimes drown." Fish suffocate whenever the oxygen supply in water dwindles below what they need to breathe and they can't get enough to supplement it. In winter, fish sometimes suffocate by myriads because of thick ice over the water. When, in a drought, numbers of fish are stranded together in a very small pool, they may suffocate. If a fish, as may occasionally happen, gets wedged between stones or tangled in the water vegetations in such a way that its gill-workings are obstructed, that too may make it suffocate, or, if we like, drown. When *I* use a word, said Humpty Dumpty, it means what I choose it to mean.

Do fish ever make a noise?

Lots of fish do. The "silence of the deep" is a concept that impresses itself early upon most of us, and no doubt it will go on forever being popular in a literary way. The deeps, however, aren't silent; nor are the shallows of the little creek pool or tide pool where we go for an afternoon of good idleness and creaturely restoration. Our underwater brother animals, like the others, make a variety of musics and comments. Some of them purr, some make boomings and whistlings, many are drummers. It is an uncommon fish that doesn't at least grunt.

Most fish possess an important organ called an air bladder. (We might have said *all* fish do, but for some awkward sharks and rays. They have a special status as not-quite-true-bony fish, and they don't have any air bladders.) Naturalists used to suppose that a fish's air bladder served the animal principally in adjusting its specific gravity as it ascended or descended in the water. It's true that fish do inflate and deflate their air bladders in accommodation to changes of pressure, though the performance doesn't work quite the way we used to think it did. The mechanics of the thing are rather complicated; we needn't go into them here. But we do need to know that our fish's air bladder is involved in a wider range of function.

For one thing, it's a hearing amplifier. We were finding out a few pages ago how acutely some fish can hear. What happens, in many of the acutest hearers, is that the fish's air bladder acts as a kind of resonance box transmitting vibrations to the fish's ear. Again, air bladders serve as supplementary breathing equipment. When the water has become stale and oxygen-exhausted, fish rise to the surface, as we were seeing, and swallow "outside" air to give them enough oxygen to keep alive. In the case of a good many fish, outer air may be taken direct from gullet into air bladder, in a return to the gill-less kind of breathing, way back in the morning of the creation, when fish breathed air just into simple respiratory sacs. Nowadays fish have gills and we have mammalian lungs; but when we're foetal we still show a gill slit in our necks, and when a fish is hard-pressed it may suck air into its air bladder as we do into our lungs. "Brotherhood," do we keep saying? Turn any stone, go into any woods or waters, and we find it.

With their air bladders fish make all sorts of astonishing sounds. Male weakfish tauten and vibrate their air bladders to make so loud a noise that we can hear it in our own outer world of air even when a weakfish is 10 fathoms below. "Drumfish" is the name most informal animalizers give to these animals, and it's a good one. The fish's noise does sound very much like the distant muffled pounding of a drum. Big Mediterranean drumfish not only drum but whistle and growl. The fish called "sirens" make a tinkly kind of music. The ones called "dog's-tongues" make a kind of twanging. Some fish chatter by grating their teeth, much as a woodchuck does when it whickers down inside its burrow under the meadow when we pass by. A company of big horse mackerel can utter a squealy grunting like so many pigs.

It's not a world of silence, down under the water. Even the striped dace in my creek, after their small plup-plupping fashion, have often turned out to be joining in the chorus of animaldom.

How can fish jump up big waterfalls?

This is a great wonder, when first we hear about it. It dissipates as we get to know fish better. They can't.

The biggest vertical leap any fish can make is not much more than perhaps 5 or 6 feet. The "waterfalls" that fish ascend are mostly very gradually slanted cascades and rapids, with plenty of whirlpools and back eddies.

But don't salmon sometimes jump up vertical waterfalls 15 or 20 feet high? Not exactly. They do sometimes get up them; but it's not by jumping. What it is, really, is a vigorous jumping take-off followed by swimming. A big fish can swim powerfully against a current; and with the momentum of a jump for a starter (not straight; always at a broad angle), a salmon can flail and beat its way for a considerable distance.

But what are we to make of the fish that swim up Niagara Falls? Almost every one of us must have heard that fish do that. Don't they? No. We may cherish as tightly as we please the astonishing thought that some fish can climb trees, for there are some Oriental perch that really can do that. But swimming up Niagara Falls? No.

This is probably the place to get ourselves set straight about a very common matter concerning the way a fish swims:

Does a fish propel itself with its fins?

Perhaps because of the way some other kinds of animals swim, or perhaps because it comes naturally to us to think of our human way of paddling or rowing a boat, the impression that fish swim this way is almost universal among us. But we lose it as soon as our animalizing extends to spending even one quiet hour watching a living fish in action. A fish's instrument of propulsion is its tail. It whips it from side to side, and its body is forced forward very much as a ship is advanced by the action of a propeller. What most of us mean by a fish's "fins"—the pectoral fins extending

from a fish's sides—are actually used by our fish as its instruments
for steering and stabilizing.

Do fish drink?

This depends on the kind of fish. The familiar fish of our fresh inland waters never drink. But fish of the salty sea, unexpectedly
enough, do drink. They drink prodigious quantities of salt water.

What we find involved here is the question of what is called
osmosis. Osmosis? This, by simplified dictionary definition, is
"diffusion which proceeds through a semipermeable membrane,
separating two solutions, and tends to equalize their concentration."
It is the rule of osmosis that the weaker concentrate flows through
the semipermeable membrane into the stronger until concentration is equalized. Or, coming down to cases and our living animal,
this is to say that brook water and pond water continually leach
into a fish through its semipermeable membrane, because a fish's
body fluid is obviously a stronger solution than fresh water, but
on the other hand an ocean fish is continually losing fluid *to* the
surrounding salt water, which is obviously a stronger concentrate
than the fish itself contains.

An ocean fish drinks sea water, its gills desalting it to potability.
A fresh-water fish has water continually seeping in through its
semipermeable gill membrane and never needs drink at all.

Do all fish have scales?

No, they don't. The vast majority of our fish-brothers do go
through the adventure of animal aliveness in this sort of covering,
as mammals in hair and birds in feathers; but we're not to think
of scales as essential to fishness. Catfish, for instance, have no scales
at all. By the way, are fish born with scales? No, they aren't. A
baby fish is born as naked of scales as a robin of feathers, and the
scales sprout later from under its skin. Does a fish grow more
scales as it increases in size? No; each separate scale just grows

larger. A scale's growth produces on it those ring markings we spoke about when we were talking of how long animals live.

In darkness or in murky water, why don't fish bump into things?

As our trout or dace slips through the clear water of the brook, it is able to contemplate its world, as we found out, with eyes that perceive color. Further, its eyes are sharp eyes. They see close objects with vivid clarity, and they reckon distances and spatial relationships with a nicety to let our fish snap at even a very small moving midge with high accuracy. All very well. But what about when the water is roiled to opacity, as it often is? How does our fish find its way then among the many obstacles in its clouded world?

Exactly speaking, it feels its way. But we are not to think of this as any sort of groping and fumbling "feeling." It is a kind of feeling that combines a sensitive touch-awareness of objects at a distance and, in a manner of speaking, a hearing of them. Our fish, unseeing, "knows" its world by what it feel-hears along its sides. The organ of its information is a median-line or lateral-line canal that runs along most fishes' sides from gill to tail. If we are to enter with any sort of understanding into a fish's world of experience, we have to know about its lateral-line canal in particular.

The canal lies just under the fish's skin, and here and there skin openings place it in direct contact with the water. A multitude of nerve endings connect the lateral line with a greater nerve beneath it, and where the lateral line comes to an end at the fish's head it branches into its brain.

A good many times in this book of ours we have been finding what a near-breakdown occurs in our human language when we try, in its terms, to formulate what the life experience of one of our fellow animals must be like as the animal undergoes it. We are in difficulty because of this language inadequacy now. What does our fish's lateral line register? It detects low-frequency vibrations.

We can say, if we like, that it "hears" . . . but what it hears are vibrations of such low frequency that they wouldn't, for us, be sounds. Or we can say, in another try, that it feels the vibrations as "touch" . . . but it is touch at a distance, touch without touching. Perhaps we come closest to it if we think of our own experience when, with our eyes closed, we undertake as we walk about to "feel" and "hear"—or at any rate "sense somehow"—massive objects before we bump into them. Those of us who are blind are often said to develop a sixth sense. It isn't, of course, really a new or extra sense. It is simply the sharpening and correlation of several sensory kinds of animal knowings that are ordinarily dulled in us because we don't use them. A fish, when it cannot see, brings into play a hearing-feeling of vibrations which is so delicately responsive that the sensory nerves all along its lateral line report to it the nearness of a boulder in the stream, the passing of another fish, the tiny shudder in the water when an invisible fisherman comes to the bank of the brook.

We have talked of seeing, hearing, and now this other hardly describable kind of fish-awareness. We'd better bring up a final question about the fish's sensory world. Can a fish detect odors? Very subtly; though as in the case of a good many other animals, including us, it isn't always easy to separate smell and taste. A fish's nostrils are equipped as smell-sensoria; but, since a fish breathes with gills, its nostrils don't lead into any passageway connecting with mouth and throat. A fish's nostrils just lead into little smelling pits and stop. On the other hand, there are taste buds on a fish's tongue; and in a great many fish there are taste buds too on other parts of its body. A few minutes ago we were speaking of the smooth naked skin of a catfish, which has no scales on it. What a catfish's body does have on it are taste buds . . . taste buds extending even to its tail. When we flip a bit of meat into the murky pond—on one of those fine "research" afternoons that make fish contemplating perhaps the finest of all animalizing excuses for a lovely idleness—the bullhead that gobbles the morsel has smelled it with a kind of all-over olfactory awareness in which no amount of animal lore will help us imaginatively participate.

Are there any fish that can live out of water?

Yes. Throughout this book of ours we have been retaining an image that came into use in our answering of one of the earliest of all our questions: the image of the creation as a garden. It's not a scientific way of speaking, of course; it's a very old religious and mythopoetic way. It speaks the truth nonetheless—it speaks it rather the more, and certainly the more widely and deeply, I think —for being worded in the language of vision, not analysis. It catches something of the greenness and flowering of this world of ours; it suggests the development of its life, from seed-simplicity to the thronging diversity of living things; it holds a hint of planting and tending . . . which at once leads into a great many other hints much too philosophical, not to say theological, for our discussing here. Well, anyway, the garden of the creation, as we saw way back at the beginning of our book, has been a slow one. The present throng of animals have come a long, long way from their start in primal seed. We look at this animal now and we see clear-cut mammalness, or we see birdness, or insectness, or whatever. But also, as we look again at animaldom, and more closely, we can see evidences of all sorts of intermediacies along the long route of growth and adaptation. We discover sorts of animals that evolved just so far and then, while the rest of their company went on to further change and sharper definition of identity, remained fixed in a long static survival that earns them now, in a popular phrase, the name "living fossils." We may discover, as one of these, lungfish.

A lungfish is altogether a fish, not an amphibian like a frog. But its air bladder amounts to an air-breathing lung, and functions as that. Some African lungfish depend so vitally on air breathing that if the fish is kept under water for any great length of time it drowns. (Can a fish drown?, we were asking. To introduce lungfish into our answer then would only have complicated things; but now we find out that certain peculiar fish, lungfish at any rate, *can* drown, in a drowning exactly analagous to the sort that can befall our human selves.)

Normally a lungfish lives the life of any other of our fish-brothers, except for its way of coming to the surface for air. When drought comes, however, and its water habitat starts drying up, a lungfish digs itself down into the ooze and curls up in a cocoon of mud. Presently, as the water evaporates and the African sun beats down, the lungfish is encased in a hard, dry ball of clay. There, breathing air with its air bladder, it remains until the rains come again to dissolve the baked clay and restore the lungfish once more to water living.

Are there any fish besides this particular "living fossil" that can live on land? There are several others. One of them is that climbing perch we mentioned a while ago. It sometimes hitches itself up a palm tree, gripping the bark with its fins.

Tree-climbing perch and lung-breathing fish that encase themselves in mud cocoons are oddities of a sort that give a lot of entertainment to our animalizing. For most of us, though, "fish" means something of a closer-to-home kind . . . the immediate pickerel that we meet in the millpond, the familiar dace in the home-farm brook. There are one or two more questions about the life-ways of fish in general, pickerel and dace as much as exotic gobies and lungfish, that we want to bring up before we conclude. After all, when drought dries the shallow pools in my brook, the trapped minnows can't do anything so spectacular as climb a tree, and there is no chance that on one of my animalizing mornings I am going to pick up a mud ball and find a speckled trout in it; but I should be prepared to defend indefinitely, all the same, the proposition that these homely little fish-brothers that I know so intimately are just as cherishable, after their fashion, as any of the others. So now these final questions, applicable to all fish-dom:

Can fish swim backward?

Naturalists get a good many letters about this, mostly from people who want to settle wagers. But like so many other animal matters, it's not a question that can be exactly "settled."

A fish can back up. It can do it with a considerable spurt of speed. But if by swimming backward we mean steady tailfirst progress through the water for any great distance, no fish is able to swim backward. This must leave the wagers to be wrangled over; but the living truth about animals, we keep finding out, doesn't always divide into neat compartments of Yes and No.

Can fish survive being frozen?

They often do. A common creek minnow may be frozen overnight in solid ice, and, when the ice melts in the sunrise, thaw out and swim off to resume its dim little minnow life in good spirits. Fish that live in far northern waters are sometimes ice-locked for months. With the return of spring they "come alive" again after a whole wintertime of frozen immobility. There are some grand spinners of animal yarns in Alaska. They tell of Kodiak bears that get to be the most enormous carnivores on earth, rearing up to a towering height of 10 feet and weighing 1,500 pounds. They tell of plucking frozen fish from the ice—fish frozen as hard as stone—and seeing the fish thaw out around the campfire and come back to life. The beauty of Alaskan whoppers is that they have a way of being quite true. Giant brown bears do get that big. Alaskan black-fish do undergo that sort of solid freezing and thaw out all right.

Do fish go to sleep?

We have been following our brotherly fish through various rounds of their life experience: what they see, what they feel, what the adventure of fishness probably seems like to them. We may suitably leave them with this very common question of whether their experience is periodically interrupted, as ours is, by sleep.

Sleep? A fish has no eyelids, has it? No. A fish's eye is perpetually open upon its world. But sensory awareness of any kind, as we have so often found out in our explorings of animal mind, involves two factors. It involves the sensory event itself—the image in the eye, the impact on the eardrum, the skin quivering to the touch—and it involves the attention of consciousness. You and I don't see everything that lies before our eyes. To put it a little ridiculously, all we see is what we notice. We don't smell everything our nose is capable to detect, or hear anything but what, in a real sense, we want to hear. With our eyes wide open we can, as it were, turn off our consciousness of the seen. We can look, with the mind, upon another landscape than the one before us. We can elect to be blind. Twenty-four hours a day our flesh remains delicately alert to pressures against it; but because we blank our consciousness of tactility we don't feel the earth pressing against our feet, the air currents drifting against us, the thousand touches upon us.

Do fish sleep? Yes. A tired fish relaxes into unconsciousness, even as you and I. What little light of mind glimmers in that small brother being of ours, down there on the gravelly bottom among the water weeds, dwindles even dimmer now, waning, drowsing, and presently it winks out. Our fish's lidless eyes are still open, still fixed on the wavering shapes of its water-world. But the inner fish, the *anima* at the core of fishness, has withdrawn to rest. Our small minnow has disappeared into the ancient nowhere of an animal asleep.

Sometimes I go prowling along my brook at midnight, to

see the fish sleeping. For some reason or other, when we see them so, lying so quiet, so wrapped in rest, a sense of their brotherhood with us—of the community of all that lives—seems to come through with a strange and special poignance.

Animal Variety

The great majority of questions that occur to us when we begin to be curious about animal life concern those brotherly creatures that belong to the five big familiar divisions: Mammals, Birds, Insects, Snakes, and Fish. Still, even in the most casual and informal introduction to animals, we can't omit a few queries that concern animals not falling into these categories.

We don't want a whole separate section devoted, say, to amphibians—the class of backboned animals falling between reptiles and fish, and including frogs, toads, newts, and salamanders. There aren't enough popular amphibian questions to warrant that. Still, if we get to wondering about animals at all, if we become even the most casual beginners at animalizing, we may very likely find ourselves wanting to know: Can toads really give you warts? Is it true they can live indefinitely sealed up inside cornerstones? Is it true that salamanders aren't hurt by fire?

As with amphibian animals, so with some others that fall outside the big, broad groups we've been considering. If an earthworm is cut in two, will both halves become new worms? Questions about those fellow creatures of ours that the stately language of zoology calls Annelida aren't very common; but *that* one is. If our book is to serve its purpose, it must bring it up. Or again, and again: Do crocodiles weep crocodile tears? Do centipedes actually have a hundred legs? Do chameleons change color to match their background?

We have been making our exploration of animaldom, in this book, in such an informally rambling and discursive sort of way, permitting ourselves interjections and asides whenever it seemed like a good idea, that it's been possible to cover a good many of these isolated and unmanageable common animal questions in the course of talking about something else. Can toads give you warts? We considered that question in connection with discussing, under Mammals, the effect of shrew bites. If you cut an earthworm in half, will both halves become new worms? *That* came up, as I recall, in the unlikely context—but reasonably enough at the time—of our finding out about the blood sweating of hippopotamuses. But even though our animalizings have been so discursive, and our pages occasionally stuffed with asides, there still remains, necessarily, a certain leftover of questions that wouldn't fit in.

So now . . . here are these stray oddments of questions to make up an Animal Variety. We won't have to be bothered by such considerations of continuity and thematic development as hitherto have held our question order to something like a patterned course. It ought to be possible here to be beautifully brisk, discontinuous, and random. Do sloths really live upside down? When the voice of the turtle is heard in the land, what sort of voice is that? Is there such a thing as a white elephant? And by the way, apropos of nothing at all, are bald eagles bald?

Can horses sleep standing up?

They can, yes; and so can many other big beasts, including elephants. We found out that birds are able to sleep in perching position, without tumbling off a twig, because of the way their toe grip automatically locks. A similar thing happens in the case of a sleeping horse. When it stands stock-still and relaxes, its leg joints automatically lock to support it. But if a horse has the opportunity to lie down, doesn't it prefer to sleep that way? No. Our recumbent horse sleeps only lightly and fitfully, and it rarely stays lying down for very long. Why? Its crushingly heavy weight, pressed against the ground, very shortly makes a horse sore and cramped and makes its breathing laborious. There used to be (and I suppose still is) a pathetic poem, taught to boys as a part of their English lessons, about the misery of a poor old horse compelled to stand in its stall while the rest of us lay at ease in our beds. The pathetic poem, a little animalizing lets us see, was built around a pathetic fallacy . . . the easy fallacy, that we've had so much to say about in this book of ours, of exaggerating our brotherhood with the animals, which is real, into a complete identification of our experience-world with theirs. We are the brother of everything that lives. We are all one company. But within this company of the creation there are developments into very, very different individualities; and enough animalizing to let us understand something of this can bring us, among other pleasant things, a freedom from considerable mis-imaginative miserableness.

Do chameleons change color to match their background?

There can be few items of animal lore, of the sort perpetuated in conversational allusions and the spirit of everybody-always-says, that are more general and enduring than the notion of chameleons' power to make these extraordinary color changes. The little lizards, however, can't do it. Our cherished tale of the chameleon driven out of its lizard wits by being placed on a Scotch plaid has to be put away—gently, and even with sorrow—with our tales of basilisks, unicorns, and the hoop snake that stung the tree.

Chameleons, like a good many other sorts of lizards, do undergo very quick changes of color. A lizard may change from bright green to pinkish-brown to almost black in fast succession; but it does so with no more intention to match its surroundings than we harbor when we blush or blanch. We need keep a chameleon under observation only for a little while to find that it's quite likely to turn sky-green when we put it on a scarlet blossom and earth-brown when we put it on a fresh green leaf. What does change its color? Well, in a wider way, very much the same things that change ours: heat and cold, sunlight and darkness, and—especially —the emotions prevailing in its small but responsive little lizard psyche.

Do crocodiles weep crocodile tears?

In fact, yes. In spirit, no. Which, being amplified, is to say this: A crocodile, lazing away in the muddy sun-warmed shallows, has only mind enough to deal with the dim affairs of its crocodilian world. The nature of its awareness can give it no such insights as would permit it to indulge in an act as intellectually intricate as hypocrisy. The tears it sheds, however, are quite real. It sheds them whenever it opens its mouth to engulf a big victim. Though we rest certain that these "crocodile tears," supposed to express mock mourning, aren't in fact set flowing in any such subtlety of spirit, we are also made very sure, just by watching crocodiles for a while, that the weeping does happen. Why? It turns out to be a simple matter of reflex and mechanics. Crocodiles' eyes water when their jaws are forced far apart, just as our own eyes water a little in the course of a large yawn.

Does a centipede have a hundred legs?

It ought to have, of course, if our names for animals were half as scrupulously exact as the innocent might suppose, watching a naturalist go about his impressive business of saying, "This little

Whatsit-bug is properly known among naturalists as a So-and-Such." But animals' names, as we soon find out in our animalizings (it's come up a good many times in this book), are quite wonderfully hit-or-miss. Most of the warblers can't warble, water thrushes aren't thrushes, few bugs are bugs, and a glass snake is a lizard. No, a centipede doesn't have a hundred legs. A common house centipede has 15 pairs. Garden centipedes have 21. Some other centipedes have anywhere up to nearly 200 legs. And millipedes? The common "thousand-legs" that frequents my own acres, and that every one of us must pretty surely encounter if we so much as turn over a stone in the woods, repays our eyestrain involved in making a firsthand count of its thousand frantically waving little legs by disclosing that they actually number 60.

These imprecisions in our way of designating animals, of course, are the reason why an occasional severe-minded scientist insists on always calling every living creature by its scientific name. A "partridge," he can rightly enough point out, may mean a pheasant, or it may mean a quail, or it may mean a ruffed grouse. (It may also, of course, mean a partridge.) *Bonasa umbellus, Colinus virginianus, Canachites canadensis canace*, and *Phasianus colchicus torquatus* leave us no possible room for misunderstanding. True. But they also leave us, as it seems to me and to my fellow naturalists who have spent their lives going animalizing for the love of the thing, very little room for *air* . . . for the spruce-smelling air, the earth-fragrant air, the wild sweet air of the living outdoors and the green woods-places where we find our animals in their living actuality. As we all know, it does something to a man, and subtly robs him, when we identify him, as in jail, by just a number. In the same way an animal—our living, breathing, brother being, our fellow personality and co-experiencer of the adventure of aliveness, after its fashion—is reduced, lessened, and nearly done away with when it becomes just a scrap of Greek or Latin. One of the most cherishable things about an animal is . . . well . . .

its animalness; and you can catch quite a lot of that animalness in "partridge" and none at all in *Bonasa umbellus* or in *Canachites canadensis canace.*

Throughout this book, along with a good many other simplifications and cheerful reductions of the erudite into the everyday, animals have been called by their plain outdoor names, naturalist's names, living-flesh-and-blood names, let an occasional confusion or ambiguity fall where it might. There's a right place, no doubt, for a ruffed grouse to be called *Bonasa umbellus*, and for a snowy-breasted, twinkly-whiskered little deer mouse to be tagged *Peromyscus maniculatus*, just as there must be a right place and a good reason, I suppose, for a medical man calling plain table salt sodium chloride. But animalizing isn't the right place. The idea of animalizing is to get to know animals: something of the how and why and wherefore of them, as we want to know those things when we go out into a summer meadow (with no Zoological Glossary in our back pocket) and encounter a waddling brotherly skunk, or when we look up at a flight of birds and (not caring at all about exactly where *Vermivora ruficapilla* fits into the *American Ornithologists' Union Check List*, Fourth Edition) think to ourselves in an animally responsive and happy-hearted sort of way, I wonder how fast birds fly?

Does a centipede have a hundred legs? No. But does it *look* as if it had a hundred legs? Is that the general living animal-impression the wiggling little fellow gives us? Does "hundred-legs" speak its personality? Beautifully. So centipede it is; and a good name too. A warbler may not exactly warble, but it does something very much more like that than anything most of us could guess from *Dendroica fusca;* and if a water thrush isn't a thrush when you count its feathers or cut it in pieces, it's a thrush, right enough, when it bobs in all its dappled enchantment before our eyes beside the rushing brook.

Do sloths really live upside down?

They do indeed, and slothfully. Sloths are one of those primitive mammals called edentates that we were talking about in the fore part of our book when we discussed how animals are classified. A sloth's a shaggy gray-brown beast (often made greenish by algae growing on it, like moss on a stone), and it passes its whole life in trees, hanging upside down from a branch by its long legs or creeping with slothful slowness, in the same position, from branch to branch. A sloth lives entirely on leaves and shoots, and gets enough moisture from them so that it never needs to come clambering down to earth for a drink. What happens if a sloth *is* stood upright on the ground? Its big claws, curved for curling up over a branch, are hopelessly knuckled under. Its legs, with the whole muscle pull reversed, go splathering. A grounded sloth generally wobbles a few paces and then collapses in a sprawl. If it's raining at the time, the sloth may also get quickly waterlogged; for even the set of its fur is adapted to upside-down life, with the hair crown on the sloth's underside and the hairs growing "downward" toward its back.

Is there such a thing as a white elephant?

This depends on how demanding we are about the exactness of our color terms. Albinism occurs in lots of animals, and now and then, very rarely, it does occur in elephants. An albino elephant, however, isn't white . . . at least not in the sense in which a white rabbit is white, or the white weasel we watch loping in its winter "ermine" across the snow. What a white elephant is—and could we ask for a wilder wonder?—is generally a pale yellowish-gray elephant with pink spots.

Are bald eagles bald?

They aren't in the present meaning that our language gives to baldness but they once were when baldness meant something else.

The way it goes is this: Our eagle, as we find out as soon as our animalizing gives us a good look at one, has a fully feathered head. Its head feathers are white. "Bald," in the days when the eagle was being named, retained its old meaning of "white." It was in *that* sense that it was used as part of a good many animal names.

The duck called a widgeon is also called a baldpate. It got that name because of white feathering on its head. A white-marked coot, in the same way, continues to be called a baldicoot; and the old term "piebald," of course, goes on being used for a white-patched horse. Are bald eagles bald? They were when the American colonists talked about them, and watched them soaring in their wild glory over the wilderness. But the old name has now become so misleading that it's going out of most naturalists' talk these days, even as the eagles have gone from so much of the American sky. The birds remaining in the wild places are "white-headed eagles" now.

What is the voice of the turtle?

It's a gentle murmurous cooing. We hear it sounding through the spring woods like the very voice of the season . . . soft as the rustle of new leaves, poignant as the smell of the fresh-furrowed fields. It must seem a very strange voice to be issuing from those reptilian brothers of ours that go waddling about the woods or gliding through the pond-murk in their encasement of plastron and carapace; and in fact it doesn't. The cooing is the voice of turtle-doves. We are up against another word-change, like the "bald" that now so misdescribes the white-headed eagles.

"Turtles," originally, was a name just for doves. It was an onomatopoetic name, and a good one, from the "turtur" syllables of the birds' soft cooing. Our shell-encased reptilian animals were tortoises. But somebody or other—most dictionaries seem to ascribe it, with a brave precision, to "sailors"—corrupted *tortue*, the French for tortoise, into "tortle" and presently "turtle"; and as a result a great many beginning animalizers go out through the spring woods or along the spring brook in a fine state of baffled astonishment.

While we're speaking of turtles (the birds), this question pops into mind: Do they really have such devotion as "turtledove" has come to symbolize? They really do. The birds stay paired all year; in nesting season they share together all the incubation, feeding, and brooding. It isn't just the male dove that coos. The birds coo back and forth to each other (and not only in mating time) in continuous endearment.

And while we're speaking of turtles (the reptiles), there is *this* common question that comes up: In an emergency, can a turtle crawl out of its shell? The belief that turtles can do this is very old and general. It was one of the first and most impressive pieces of animal lore that I learned in my boyhood from an old gardener. In his version, which appears still to be the most popular and which must cause turtles to be subjected to a good many unpleasant experiments, a turtle creeps out of its shell to get away from the heat of a fire. Can a turtle do that? No. Our bony-shelled brother in attached inescapably to the armor of its covering.

Do turtles (the reptiles) have any voice at all? If we tease or frighten a turtle into pulling in its head, we discover that it often emits a hiss. It isn't a "voice," exactly. It's caused by the turtle's breath being forced out suddenly to make room for its indrawn head inside its shell.

Can salamanders
live in fire?

No better, rather worse, than our hapless turtles. If we do any animalizing at all, the question will hardly survive even the beginnings of our beginnings. A soft-skinned little salamander in its newt stage can live only in water, and even during its land sojourn it is so susceptible to dryness that it doesn't venture far from the sanctuary of the leaf mold or the cool damp darkness of its retreat in an old stump. But the idea of our Introduction is to introduce, and to do that by bringing up the commonest animal questions; and this one is one of the commonest.

The fire-impervious salamander goes back to the medieval theory of elementals; and back beyond that it dates probably to some of man's earliest mythologizings. The actual salamander, our amphibious brother that we meet in the damp, ferny places of the actual woods or along the reed-bordered actual brook, is an amiable and quite lovely little animal with a soft moist skin and a proclivity for eating tiny snails and crustaceans. Is it scaly like a dragon? No; no scales. Is it poisonous? Not a bit.

Can a pelican's beak hold more than its belly can?

For once, a popular old rhyme has told us an animal-truth. A pelican's beak—or, if we're to be entirely precise, the throat pouch beneath it—is a maw of astonishing capacity. A pelican uses it, a good deal of the time, as a fish-scoop. Plunging into a school of fish with its beak agape, it grabs as many fish as it can, closes its beak to let the water drain out and the fish settle into its pouch, and then opens its beak again for another scooping lunge. A good many birds, as we found out in our section of bird-life questions, feed their babies by regurgitation. Many, such as doves and herons, never feed the youngsters in any other way; and this is also true of pelicans. At feeding time, a pelican brings up a partially pre-digested meal into its pouch, stands quietly with its mouth open, and the babies feed from the pouch as from a bowl.

How much can a pelican's pouch hold? When it's distended with a big fish-catch it can hold upwards of 25 pounds.

Why don't spiders get snared in their own webs?

Though spiders aren't insects, they are so like them in many ways that a great deal of what we found out about insects amounts, in effect, to a finding-out about spiders too. However, there are a few questions about spiders in particular that still need answering, this web question being only the commonest of them; so instead of just taking this one up briskly and all alone, suppose we come at it, in our inveterate fashion, as the end question of a little clump of others. The whole thing won't take long.

Do all spiders spin webs? No. Some species just prowl around and find their prey at random. Some others take their prey from ambush; they hide in flowers and pounce on the insects that visit them. Web weavers, and particularly the ones called orb weavers, however, are of course the spiders most likely to enlist our first animalizing interest.

Does a spider spin silk just for spider-web making? No. Spiders spin fine silk to make their egg sacs; they spin coarser silk, of many fine strands together, with which to lasso and secure their prey; and most spiders as they go about their wanderings spin continually a filament called their dragline. It's by means of its dragline that a spider suddenly raises or lowers itself when we see it dangling "in mid air"; and it's by throwing a filament of dragline into the wind that a spider is whisked aloft and taken, so to speak, ballooning across the countryside. The silk that issues from the little spinnerets on a spider's abdomen isn't just a single kind of sub-

K

stance. Spiders spin no less than seven different kinds of silk; and even one individual spider can spin five.

Now then, the web. How does our black-and-golden orb weaver construct this intricate wheel? First, cross lines between two supports to make a square. Then diagonals across the corners, then connectives of the diagonals. Now radii: The spider stretches a thread across the web's diameter, returns to the center of this thread, fastens a new one, and proceeds again toward the periphery. With each trip from the web's center to its circumference a new wheel spoke is added. Finally, when all the radii are ready (21 of them, as a general thing) the spider spins cross supports to give them strength. The spider starts now from the hub, and moves around the web in a widening circle. At each radius the silk strand now being secreted is fastened and drawn tight. When at last the spider's spirals bring it to the web's outer edge, the radii are all joined by circles of silk supports.

Is the web finished now? Not quite; and here, at last, we answer the web question that started us. The web has been spun of a dry and not very elastic sort of thread. Now, as its final touch, the spider goes over it again, spinning a new kind of thread, gummy and sticky. It breaks its original guy spirals and replaces them with this. *This* is the spider web that catches prey. This is the viscid web-stuff that the spider carefully avoids after spinning it. And it's in this gummy network, finally, that the spider always leaves a "free zone" . . . a safe area where it can go scuttling with no danger of being entangled.

Any other urgent spider questions, before we go? Well, one, perhaps. What's gossamer? It's fine wind-drifted strands of the delicate draglines that spiders spin.

How do birds effect their mating?

Way back near the start of this book of ours, we brought up a lot of questions about animals' sexual behaviors. There is a certain rightness in our finding ourselves concluding, now, with a question on the same theme. It's not just that sex is a central thing in the life on this green earth of ours. So is feeding. So is breath. It's that sex is so greatly a misunderstood thing, a shied-away-from thing, that it's the subject for more abounding and persistent myths and misinformations in our animal lore than almost anything else. Whatever else we may gain from animalizing, we stand to gain an equanimity about sex and some clear factualities to let us see it as no queerer a thing than breathing, no stranger a thing than sleep. Nasty? Not this strong clean thing that happens when foxes meet, out under the moon. Not this thing of songs and fluttering praise, among the birds. Not this stir that goes right down to the first stir in the first cell, in the morning of this garden. If animalizing lets us know this, we have been done one of its great services.

Now, about our birds. When we see two sparrows fluttering briefly together in what appears to be a copulation, it seems scarcely possible that this can be taking place. How can it? It can because birds breed by a simple application of cloaca to cloaca. A bird's cloaca, the final section of its alimentary tract, serves it both for excretion and reproduction. In breeding time a male bird's testes are greatly enlarged; the female's ovary swells to a ripened bunch of eggs-to-be. When the birds come together, cloaca is pressed briefly to cloaca and the male's sperm passes from the sperm ducts, through the cloaca, into the cloaca of the female. No male bird, then, actually has an intromittent sexual organ, like a mammal's? It isn't common; but a few birds do. Take ducks. They have the special difficulty of breeding on the water. It is facilitated by the drake's having a true sexual organ.

When we say "ovary" or "testis" about a bird, the words come somehow with a shock of strangeness. As a matter of fact, no matter what veteran animalizers we become, there is always something of this sense of startlingness in our realization of how very like our own bodies other animals' bodies are, how akin to our minds their minds, how close they are to us in all their waking and sleeping. The reminder is continually brought home to us. It's a good one

to have. A grasshopper lights on our arm and we contemplate it.
Surely this tiny being doesn't have inside it, say, a heart? Why yes,
it has a heart . . . and corpuscular blood, and an esophagus, and
Malpighian tubes to serve it as kidneys. That phoebe darting over
there in the sunlight . . . surely that little bird doesn't have, say,
a gall bladder? Why, yes, and a liver and a pancreas, and something of a glimmer of mind, after its fashion, and a life adventure
to be lived.

Look where we will among the animals, and it is brought home
to us. We are all in community. We are all in kinship. It is all a
brotherhood, this life of ours together, under the warmth of the
common sun that broods us all.

The Adventure
of Animals

We have come to the end of our questions. In the terms of the scope set at the outset, that means we have come to the end of our book.

It had been planned that the thousand commonest questions about animal life—the commonest, at any rate, in my own experience as a naturalist to whom a good many inquiring letters come—would be raised and answered; and it had been planned that these questions would be given both a certain degree of classification and arrangement, so that our book might give us something of the structure and relationships of animaldom instead of just being a question-and-answer hodgepodge, and also a certain fullness in the answering, so that instead of our just finding out (for instance) that opossums do play possum or that snakes don't undulate up and down, we might get some understanding of the whys and wherefores behind these facts and might explore, while about it, some of the animal facts related to them.

In the matter of formal arrangement, we have at times deviated from our original plan, when this seemed necessary and logical. In animalizing, a question about whether it is instinctive for dogs to hate cats is likely to bring up in our minds, by a very natural and human sort of association, the question, say, of whether it is also instinctive for silkworms to eat mulberry leaves. Our sequence of questions, and our division of them into categories, have now and then been cheerfully violated in a frank succumbing to the spirit of that-reminds-me.

Such a spirit may result in a certain number of insects getting in among the mammals, or a bird inquiry popping up among the snakes, after a fashion to make the formal look down their noses; but it is nevertheless the spirit, I think, in which most of us do actually go about our introductory lookings at animals and our wonderings about them. What becomes of houseflies in the winter-time? They do thus and such. Well then, next, since we're talking about flies, how can a fly walk upside down on the ceiling? The one question leads (or if you like, zigzags) into the other one; for our minds, as we contemplate living animals, don't always work according to the stately patterns of formal inquiry, wherein the study of locomotion would be a very distant matter from the study of hibernation or the study of the physiology of dormancy. A merely hodgepodge book about animals would be a sorry one; but an inhuman one might be a worse. And so at times our progress may have seemed as meandering, and our attention as distractible, as when we're out for an animalizing hike through the woods on a June morning.

Having now done what I can to justify and even ennoble the occasional randomness of the structure into which our animal questions have been assembled, there remain to be reviewed the other intentions with which our book started out: the intention to go in for a certain fullness in answering some of the questions so that the ways of animaldom might be understood in some related and reasonable way instead of just appearing in little disparate chopped-up bits of factuality, and the intention to cover questions to the number of no less than a full thousand. With respect to these two intentions, happily, there doesn't have to be anything even dimly suspicious as special pleading to establish the case for fulfillment.

A certain fullness in some of the answerings? There can't be much doubt, I should imagine, that *that* expectation has been carried out, all right. I think it's only too likely that occasionally some of our answers may have put an impetuous reader in mind of that celebrated book about penguins which the little girl received as a gift from an aunt, and for which she expressed her thanks in a grave note saying that she had found the volume most interesting and that indeed it had told her more about penguins, really, than she had ever wanted to know. I realize that every now and then an apparently simple, straightforward animal question, which you'd suppose might have taken fifty words to answer, has sent us off on a round-up of a whole brace of related questions, and that sometimes, in fact, the answer hasn't even stopped short of an excursion into something like philosophy or something verging strangely close to theology. I am particularly keenly aware of the rather vast lot of wordage having to do with animals' inner lives: the detailed explorings and reexplorings of what, as our best guess can make it out, coon life or crow life or whatever is like from the inside looking out. The fullness of some of our answers, I feel sure, must sometimes have seemed like an overfullness.

But, after all, there was no promise at the start of our book that this wouldn't happen. We said there would be some fullness; we didn't promise where it would stop. And I think that if we're to go at animalizing with any sort of sound foundational understanding, the answers to some of our very first and most elementary questions—such ones, for instance, as concern the nature of the animals' minds—can hardly be made too full and careful. Does a chipmunk think? Give a quick answer to that, a "snap" answer, and we get nothing at all of any real increase in understanding. Are most animals harmful or beneficial? That doesn't call for a statistic. It calls for an insight into the over-allness of animaldom; and we can hardly bring up in even the roughest and most simplified way the considerations to provide that insight without spending a considerable parcel of paragraphs on it.

So much for our occasional fullnesses. I can't regret them. I do regret in a lively way that in some particular connections there weren't rather more of them. (Thinking back now, for instance, I don't believe the question about whether there are any iridescent mammals should have been just tossed aside with a hurried answer that such shimmering and surprising brothers of ours do exist and that some African moles and water moles do have such a sheen.)

But now to the matter of the total number of animal questions we have managed to raise and answer, quickly or roundabout. Frankly, now that they lie behind us, I permit myself to feel appalled. The initial idea was that a thousand questions should be answered in the course of our pages. But what has actually happened, as we have gone along and along and along with our asides and interjections and occasional convolutions to clump a lot of related questions together in answering one large lead question, is that we have overshot our mark in quite a whopping way. I have not totaled up our questions. Nothing would induce me to. But I did (having after all made a commitment at the start) keep a count until the thousand mark. I don't now recall on just which page this millennial point was reached, but I know it was a long while ago. In the spirit of a baker's dozen, our naturalist's thousand has turned out to be overspilling measure.

And that brings me, now, to what is the real substance of this last chapter—to the point where I want for the rest of our time together to be altogether serious.

A main thing I have wanted to do in this book, obviously enough, is answer questions about animals. But I have wanted all the while to convey the realization that answering a thousand questions about animals, or answering ten thousand or a hundred thousand such questions, leaves us with most questions about animals still unanswered. We have described this book as an introduction to animals. It would be not only more modest, but a good deal more accurate, if it could be described as just an introduction to an introduction, and it would be more accurate still for it to be thought of as just a bundle of little notes for an introduction to a foreword to a preface. This would still be true if our volume were twice as big as it is, and it would continue true if, instead of being one book, it were a shelfful. It isn't in the least mystical, nor even the slightest literal exaggeration, to say that the lore of animals stretches to infinity. A man I know who is an astronomer wrote some years ago an enormous report summarizing the discoveries in astronomy that had taken place during the year preceding his writing. His colossal document concluded like this: "These discoveries have served chiefly to bring us to awareness of infinitely greater mysteries than hitherto we had known existed." Exactly. Precisely. And what is true of the distant lights in the night sky is very, very true of the squirrel on our immediate window sill, the tanagers nesting in our home woods, and the curled-up little millipede we uncover when we kick over the stone nearest our foot.

There's no getting to the end of animals, no making our way through the subject and coming out on the other side. There is no time, ever, when we can say: "Now I know about animals." There is only a time when we can say: "Now I know a *little* about animals." Such a time occurs when, having started out from scratch, from the presumed status of virtually total strangers to our subject, we finish the consideration of ten hundred animal questions, which is what the program of this book has been. We know now, I hope, a little more about animals than we did 280-and-some pages ago. But it's very, very little. And it doesn't get to be much more if we live to be ninety-five and spend every waking hour of it in a devoted animalizing. Did Charles Darwin know much about animals? Well, a little something. Did Burroughs and Ernest Thompson Seton and John Muir manage to amass a great animal lore, as they went prowling this beloved earth of theirs, this garden of the creation, year after year? Well, a few fragments. But to get to *know about animals?* Why, God bless us all, there isn't anywhere time enough in a life span to get to know all about one mouse.

Now I've kept saying this, and here I am saying it all over again with particular emphasis, for a particular reason, and the particular reason is this: I hope some readers of mine are going to be persuaded

K*

into taking up animalizing. I hope that no reader—not even the most naïve and most easily impressible, if there are any—is going to suppose that this book has been written, or is to be read, with the thought that it "covers" its subject. It isn't meant to cover it; it has the more possible hope of just introducing it. What I hope this book may do, along with providing some answers to some questions that get asked a lot, is to *start* things. I hope it may start some readers to animalizing on their own. What I hope is that some little piquant or pregnant oddment about animals discovered from this book—say the reasons for the markings on birds' eggs, or the facts about how bats find their way in the dark by radar, or any other stray fact or reflection in the multitude—may catch the reader's interest and kindle it into an enthusiasm. And then what I hope is that this enthusiasm will be set soaring by the realization that the whole of the animal lore in this book amounts to nothing, nothing at all, compared to what it lies open to anyone in the world to find out about animals if he or she cares to take up animalizing and go ahead with it; and I hope that the grand upshot of all this will be a happy-hearted new life member of the company of animalizers. For I think, of course, that getting to know what we can about animals, entering into an intelligently insighted intimacy with our brothers that coinhabit this earth-scene with us, is easily the best and greatest adventure in the world.

Naturally I think so. If I thought otherwise, I'd be doing something quite different with my life. I'd be serving society usefully as a plumber or a banker or a manufacturer of raincoat lapels or some such solid thing, instead of passing my days pestering a curator-crony for further facts about pangolins' tails, corresponding with a trapper up at Great Bear Lake to see if I can't add something new to my supply of wolf lore, and daily in all weathers prowling around and around the hundred-and-some acres of my living laboratory with an entranced expression and nothing in my wallet but the disintegrating skeleton of an old newt.

No doubt everyone who has some engrossing interest in life

thinks it is the best of all interests. I do believe, though, that the case for animalizing is something a good deal more substantial than the case for any merely whimful hobby, any mere (God forgive us for having even *invented* such a word!) "pastime." Animals don't do anything so deadly as pass our time. What they do is restore us to a very old garden, that we lost a long time ago but that ought to be our homeland; and what they do is broaden out our vision of the brotherhood of all things created; and what they do is plank us down, when we get too smart by half, into the old original wisdoms of simplicity. Those aren't all the things they do, of course. They keep us from ever being bored. They remind us continually of what in our tired preoccupations we'd nearly forgotten, the meaning of "animal spirits." They present plenty of comicalities, to make us grin like children, which is a sort of grin we should never have stopped grinning; and when we are being serious about them—listening, with hushed spirits, to the song of a wood thrush in a green glen in the dusk of a summer evening; watching with eager eyes and absorbed spirits the caperings of a vixen and her foxlets playing at their den-side in a sunny field— they can at once break our hearts and heal them, and they can pour in upon us a perfectly extraordinary peace.

All through this book I have been persistently using the word "animalizing," in spite of its not having existed hitherto; and I shouldn't wonder if sometimes this has been a little irritating. But I've not done it to be whimsical, but with the serious intention of keeping the fact before us that we can devote ourselves to animal lore, and can make animals a rewarding and meaningful part of our lives, and can go from knowledge to ever deeper knowledge about them, without having to go in for a training in the technical profundities of zoology, entomology, ornithology, or any of the other strict official "ologies." We want to have always a great respect for science, and we want to assimilate all the animal science we can in a spirit of carefulness and accuracy. But in addition to science, alongside science, and in a certain sense beyond science, there is, so to put it, the living lore of the living animal. There is what we can see for ourselves, watching that bird in that tree out there. There is what we can learn about whales, not merely from a whale monograph but from that old sea captain down on the wharf. There is the fox fact to be picked up, not in a university, but in our southeast Forty-Acre; and there is the whole living world of living brothers of ours to be met and known as we walk among them, in the spring woods, in the golden pastures of October, in the Christmas snow. All that's the sort of thing I have meant to say by the word "animalizing."

Animalizing has no expenses. It poses no debarring requirements for any of us. You can be ninety-five years old and in a wheelchair, and still be an animalizer. You can have just had to take a pauper's oath; the rabbits are still out there, on the moonlit grass, for you to watch. You can be a traveler, with all the animaldom around the world available to you; or you can be held fast to one place, no matter where that may be, and still there is animaldom around you to infinity. I have done a bit of peering and probing among animals in the tropics and in Europe and some other places; but a long time ago, really as soon as I had settled into the realization that I must follow the life-way of a writer-naturalist because that was where my heart was and I might just as well give up any pretense of being a more responsible sort of citizen, I planted myself in one spot— the hundred-and-some country acres that I'm everlastingly calling my living laboratory—and here, by election, I have stayed put. A hundred-and-some acres is a plenty big enough world of animals. It's a great deal too big for me ever to do more than touch the edge of it, take the first small steps into understanding of it, even if I should live to be a very old man.

Why did the lynx up at the head of my old wood road make such a queerly wide-spaced track in the loam the other morning? I don't know. What temperature does my creek water have to get to be before the last trout comes out from under the bank, down in that shadowy pool where the great old willow grows? I don't know. Sometimes a woodchuck comes digging up out of its hibernation on a bitterly cold day in midwinter, and goes traipsing off across the crusted snow until it has found some withered weeds and eaten them, and then it goes traipsing back again and resumes its stertorous sleep below the frost line. Why does it do that? I don't know. I don't know these things about animals, and I don't know ten thousand million other things. There's plenty of animalizing, in this world of a hundred-and-some acres, to keep me enthralled for a lifetime. There's good animalizing to be done if you're fourteen or if you're eighty-four, if you're well or ill, if you're out hiking over the rolling uplands or if you're stuck in jail. (This isn't just a bad-tasting joke. The most fascinating pigeon lore ever to come my way came to me from a convict in a penitentiary. He'd had nothing to watch, over the years, but some pigeons outside his cell; and that had been enough to arouse his Adamite responsiveness to the wonder of the world; and he'd put his heart into it.) The adventure of animals is open to us all.

I think that there's a great lot of fun in animals, and a great lot of help and healing and sunny sanity. Animalizing is a good and happy adventure, and I hope there may have been some things in this introduction to persuade a lot of persons to join me in it.

Index

A

Air, need of animals for, 15, 24–25
Air bladder of fish, 256–257
Allen, Dr. Arthur A., 134
Alligators, 192
Amoebas, 15
Amphibians, 8, 267
Anacondas, 228, 229
Anemones, sea, 79
Angle-wings, 193
Angleworms (*see* Earthworms)
"Animalizer," 28–29
Annelids, 5, 8
Ant bears, 58
Anteaters, 9, 50, 58
Antelope, 21, 67, 98
Anthropoid apes, 9, 14
Antivenin, 235–236
Ants, 181, 223
    colony life of, 198–202
    winged, 198–199
Apes, 9, 14, 23, 34, 86
Arachnids, 172
    species of, 5
Armadillos, 9
Arthropods, 5, 7, 8
Atlas moths, 182–183
Atmosphere, effect on animals of, 15, 24–25
Auks, 124

B

Baby animals, sizes of, 75–76
Backward flight of birds, 121

Badgers, 101–102
Bald eagles, 273–274
Baldicoots, 274
Baldpates, 274
Banana flies, 186
Barn swallow, 148
Bass, 33, 253
Bats, 9, 34, 51, 54–56
    migration of, 54
    radar equipment of, 54–55
    vampire, 55
Bear animalcules, 35
Bears, 67, 83, 109, 248
    ant, 58
    birth of, 75
    family life of, 70
    gestation period of, 73–74
    grizzly, 74, 99
    hibernation of, 94–95
    honey, 58
    hugging enemy to death, 93–94
    Kadiak, 264
    longevity of, 34
    speed of, 99
Beavers, 9, 22, 59–61, 66, 71
    building skills of, 59–60
    gestation period of, 73
    tails of, 59
    tree-cutting of, 60
Bees, 87, 178, 180–181, 237
    community life of, 202–206
    life cycle of, 206–207
    time-telling ability of, 208–213
Beetles, anobiid, 154
    sexton, 112–116

291

Glossary

Although it is one of the merits of this book that technical words have been avoided wherever possible, some such words were unavoidable. This glossary provides a simple definition of terms that are likely to be unknown to non-scientific readers.

ASEPSIS. Cleansing of wounds.

BIPEDAL. Two-legged.

CADAVER. A creature that feeds on dead flesh, etc. ; also a corpse.

CAECUM. The first part of a mammal's large intestine.

CARAPACE. The upper shell of crustaceans.

CHITINOUS. Horny, cf. the shell of crustaceans.

CLOACA. The excrement cavity in birds, reptiles, etc.

CORVINE. Like a crow.

COWBIRD. A species of American blackbird.

EMPATHY. The ability to identify oneself with another being.

FORMICARY. A colony of ants.

GNU. An oxlike antelope.

GANGLION. Part of a nerve.

HEPATICA. Liver-coloured.

HERBIVORES. Plant-eating animals.

HERMAPHRODITES. Creatures having both male and female sexuality.

HERPETOLOGICAL. To do with the study of reptiles.

INTEGUMENT. Skin or rind.

KATYDID. A large green insect, common in America.

LIANAS. Tropical forest plants.

MILT. The roe of male fish.

NUMEN EST. Latin for "There is a spirit in it, or them."

OOLOGY. The study of birds' eggs.

ORIOLE. An American bird with black and yellow plumage.

OVULATION. Egg-laying.

PARAMACIUM. A genus of the lowest link in the animal kingdom.

PHOERE. An American fly-catching bird.

PERINEAL. Adjective of perineum, the region of the body between the anus and scrotum.

PLASTRON. Undershell of a tortoise.

PROTEROZOIC. Living in very early times.

THEODICIST. One who supports the theory of a divine creation of the universe.

TOXICOLOGY. The study of poisons.

URANIUM. A heavy white metallic element.

WHIPOORWILL. An American bird, like a nightjar.

6